Signal Processing of Underwater Acoustic Waves

by C. W. Horton, Sr.

The University of Texas at Austin
Austin, Texas
for the Naval Ship Systems Command
Department of the Navy

November 1969

UNITED STATES

GOVERNMENT PRINTING OFFICE

WASHINGTON: 1969

Library of Congress Catalogue Number: 74-603409

For sale by the Superintendent of Documents, U.S. Government Printing Office
Washington, D.C. 20402 - Price $3

PREFACE

This is an introductory book intended for scientists and engineers who are involved in the construction, design, evaluation, or operation of sonar systems. Although an effort has been made to provide all of the necessary background material, a slight familiarity with the theory of probability has been presumed. In view of the introductory nature of the book, the amount of material presented has been limited purposely. The expert who looks at the book will no doubt complain about the topics which have been omitted. For example, the important topic of parameter estimation is mentioned only briefly. As the late Professor H. A. Wilson said, "It is important for the student to learn some facts and to get to understand some methods and fundamental principles; if he learns nothing about certain phenomena no harm is done and he can make up the deficiency in his knowledge at a later date if necessary." If the book enables the reader to follow the current literature on signal processing, it has achieved its goal.

The writer wishes to take this opportunity to thank the many people with whom he has had the pleasure of discussing signal processing. Among these are Mr. P. G. Redgment and Dr. E. J. Risness, Admiralty Underwater Weapons Establishment, Portland, England; Professor G. Bonnet and Mr. P. Y. Arquès, Centre d'Étude des Phénomènes Aléatoires, Université de Grenoble, Grenoble, France; Dr. H. Mermoz, Laboratoire D. S. M., Le Brusc, (Var) France; Mr. A. Bruce and Mr. R. Laval, SACLANT ASW Research Centre, La Spezia, Italy; Dr. C. van Schooneveld, Physisch Laboratorium, Organization RVO-TNO, The Hague, Netherlands; and Mr. I. Engelsen and Dr. F. Bryn, Norwegian Defence Research Establishment, Horten, Norway.

The author is greatly indebted to the following scientists who were kind enough to read critically parts of an earlier draft, point out errors, and suggest improvements: F. Bryn; T. L. Brownyard, Naval Ordnance Systems Command; T. Kooij, SACLANT ASW Research Centre, La Spezia, Italy; M. Moll, Arthur D. Little, Inc.; David Middleton; P. G. Redgment; E. J. Risness; Captain S. W. W. Shor, USN; C. van Schooneveld; and E. C. Westerfield, U. S. Navy Electronics Laboratory. He is also greatly indebted to Mrs. Patricia Nelson, of Applied Research Laboratories (formerly Defense Research Laboratory), The University of Texas at Austin, who typed the entire manuscript.

The book has been used as the text in a graduate physics course. The material can be covered, with a few omissions, easily in one semester. Answers are provided for some of the problems to provide greater flexibility in the use of the text for both organized classes and individual study.

The writer is greatly indebted to Captain S. W. W. Shor, USN, and Mr. Carey D. Smith for the interest they have shown in the work and for many helpful discussions. The book was supported by Naval Ship Systems Command under Contract NObsr-93163 with Defense Research Laboratory, The University of Texas.

C. W. Horton, Sr.
August 1968
Austin, Texas

CONTENTS

Chapter 1

SURVEY OF THE PROBLEM

1.1 Qualitative Description of Signals

In the operation of a sonar system the operator is repeatedly faced with the problem of detecting a signal which is obscured by noise. This signal may be an echo resulting from a transmitted signal over which the operator has some control, or it may have its origin in some external source. These two modes of operation are commonly distinguished as active and passive sonar, respectively. Similar situations arise in radar surveillance and in seismic explorations so that one may draw on all three disciplines for techniques and for illustrations of the basic principles.

Since there are many ways in which one can think about signal detection, it is desirable to define a few terms to denote special cases. The word *detection* will be used when the question to be answered is, "Are one or more signals present?" When the system is designed to provide an answer to this question, either deterministic or probabilistic, one speaks of *hypothesis testing*. The case of a single signal occurs so often that many systems are designed to provide only two answers, "Yes, a signal is present," or "No, there is no signal." One can make the problem more complicated by endeavoring to classify the signal into categories. Decisions of this latter kind will be referred to as *target classification*.

Normally a piece of detection equipment is designed to operate in a fixed mode and the parameters such as integrating time of rectifier circuits or persistence of the oscilloscope tube for visual detection cannot be changed readily. There will always be some uncertain signals which the observer will be hesitant to reject or accept. In these cases the operator might have the feeling that if the integrating time of the detector or the persistence of the oscilloscope tube were longer, he could reach a decision about the existence of the signal. This intuitive feeling has been formulated into a theory of detection by Wald (1950). When one is able to vary deliberately the interval over which one stores data in the reception system in order to achieve a certain level of certainty, one speaks of *sequential detection*.

Frequently it is desirable to determine not only the presence or absence of the signal but also one or more parameters associated with the signal. The parameters of interest can vary widely from a simple quantity such as time of arrival or target bearing to the recovery of the complete wave form. When a system is designed to recover one or more parameters associated with the signal, one speaks of *signal extraction.*

The word signal was not defined and it was assumed that the reader had an intuitive feeling for the word. Some elaboration may be in order since the definition of signal is subjective and depends on the application. One may say that "signal" is what one wants to observe and noise is anything that obscures the observation. Thus, a tuna fisherman who is searching the ocean with the aid of sonar equipment will be overjoyed with sounds that are impairing the performance of a nearby sonar system engaged in tracking a submarine. Quite literally, one man's signal is another man's noise.

Signals come in all shapes and forms. In active sonar systems one may use simple sinusoidal signals of fixed duration and modulations thereof. There are impulsive signals such as those made with explosions or thumpers. At the other extreme one may make use of pseudorandom signals. In passive systems, the signals whose detection are sought may be noise in the conventional meaning of the word; noise produced by propellers or underwater swimmers, for example. It should be evident that one of our problems will be the formulation of mathematical techniques that can be used to describe the signal.

Although the source in an active sonar search system may be designed to transmit a signal of known shape, there is no guarantee that the returned signal whose detection is sought will be similar. In fact, there are many factors which act to change the signal. The amplitude loss associated with inverse spherical spreading is most unfortunate for the detection system but it does not entail any distortion of the wave shape. (Incidentally, this happy state of affairs does not apply to two-dimensional waves except in the far field where the wave can be approximated locally as a plane wave.) The acoustic medium has an attenuation factor which depends on the frequency. This produces a slight distortion of the wave shape and a corresponding change in the energy spectrum of the pulse. The major changes in the wave form result from acoustic boundaries and inhomogeneities in the medium. These effects will be described in Sections 1.5 and 1.6.

When echoes are produced by extended targets such as submarines, there are two distinct ways in which the echo structure is affected. First, there is the interference between reflections from the different structural features on the hull of the submarine. This interference leads to a target strength that fluctuates rapidly with changes in the aspect. Secondly, there is the elongation of the composite echo due to the distribution of reflecting features along the submarine. This means that the duration of the composite echo is dependent in a simple manner on the aspect angle. If T is the duration of the echo from a point scatterer, and L is the length of the submarine, the duration of the returned echo will be $T + (2L/c) \cos \theta$, where θ is the acute angle between the major axis of the submarine and the line joining the source and the submarine. c is the velocity of sound in the water. Of course, $L \cos \theta$ must be replaced by the beam width of the submarine when θ is near 90°.

A final source of pulse distortion is the Doppler shifts produced by the relative motions between the source, the medium, the bottom, and the targets. Since the source, the medium, and the target (or detector in passive listening) may each have a different vector velocity relative to the bottom, the variety of effects may be quite large. The magnitude of this effect will be discussed in Section 1.3.

1.2 Qualitative Description of the Sources of Noise

The noise source that is easiest to describe and to introduce into the calculations is the thermal noise produced in the detection equipment itself. Usually the properties of this noise are completely unrelated to those of the signal. In this case the reduction of internal noise in the equipment can be attempted without particular regard for the type of signal that will be detected. In sonar and seismic studies the ambient noise in the wave field is so large that the internal noise of the equipment seldom limits the performance. On the other hand, detection systems utilizing electromagnetic signals are often limited in their performance by internal noise in the receiver.

There is a source of noise intermediate between internal noise of the equipment and ambient noise of the ocean. This source results from the motion of the ship or platform on which the array is mounted through the water. The noise field generated in this manner depends on the speed of the ship and, in the case of surface ships, on the sea state. To some extent this noise can be lessened by a careful choice for the location of the transducer and by proper design of the covering dome.

The ambient acoustic wave fields in the earth and in the ocean often are quite energetic and contain a wide range of frequencies. The study of these noise fields forms an important and necessary prelude to any serious design of optimum detection systems. In the ocean, for example, one finds, in addition to the biological sources already mentioned, noises due to wave action at the surface of the water, noises due to collapse of air bubbles entrained in the water, and noises produced by meteorological conditions such as precipitation. In the case of passive detection, these noise fields furnish the noise background out of which signals must be recovered.

Whenever one engages in active signal detection, the production of the signal entails a large production of noise background which tends to obscure the signal. This noise* is particularly difficult to treat because it usually has

*Throughout the book the word noise will be used in its most general sense to mean anything that obscures the desired signal. This is to some extent a subjective definition but it is convenient.

the same frequency characteristics as the signal, since both the noise and the signal are produced by the reflection or scattering of the transmitted energy. For example, in sonar the volume, bottom, and surface reverberation are caused by reflection of the transmitted signal from irregularities in the body of the water and from the lower and upper surfaces of the water, respectively. If one endeavors to increase the energy in the returned signal by increasing the power of the transmitter, these reverberent sources of noise increase proportionately. If one samples the noise as a function of time after the transmission of the signal, one can see the transition from reverberation noise to ambient noise very clearly. At the beginning the power spectrum of the returning noise resembles that of the transmitted signal very closely. As time goes by the power in the reverberation decreases but the power level of the ambient noise remains constant and eventually dominates.

An interesting situation arises in seismic exploration which, although it is not directly related to sonar, furnishes an interesting example of how one may utilize the properties of the noise in its elimination. The commonly used source of energy in seismic exploration is dynamite, the explosion of which produces energy in a wide band of frequencies. The acoustic reflections from the deep rock strata have a dominant band of energy in the range of 20 Hz to 70 Hz. However, the explosion produces large amplitude low velocity surface waves whose frequencies extend from 5 Hz to 20 Hz or so. In the early attempts at exploration, before the existence of this frequency separation was realized, the detection and recording systems were overloaded by this low frequency wave, so that there was no sensitivity available for the lower amplitude, higher frequency signals. The separation of these two overlapping bands of energy is a relatively simple example of the design of a signal detection system. In this particular case an alternate solution may be available, since it is possible sometimes to separate the two bands of energy on the basis of travel times by a proper choice of distance between the source and the receiver.

Another source of noise that may be serious is man-made countermeasures. These may be active sources such as prisoners of war running so as to hide the noise of digging or passive sources such as chaff used as a radar countermeasure. These noise sources will not be treated here but they can be analyzed by the same techniques used to study other noises.

1.3 Comparison of Sonar, Radar, and Seismic Parameters

It was mentioned in Section 1.1 that there are similarities between sonar, radar, and seismic systems of signal processing. Although this is true there are also striking differences in the media which lead to significant differences in the methods of signal processing used in these three systems. In this section the basic physical parameters of the media and of the systems are discussed in order to focus attention on the critical differences. There is a wide range of values for many of the parameters so that only representative values are given.

Table 1.1 lists representative values of the chief physical parameters of the three systems. The designer of sonar and radar systems has a wide choice in the operating frequencies, but only one value is used in the table in order not to complicate the presentation. In the seismic system the choice of operating frequency is limited severely by the attenuation properties of the earth. Associated with this restriction is the fact that seismic signals arriving at the detector are broad-band signals while the sonar and radar pulses are narrow-band.

One striking feature is shown by column 4 of Table 1.1. Despite the wide range of wave velocities between the three media, the pulse lengths are surprisingly similar. This would suggest that the three methods have similar resolution but this is not true. The seismic method is at a great disadvantage, first because the operator cannot change his frequency, and second because the reflection coefficient of the rock interfaces are much smaller than the reflection coefficients of sonar and radar targets. The resolution of sonar systems is inferior to that of radar systems but the reasons are more subtle. First, the effect of the ocean on acoustic wave propagation is more severe than the effect of the atmosphere on electromagnetic waves. Second, the significantly higher frequencies used in radar systems enables one to use a wider bandwidth for the signals. This permits one to do much more signal processing on radar signals. Third, the effects of Doppler shifts described in the next section degrade the performance of the sonar system by a greater amount.

If a stationary source is used to echo range against a moving target, the frequency of the returning echo will be shifted by an amount $\pm 2vf/c$ where c is the velocity of the wave in the medium, f is the frequency of the signal, and v is the radial component of the velocity of the target. If the signal is a pulse and hence is composed of a band of frequencies, each component is shifted by this amount. This shift is known as the *Doppler Shift.* Motion of the source produces a similar shift in frequency but this can often be corrected for since the motion of the source is known. In sonar systems this device is called an *Own Doppler Nullifier.*

TABLE 1.1

Brief Summary of Representative Sonar, Radar, and Seismic Characteristics

System	Wave Velocity m/sec	Pulse Duration	Pulse Length m	Pulse Repetition Rate sec^{-1}	Wave-length m	Size of Mobile Array m
Sonar	1,500	2–200 ms	3–300	0.1	0.3	10
Radar	3×10^8	0.1–10 μs	30–3,000	2,000–200	0.03	2
Seismic	1,600–7,000	50 ms	80–350	(*)	40–175	---

*Pulse repetition rate in the seismic case affects only the economics of the exploration.

Table 1.2 shows the effects of target motion on Doppler shifts for representative velocities and pulse lengths. If a sonar receiver processes all echoes with one channel, the bandwidth of the receiver must be 20 times as wide as it would be in the absence of Doppler. This will result in a serious impairment of performance when the signal level is comparable to the noise level unless one divides the Doppler band by using approximately 20 receiver channels, each with a bandwidth comparable to that of the signal. Of course, the relative outputs of these channels can be used to indicate the radial velocity of the target. In the case of radar, the range of possible frequency shifts encountered with airplanes is only 0.06 times the bandwidth of the pulse. Thus the receiver can accommodate the Doppler shift without seriously increasing the noise power.

TABLE 1.2

Representative Target Velocities and Doppler Shifts

System	Target	Target Velocity m/sec	Wave Velocity m/sec	Doppler Shift $\Delta f/f$ %	Bandwidth of CW Pulse $\Delta f/f$ %
Sonar	Ship	± 15	1,500	± 2	0.2
Radar	Airplane	± 500	3×10^8	± 0.0003	0.01

The sonar, radar, and seismic media all have inhomogeneities. These can be classified into large scale inhomogeneities associated primarily with the horizontal stratifications of the earth, water, and atmosphere and small scale inhomogeneities associated with turbulence in the water and air and lithologic variations in the earth. The interaction between the ocean and the atmosphere sometimes produces strong temperature gradients in the first few hundred meters either side of the interface. At times the resulting velocity gradient produces a wave duct or channel in either the water or the atmosphere which can transmit acoustic or electromagnetic waves over surprising distances.

The velocity gradient dc/dz in the surface channel for acoustic waves in the ocean may be as large as 0.3 sec^{-1} while the corresponding gradient for electromagnetic waves in the atmosphere may be as large as 30 sec^{-1}. A more useful comparison is the gradient of the index of refraction, n, since this governs the radius of curvature of the rays. Representative maximum values are $|dn/dz| = 2 \times 10^{-4}\ \text{m}^{-1}$ for acoustic waves and $|dn/dz| = 10^{-7}\ \text{m}^{-1}$ for electromagnetic waves where z is the distance from the interface. It can be shown that when the velocity is a linear function of z, the geometric ray is a circle whose radius depends on dn/dz and the angle of inclination of the ray. The relationship is such that for the maximum values of dn/dz just quoted

$$\frac{\text{radius of electromagnetic ray}}{\text{radius of acoustic ray}} = 2{,}000$$

provided the two rays have the same inclination. Since these numbers are near maximum values, one may only conclude that acoustic rays in the surface ducts can have significantly greater curvature than the corresponding radar rays. Actually, surface ducts occur much more frequently in the water than in the air. The existence of ducts is important both for the effect on range and also for the effect on ambient noise resulting from sources located at the surface.

Surface ducting occurs in seismic exploration when high velocity formations occur near the surface. The effect is so severe in some areas, such as the Edwards Plateau of Texas, that seismic exploration is extremely difficult.

In the deep ocean the acoustic velocity reaches a minimum in the SOFAR channel and increases monotonically below this with a velocity gradient which, in the Atlantic Ocean, is approximately 0.014 $\sec^{-1}$. If the ionosphere is excluded from the discussion there is no counterpart of the SOFAR channel in the atmosphere. On the other hand, seismic wave velocity increases almost monotonically with depth because of the compaction produced by the overburden. In sedimentary columns the velocity gradient for longitudinal waves does not vary greatly from the value 0.6 $\sec^{-1}$.

The air and the ocean are similar in that each has a temperature microstructure that produces local inhomogeneities in the velocity. The size and intensity of these regions of abnormal velocities depend significantly on the vertical distribution of the horizontal velocity of the medium, the temperature gradient, and the distance from the air-water interface. However, as a simple generalization one may say that in the ocean these "patches" have a characteristic size of 0.6 m and a RMS value of 7×10^{-5} for the index of refraction. In the atmosphere the corresponding values are 125 m and 3×10^{-6}. When the sizes of the patches are expressed in wavelengths, the disparity in size is even larger. These numbers suggest that the fluctuations in phase and amplitude caused by temperature microstructure are smaller in the ocean than in the atmosphere. The attenuation of sonar waves in the ocean is due primarily to loss mechanisms in the medium and it is only at very low frequencies, a few hundred Hertz, say, that attenuation by temperature inhomogeneities is significant.

1.4 Target Strength and the Sonar Range Equation

The elementary discussion of sonar performance based on an infinite, homogeneous medium usually proceeds as follows. The source transducer radiates a wave which produces an intensity I_T at the target. The power contained in some area of this wave front is intercepted by the target and reradiated as a new source. Thus the intensity of the returned signal is affected by the inverse square law of spherical waves and the attenuation two times, once on the path from the source to the target and on the return path. The returning acoustic intensity produces an output power S' at the electrical terminals of the transducer. At the same time the acoustic noise in the water has some intensity in the water and a corresponding electrical power N' at the electrical terminals of the transducer.

Often the performance of a sonar system can be described approximately by saying that there is a number M' called the recognition differential such that if $S' \geqslant M'N'$, the target can be detected successfully 50% of the time. It should be noted that when the acoustic noise intensity in the water is defined properly the ratio S'/N' is equal to the corresponding ratio of acoustic intensities in the water. When all of the quantities are expressed in decibels, one has the sonar range equation

$$M = S\text{-}N = S_o + T - 2[20 \log r + ar] - N, \tag{1.1}$$

where

M = recognition differential of system in dB
S_o = source level in dB at one yard
T = target strength, dB
r = range in yards
a = attenuation in dB per yard
N = noise level in dB
S = returned acoustic intensity produced by target.

Typical values of the quantities in Eq. (1.1) are T = 15 to 20 dB, S_o = 100 to 140 dB, N = -40 to -60 dB, and $M \cong 0$ dB. Actual values can deviate significantly from these illustrative numbers. The attenuation constant, a, depends on the frequency in a complicated manner, but in the vicinity of 5 kHz one has a good approximation in the formula $a = 0.01f^2$ dB per kiloyard when f is expressed in kiloHertz.

The major advantages of Eq. (1.1) are twofold. First, it provides an easy approximation to the expected range of a sonar system, and second, it enables anyone who can add and subtract to speak glibly about sonar performance. The major disadvantage is that it involves only the simple average involved in computing power. All sophistication in signal processing, all unknown statistical parameters, and all information contained in the signal wave form are hidden in the term M, the recognition differential.

When one attempts to modify Eq. (1.1) so as to include the effects of inhomogeneities in the medium and of acoustic boundaries, there is no place to start and it is necessary to introduce empirical modifications in M. These arguments make it clear that one cannot study signal processing by starting with power averages, but instead, one must consider the distribution in space and time of the acoustic wave fields associated with the signals and the noise.

1.5 Reflection and Scattering from Boundaries

The performance of sonar and seismic systems is impaired by the unwanted energy reflected and scattered by velocity discontinuities at the surface and in the interior of the ocean and the earth. For example, three possible travel paths are shown in Fig. 1.1 for a source and target in water of moderate depth. In the case of active sonar there are six possible combinations of these paths with six different travel times. Even if the water is deep enough or the bottom reflects so poorly that the path QBT can be neglected, there are still three possible travel times which can produce interference and wave form distortion. The ocean surface is usually a very good reflector so that the two paths $\overline{QT}$ and $\overline{QST}$ tend to give nearly perfect constructive or destructive interference when the path difference measured in half wavelengths is an integral number. Thus even a moderate movement of the source Q or the target T will lead to large variations of the reflection amplitude and wave shape.

When the distance $\overline{QT}$ is several times the water depth, the travel time for the paths $\overline{QT}$ and $\overline{QBT}$ differ so little that the signals overlap to give further amplitude fluctuation and wave shape distortion. Some of the wave energy penetrates the ocean bottom and is lost. The energy that is reflected can be divided into two parts. One part may be associated with a specular reflection from an average plane surface which preserves a wave pattern that is coherent in space and time. The remaining energy is distributed in a stochastic wave field which has very limited coherence in space and time. A realistic view is that each hill and depression on the bottom acts as a small localized scatterer so that the acoustic wave field at any point is the result of the superposition of a large number of waves of small amplitude and random phase. The distribution of energy between the coherent, reflected wave and the stochastic, scattered wave field depends on the roughness.

Even though the problem of the reflection of waves from a target in a stratified medium is deterministic in principle, the motion of the source Q and

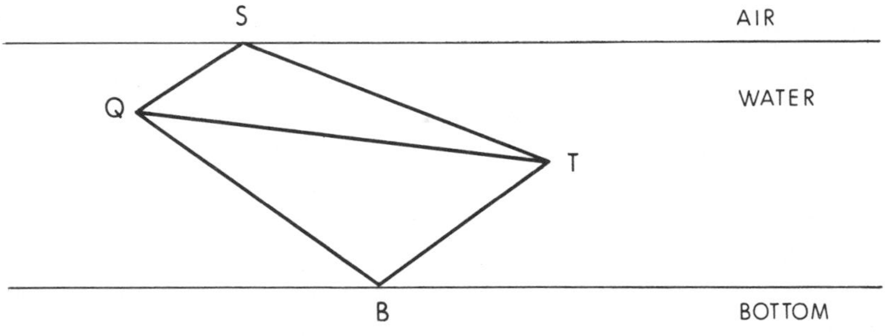

Figure 1.1–Three possible paths from the source Q to the target T.

the target T, as well as the roughness of the interfaces, conspire to produce a stochastic noise field at the transducer as well as a slow variation of wave shape and amplitude in the received echo.

The preceding discussion was phrased in terms of forward scattering and the resulting distortion of the target echo. Frequently the backscattering from the surface and the bottom produces a stochastic wave field of large amplitude that obscures the echo. This phenomena is known as reverberation and is classified as surface and volume reverberation according as the scattering objects are distributed over a surface or throughout a volume of the medium. It is easy to show that the intensity of surface reverberation decreases as t^{-3} where t is the time measured after the production of the acoustic signal. This conclusion is misleading, however, since it suggests that the reverberation level decreases with time more slowly than the returned acoustic intensity of a given target. Actually the backscattering strength decreases with grazing angle so that as the time increases the reverberation level decreases more rapidly than t^{-4}. Thus at sufficiently long ranges the target echo is obscured by ambient acoustic noise rather than by reverberation noise.

1.6 Effects of an Inhomogeneous Medium

The nature of the local inhomogeneities in the water was described in Section 1.3. The local variations of amplitude and phase that result from these inhomogeneities can be understood most easily by considering the wave front illustrated in Fig. 1.2. If the direction to the target is determined by measuring the phase difference between the two signals received at hydrophones located at W_1 and W_2, the indicated direction will be in error because of the perturbations in the wave front. Further, the size and location of these inhomogeneities are random functions of time and space so that the measured value of target direction will fluctuate about the true direction. There will also be fluctuations in the signal amplitude associated with the deformations of the wave surface. These fluctuations are equivalent to noise signals at W_1 and W_2 which degrade the performance of any signal processing system.

1.7 Criteria for Measuring the Success of Detection

Now that the properties of signals and of noise have been described briefly it is possible to sketch the problem of determining the best way to recover the signal. One would like to formulate some criterion of success for this operation for two reasons. First, one cannot decide how to optimize a system unless one has a quantitative measure of success. Secondly, one would like to judge the performance of an actual system by comparing it with the performance of the optimum ideal system of the same class. It is evident from the discussion of Section 1.1 that there cannot be a single criterion applicable to all systems.

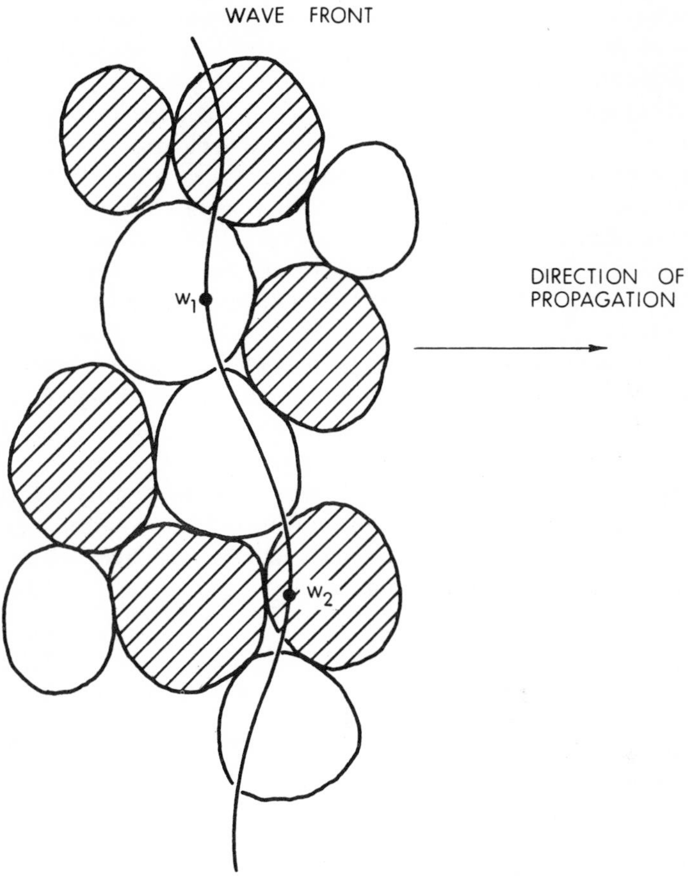

Figure 1.2–The acoustic wave front in an inhomogeneous medium. The shaded (unshaded) regions have temperatures above (below) the average value.

The peak amplitude of the signal response is frequently used as a parameter to judge the performance of a system. In this case one designs a system which will maximize the ratio of the peak amplitude of the signal to the root-mean-square amplitude of the noise. Another criterion frequently used involves the ratio of the energy contained in the signal to the noise energy contained in a specified interval of time. In this case the ratio of the energy in the signal to the power per Hz contained in the noise is maximized. Again one may desire the recovery of a wave form so that the criterion that is applied is a measure of the difference between the input wave form and the output.

If one has designed a detection system whose output consists of an assertion regarding the presence or absence of a signal, one wishes to evaluate the performance by some measure of the correctness of the decision. There are two ways in which the decision can be wrong. The system can assert that a signal is present when in fact there is none, and a system can indicate that a signal is not present when one is present. A simple criterion that is often used is obtained by assigning a cost or loss to each kind of error. The design of an optimum system is obtained by minimizing the average loss. This criterion may be generalized by introducing in addition costs for the two correct decisions of deciding that a signal is present or that a signal is absent. Alternately, one may not wish to assign costs explicitly but simply calculate probabilities of detection and of false alarms and state operating conditions in terms of these quantities.

It is clear that one cannot optimize the various processes described above without assigning some limitation to the classes of signals, noise, and systems considered. For example, one may specify the properties of the signals that are considered and the nature of the noise and then design a system that will be optimum according to a specific criterion. In order to carry out such an analysis a limitation on the class of systems that will be considered must be introduced. If only linear systems are considered, one can obtain the optimum for this class of systems. On the other hand, if the investigation is enlarged to include nonlinear systems, one would expect to obtain a better system provided the linear systems first considered are a subset of the larger class of nonlinear systems. Consequently, in order that an optimization process be meaningful one must state with exactness the nature of the signals and the noise, specify criterion of performance that will be utilized, and stipulate the class of systems over which the optimization will be carried out. A change in any one of the four elements of the problem may lead to new conclusions.

There are several criteria that are regularly applied to the evaluation of a detection system. One may define a signal-to-noise ratio and maximize this ratio or define a loss for the detection system and minimize it. Sometimes it is possible to calculate *a posteriori* probabilities and select the hypothesis which has the largest *a posteriori* probability. In connection with the discussion of *a posteriori* probabilities, Section 5.1, it will be found that a simpler detection system can be defined in terms of an alternate concept, the *likelihood function.* The performance of the system can be evaluated in a realistic manner on the assumption that a signal is present when the likelihood function exceeds a preset threshold. One can also define suitable quantities to which a least-squares test can be applied. These criteria are not mutually exclusive. For example, cost functions can be chosen which lead to a least-squares fit or to a maximum signal-to-noise ratio.

1.8 Directional Arrays

In the discussion so far it has been tacitly assumed that the signal and noise are scalar quantities which constitute the input to the system and that the only operations permissible are those that can be applied in the time domain or the frequency domain. This is not true since the signal arrives in the form of a wave propagated in a medium–water for underwater sound, water or earth for seismic waves, and air, water, or earth for electromagnetic waves. This fact enlarges substantially the problem of designing an optimum detection system since one may utilize the spatial dimensions of the sensors to discriminate against noise. In the case of underwater sound the introduction of the transducer array produces a serious conflict for the designer. Since the attenuation per unit travel distance in water increases with the frequency of the signal, the range of a system can be increased by decreasing the operating frequency. This change, however, will degrade the directivity pattern of the transducer unless its physical dimensions are increased at the same time. Usually the physical dimensions of the transducer are already limited by some external constraint so the desire to increase the range is foiled. Some of these limitations can be avoided if one is willing to use nonlinear processes such as the time averages of products in the detection system. However, it turns out that this improvement is obtained at the expense of wider bandwidths in the signal or longer integrating times in the detector. These changes lead eventually to reduced sensitivity in the transducer or reduced search rate, which in turn reduce the effective range. Thus one is led to expect that the restraints imposed by the medium and the platform lead to a true maximum in the performance of the system which can be established by a suitably clever analysis.

1.9 Suggestions for Further Reading

The best introductory work on signal processing is the book by Woodward (1953). The article by Siebert (1956) is not elementary but it gives an interesting survey of many aspects of the problem. The book by Helstrom (1960) has a fair amount of mathematics but it is extremely readable. The article by Middleton and van Meter (1956) is excellent in its own right and it is a good introduction to the monographic book by Middleton (1960). The latter text answers a surprisingly large fraction of the questions that one needs to ask about the theory of signal processing. A later book by Middleton (1965) provides material that is supplementary to the earlier and larger book.

In addition to these general treatises the reader is referred to two symposia held in 1964 and devoted primarily to signal processing in underwater acoustics (Bonnet, 1964b, and Tucker, 1964). Although the papers are intended for specialists they form a good introduction to the subject matter and provide extensive bibliographic references.

There are several excellent books on the physics of acoustic media. The subject of propagation in the ocean is discussed by Officer (1958) and Tolstoy and Clay (1966). Propagation in layered media is discussed thoroughly by Brekhovskikh (1960). Propagation through an inhomogeneous medium is analyzed by Chernov (1960), and the scattering of waves by a rough surface is summarized extensively by Beckmann and Spizzichino (1963).

The reader should refer to the papers by Faure (1964) and Middleton (1967) and the book by Ol'shevskii (1967) for a discussion of reverberation and for references to other work on this subject. The use of arrays for acoustic transmission through a noisy ocean is discussed by Clay (1966). References to geophysical applications are described in three special issues of *Geophysics* edited by Van Melle (1964a, 1964b) and Flinn (1967). The reader may also refer to a paper by Capon *et al* (1967) for the application of signal processing to seismic arrays.

PROBLEMS

1.1 A formula for Doppler shift may be calculated easily from a model in which two men stand on the bank of a river. The velocity of the water in the river may be thought of as the wave velocity in the medium. One man, A, who is located upstream throws corks into the river at equal time intervals T, which may be thought of as the period of the source. The other man, B, who is located downstream measures the time interval T' between the successive passages of corks. T' is the period of the received wave. If the men do not move, $T = T'$ and there is no Doppler shift. Let v_A and v_B be the magnitudes of the velocities of the two men.

(a) Use this model to calculate the Doppler shift when $v_A = 0$ and v_B is directed downstream.

(b) Modify this model to explain the Doppler shift of the returning echo when the target is moving.

(c) Derive the approximate formula quoted in Sec. 1.3 when $v_B/c \ll 1$.

1.2 Snell's law states that the angle of incidence, i, and the angle of refraction, r, of a geometric ray are related by $V_2 \sin i = V_1 \sin r$ for the Model in Fig. 1.3. A medium whose velocity is a function of depth, $c = c(z)$, can be approximated by a sequence of layers each of thickness h and velocity $c_1, c_2, \ldots$ as in Fig. 1.4.

Set up a recurrence relationship for the angles, i_n, of the geometric ray, and carry out the limiting process as $h \to 0$. Show that when the velocity function $c(z)$ is continuous, one obtains

$$x(z) = x(0) + \sin i_o \int_0^z \frac{dz}{\left\{\left[\frac{c(0)}{c(z)}\right]^2 - \sin^2 i_o\right\}^{1/2}}$$

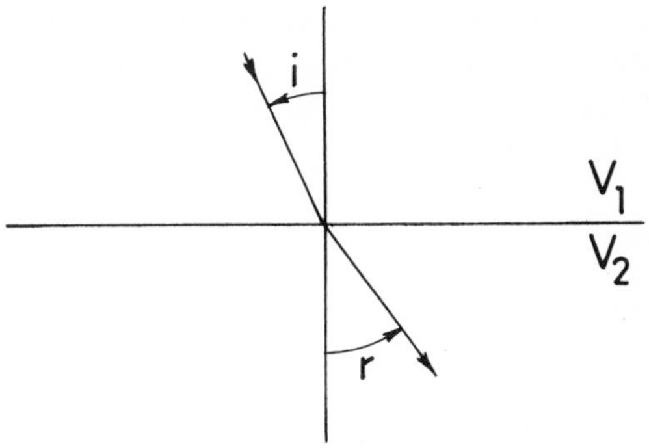

Figure 1.3–Illustration of Snell's Law.

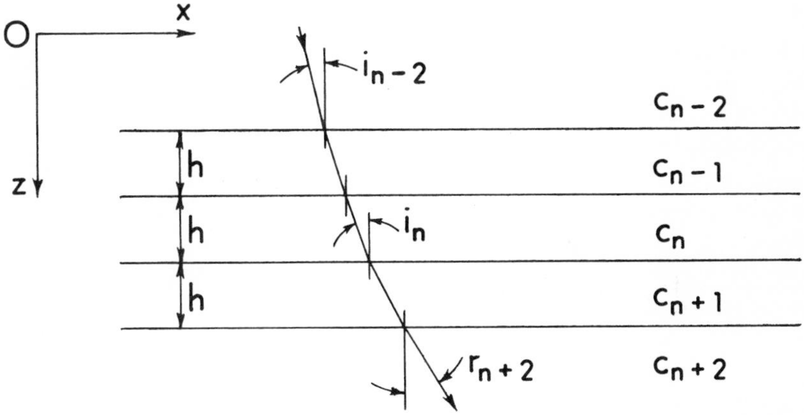

Figure 1.4–Ray propagation in a stratified medium.

as the equation for the ray path. In this equation $c(0)$ = velocity at $z = 0$ and i_o is the angle between the tangent to the ray and the z-axis at $z = 0$.

1.3 Use the result of Problem 1.2 to show that ray paths are circular arcs when $c(z) = c_o + gz$; c_o and g are constants. Express the radius of the circle and the coordinates of the center in terms of c_o, g, and i_o.

1.4 Assume in Fig. 1.1 that the source Q is 10 m below the surface and the target T is 110 m below the surface. A pulse 2 ms in duration is transmitted and two echoes are received. If one echo travels by the path $\overline{QT}$ and returns by $\overline{TQ}$ while the other echo travels by the path $\overline{QT}$ and returns by $\overline{TSQ}$, what is the largest horizontal range between Q and T at which the pulses do not overlap? Use c = 1,500 m/sec.

1.5 Use Eq. (1.1) to calculate the range at which a target can be detected 50% of the time for the values $M = 0$ dB, $S_o = 110$ dB, $T = 10$ dB, $a = 0$, and $N = -50$ dB. What is the range when the frequency is 5 kHz and attenuation is introduced?

1.6 Give a detailed derivation of Eq. (1.1).

1.7 Modify Eq. (1.1) so that it will apply to passive listening.

Chapter II

ANALYTIC DESCRIPTION OF A SIGNAL

2.1 The Fourier Integral

Whether one thinks of the transmitted signal as an electric voltage (or current) applied to an electromechanical transducer, the motional current of the active face of the transducer, or the acoustic pressure produced in the water, the signal is a real function of time which has a finite duration, finite energy, and, practically speaking, a finite frequency range. It will be shown that there is a mathematical contradiction inherent in the last statement. Suppose that the signal is a real function of time which will be denoted $E(t)$. From an empirical point of view it is clear that any signal produced by an experimenter must satisfy the condition

$$E(t) \equiv 0, \; |t| > T, \; T > 0, \tag{2.1}$$

where T is a suitably large time. This statement follows from the fact that the equipment has a date of construction and it will be dismantled at some later date. It will be convenient many times to approximate $E(t)$ by analytic functions such as $\exp[-at^2]$ or $\exp[-at]$ which do not satisfy Eq. (2.1). Consequently, it is not desirable to restrict the discussion by imposing the restriction (2.1).

One can introduce a less restrictive condition on the function $E(t)$ that has considerable mathematical merit and which can be justified from physical considerations. If $E(t)$ is an electric voltage in volts that is developed across a one ohm resistor, the energy dissipated in the interval of time Δt seconds is approximately one mho $\times\, E^2(t)\Delta t$ joules. The approximation becomes better as Δt becomes smaller provided $E(t)$ is continuous in the interval Δt. Consequently, the following discussion will be restricted to signals $E(t)$ that satisfy the restriction

$$\int_{-\infty}^{+\infty} E^2(t)\, dt \quad \text{is bounded.} \tag{2.2}$$

It will be assumed that the reader has some knowledge of Fourier transforms so that it is necessary only to describe the notation that will be used and list a few of the principle formulas. The standard reference is Titchmarsh (1959), but this book requires considerable mathematical maturity on the part of the reader. A more elementary but excellent account may be found in Guillemin (1949). This book, like all of his other books, is pleasant to read and is ideally suited for scientists with a background in engineering or experimental physics.

It is desirable to use a notation for Fourier transform pairs that enables one to associate them immediately. One convention frequently used is that followed by Titchmarsh who uses the lower case letter, say $e(t)$, for the function and the corresponding upper case letter, $E(f)$, for the transform. However, it will be found desirable to save upper case letters for special usages so the practice of Beran and Parrent (1964) will be followed. A circumflex will be used to denote the Fourier transform of any function. Thus $\hat{e}(f)$ and $\hat{E}(f)$ are the Fourier transforms of $e(t)$ and $E(t)$, respectively.

The following statement is a paraphrase of theorem 23 of Titchmarsh (1959). If a complex function $E(t)$ is such that

$$\lim_{T \to \infty} \int_{-T}^{+T} |E(t)|\, dt < \infty$$

and it is continuous for all t, there exists a function $\hat{E}(f)$, called the Fourier transform of $E(t)$, such that

$$E(t) = \int_{-\infty}^{+\infty} \hat{E}(f)\, e^{+i2\pi ft}\, df \tag{2.3}$$

and

$$\hat{E}(f) = \int_{-\infty}^{+\infty} E(t)\, e^{-i2\pi ft}\, dt. \tag{2.4}$$

The condition of continuity can be relaxed to one of a countable number of discontinuities of bounded variation. At any point of discontinuity of $E(t)$, Eq. (2.3) must be replaced by

$$\frac{1}{2}\left\{E(t+0) + E(t-0)\right\} = \int_{-\infty}^{+\infty} \hat{E}(f)\, e^{+i2\pi ft}\, df. \tag{2.5}$$

This situation will arise, for example, if one calculates the Fourier transform of a dc pulse $E(t) = 1$, $|t| < T/2$, $E(t) = 0$, $|t| > T/2$.

A short table of Fourier transforms is given in Appendix 2.1.

The integrals in Eqs. (2.3) to (2.5) may be interpreted as ordinary (improper) Riemann integrals familiar to all students of calculus. They are valid, however, if interpreted as Lebesgue integrals. The nature of Lebesgue integrals will be discussed briefly in Section 4.2.3.

One will notice that the exponentials in Eqs. (2.3) and (2.4) contain a factor 2π. This factor is distributed differently by different authors so that a minor confusion sometimes arises. Some mathematicians prefer to emphasize the symmetry by distributing this factor as $1/\sqrt{2\pi}$ in front of each integral. In books that stress engineering applications the variable f is sometimes replaced by $\omega/2\pi$. In this case a factor $1/2\pi$ occurs in the right member of Eq. (2.3). One also finds in some engineering texts that i has been replaced by j.

One of the primary interests in this book is the study of real signals $E(t)$. When $E(t)$ is real, one sees from Eq. (2.4) that $\hat{E}(f)$ will be real if $E(-t) = E(+t)$, a condition that is not generally satisfied. Also, $\hat{E}(f)$ will not vanish for all negative frequencies for real pulses.

There are two formulas that will be used frequently. If $E(t)$ and $G(t)$ are two functions which may be complex and if $\hat{E}(f)$ and $\hat{G}(f)$ are their Fourier transforms, one has the Parseval formula (see Titchmarsh, p. 50)

$$\int_{-\infty}^{+\infty} \hat{E}(f)\,\hat{G}^*(f)\,df = \int_{-\infty}^{+\infty} E(t)\,G^*(t)\,dt, \tag{2.6}$$

where the asterisk denotes complex conjugate. The Fourier transform of the product $E(t)\,G(t)$ can be shown to be the convolution of $\hat{E}(f)$ and $\hat{G}(f)$; that is the Fourier transform of $E(t)\,G(t)$ is given by

$$\hat{E}(f) * \hat{G}(f) \equiv \int_{-\infty}^{+\infty} \hat{E}(f_1)\,\hat{G}(f-f_1)\,df_1 \tag{2.7}$$

This equation may be considered as the definition of $\hat{E}(f) * \hat{G}(f)$. A converse formula is valid for the function whose transform is $\hat{E}(f)\,\hat{G}(f)$.

When the signal $E(t)$ is real, Eq. (2.6) implies

$$\int_{-\infty}^{+\infty} E^2(t)\,dt = \int_{-\infty}^{+\infty} |\hat{E}(f)|^2\,df. \tag{2.8}$$

This result can be interpreted in a most useful manner. If $E(t)$ is thought of as a potential difference in volts developed across a one ohm resistor, the integral on the right of Eq. (2.8) becomes, when multiplied by one mho, the total energy dissipated in the resistor. Consequently, one is tempted to interpret the integrand on the right as follows:

$$1 \text{ mho} \times |\hat{E}(f_i)|^2\,\Delta f = \text{energy dissipated in the frequency band } (f, f+\Delta f) \quad \ldots . \tag{2.9}$$

where f_i is a value, $f \leqslant f_i \leqslant f + \Delta f$, dictated by the theorem of the mean. Equation (2.9) is an assumption that is justified on the heuristic grounds that it gives results in agreement with experiment, but, in principle, any quantity could be added to the left of Eq. (2.9) so long as it did not change the value of the integral in the right member of Eq. (2.8). The function $|E(f)|^2$ will be called the *energy spectrum* of the signal. The reader should note that it is defined for negative as well as positive frequencies.

Since the integral on the right side of Eq. (2.3) must be real for real signals, one concludes that

$$E(-f) = E^*(f) \tag{2.10}$$

and

$$|\hat{E}(-f)|^2 = |\hat{E}(f)|^2 . \tag{2.11}$$

This shows that the distribution of energy versus frequency is symmetric about $f = 0$, and one may, in discussing the energy of real pulses, restrict the discussion to positive frequencies by adding a factor of two to the left member of Eq. (2.9).

2.2 Application of the Fourier Integral to Linear Networks

The Fourier integral will be used most extensively in the following work so it may be well to develop a few of its consequences. This will not only illustrate the transform relation but will provide results for future references. A common device in electronics is a linear network such that when an input voltage $E_i \exp(+i\omega t)$, $\omega = 2\pi f$, is introduced at the input, as in Fig. 2.1, an output voltage $E_o \exp(+i\omega t)$ results which is related to the input by

$$E_o e^{+i2\pi ft} = \hat{Y}(f)\, E_i e^{+i2\pi ft} \ , \tag{2.12}$$

a relationship that must be defined for all f. The reader will note that $\hat{Y}(f)$ is a dimensionless quantity. It is possible and not uncommon to build devices other than lumped constant networks that perform linear operations on $E_i(t)$ which can be described by Eq. (2.12). For convenience such devices will be called generalized networks.

The reader will have noticed that the input voltages in Eq. (2.12) and Fig. 2.1 are complex quantities whereas it was stated earlier that real signals were of primary interest. The orthodox attitude in mathematical physics is that only real quantities can have physical significance. Whenever a complex quantity such as $E_i \exp(+i\omega t)$ is used to represent a physical quantity, it is understood that at all times either the real part or the imaginary part of the

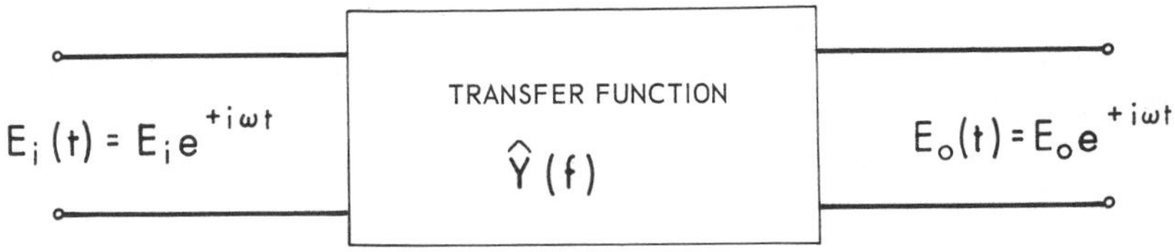

Figure 2.1 – A generalized, linear network.

complex quantity must be interpreted as the physical quantity. The use of complex numbers in the analysis is abundantly justified by the greater ease of the manipulations.

When an arbitrary real signal $E_i(t)$ is applied to the input of the generalized network, one may use Eq. (2.4) to resolve the signal into sinusoidal components and apply each of these to the input of the network. Since the network is linear, the output is the sum of the outputs for each of the sinusoidal inputs. One has

$$E_o(t) = \int_{-\infty}^{+\infty} \hat{Y}(f)\, \hat{E}_i(f)\, e^{+i2\pi ft}\, df. \tag{2.13}$$

This equation shows that $\hat{Y}(f)\ \hat{E}_i(f)$ is the Fourier transform of $E_o(t)$, but according to the remark after Eq. (2.7) this means that $E_o(t)$ is the convolution of $Y(t)$ and $E_i(t)$, or[1]

$$E_o(t) = \int_{-\infty}^{+\infty} Y(\tau)\, E_i(t-\tau)\, d\tau\, . \tag{2.14}$$

It is the quantity $\hat{E}_i(f)\, df$ and not $\hat{E}_i(f)$ that has the same physical dimensions as those of $E_o(t)$. Thus if the dimensions of $E_o(t)$ are volts, say, the dimensions of $\hat{E}_i(f)$ are volt seconds. The dimensions of $Y(\tau)$ are second^{-1}.

The generalized network is said to be physically realizable if (1) the response $E_o(t)$ is identically zero for all $t < 0$ when $E_i(t) = \delta(t)$, the Dirac delta function[2], and (2) the amplitude and argument of the complex function $\hat{Y}(f)$ are even and odd functions of f, respectively. The first restriction insures that one does not violate causality by having an output before there is an input, while the second condition insures that $E_o(t)$ is a real function of time if $E_i(t)$ is real.

[1] The proof of this assertion is not readily apparent from the material presented. A demonstration will be given in the next session.

[2] The Dirac delta function will be discussed in the next section.

When Eq. (2.14) is considered in the light of condition (1), it is noticed that $Y(\tau)$ must vanish identically for $\tau < 0$. This means that Eq. (2.14) may be written as

$$E_o(t) = \int_{0-}^{+\infty} Y(\tau)\, E_i(t-\tau)\; d\tau \tag{2.15}$$

whenever the network satisfies the conditions of physical realizability. The lower limit of the integral is written as 0- to insure that one integrates "across" the point $\tau = 0$. This is necessary since $Y(\tau)$ may contain a Dirac delta function, $\delta(\tau)$.

2.3 The Relation between Signal Length and Bandwidth

The existence of Fourier transforms assures one that the shape of a pulse $E(t)$ and its energy spectrum $|\hat{E}(f)|^2$ cannot be specified independently. As an example of this relationship consider a dc pulse whose shape can be approximated by the error function

$$E(t) = \frac{1}{\sqrt{2\pi}\sigma}\; e^{-t^2/2\sigma^2} \; . \tag{2.16}$$

The total area under this curve is unity and the shape of the curve becomes more sharply pointed as σ approaches zero. If one carries out the integration required to find the Fourier transform, one obtains

$$\hat{E}(f) = e^{-\frac{1}{2}(2\pi f\sigma)^2} \tag{2.17}$$

When Eqs. (2.16) and (2.17) are compared, one sees that they have an inverse dependence on σ. As σ is made progressively smaller, the signal $E(t)$ becomes shorter in time, but the corresponding energy spectrum $\hat{E}(f)$ becomes broader. If one defines the time duration T of the signal as the time during which $E(t)/E(o)$ is greater than e^{-1}, say, and the bandwidth W of the pulse as the frequency range over which $\hat{E}(f)$ is greater than e^{-1}, one finds

$$WT \cong 1 \; . \tag{2.18}$$

Equation (2.18) was derived for the special case of a dc pulse with a Gaussian shape. The reader will find it instructive to carry through a similar analysis for the pulse obtained by multiplying the right-hand member of Eq. (2.16) by $\cos \omega_0 t$. A short calculation will show that Eq. (2.18) is valid for this modulated pulse as well as for the tone burst $E(t) = \cos(\omega_0 t + \Phi)$, $|t| < T/2$, $E(t) \equiv 0$, $|t| > T/2$. Here Φ is a constant phase angle.

The equality (2.18) is a specialized relation that must be replaced by the inequality $WT \geqslant 1$ when one considers general pulse shapes. One can define a time duration T and the bandwidth W for an arbitrary signal and prove that $W\,T$ is greater than or equal to ($\geqslant$) a constant near unity for all pulses. A demonstration of this statement is given in an interesting paper by Gabor (1946). Actually the mathematical principles involved are closely related to the famous uncertainty principle of Heisenberg in quantum mechanics. The resemblance is not surprising when one remembers that in quantum mechanics a component of the momentum is the Fourier transform of the corresponding positional coordinate.

The limiting forms of Eqs. (2.16) and (2.17) as $\sigma \to 0$ are of especial interest since $E(t)$ approaches the well known Dirac delta function $\delta(t)$. This is a function that is identically zero for $t \neq 0$ and for which

$$\int_{-a}^{+b} \delta(t)\,dt = 1\,, \quad a, b > 0\,. \tag{2.19}$$

Integrals that involve the delta function are easily evaluated since

$$\int_{-a}^{+b} f(t)\,\delta(t)\,dt = f(0)\,, \quad a, b > 0 \tag{2.20}$$

provided $f(t)$ is continuous at $t = 0$. The reader should note that the dimensions of δ are $\sec^{-1}$ in this case.

One has from Eqs. (2.16) and (2.17)

$$\lim_{\sigma \to 0} E(t) = \delta(t)$$

and

$$\lim_{\sigma \to 0} \hat{E}(f) = 1\,.$$

Consequently, one is tempted to consider $\delta(t)$ and the constant unity as Fourier transforms of one another. Hence, one writes in a purely formal manner

$$\delta(t) = \int_{-\infty}^{+\infty} e^{+i2\pi ft}\,df \tag{2.21}$$

$$1 = \int_{-\infty}^{+\infty} \delta(t)\,e^{-i2\pi ft}\,dt\,. \tag{2.22}$$

The arguments leading to these equations were based on an appeal to one's physical intuition, but clearly, the integral in Eq. (2.21) does not exist in the mathematical sense of the word. Nonetheless, these Fourier transforms may be used in analysis and will give correct answers. The reader who is interested in learning more about the historical and analytic background of the delta function is referred to Chapter V of the book by van der Pol and Bremmer (1950).

As an illustration of the usefulness of the delta function, let us derive Eq. (2.14) from (2.13). Replace $\hat{Y}(f)$ and $\hat{E}_i(f)$ by their transforms and change the order of integration. This yields

$$E_o(t) = \int_{-\infty}^{+\infty} Y(\tau_1)\, d\tau_1 \int_{-\infty}^{+\infty} E_i(\tau_2)\, d\tau_2 \int_{-\infty}^{+\infty} e^{-i2\pi f\,(\tau_1 + \tau_2 - t)}\, df .$$

The inner integral is the same as that in Eq. (2.21) except that t is replaced by $t - \tau_1 - \tau_2$. Consequently, one has (making use of the symmetry of the delta function)

$$E_o(t) = \int_{-\infty}^{+\infty} Y(\tau_1)\, d\tau_1 \int_{-\infty}^{+\infty} E_i(\tau_2)\, \delta(\tau_2 - (t - \tau_1))\, d\tau_2 .$$

By using a slight modification of Eq. (2.20) one arrives at the desired result.

$$E_o(t) = \int_{-\infty}^{+\infty} Y(\tau_1)\, E_i\,(t - \tau_1)\, d\tau_1 .$$

The generalized linear network in Fig. 2.1 was characterized by the frequency response $\hat{Y}(f)$. Needless to say, one could use the Fourier transform $Y(t)$ equally well. This function is normally introduced into the analysis in a different manner. Suppose that the input to the network is the delta function $\delta(t)$. The corresponding output function $h(t)$ is called the *impulse response.* One sees immediately from Eq. (2.15) that when the input function $E_i(t) = \delta(t)$, the output function $E_o(t)$, which by definition is the impulse response $h(t)$, is given by

$$E_o(t) = h(t) = Y(t) . \tag{2.23}$$

Thus one has the important result that the frequency response $\hat{Y}(f)$ and the impulse response are Fourier transforms of one another.

The discussion of the delta function has caused us to digress from the original topic of this section, namely, the relation between time duration T and bandwidth W. The connection between T and W given by Eq. (2.18) is typical of many design restrictions that will be encountered below. If one wishes to measure the time of arrival of a signal with great precision, one makes T very small, but this gain in accuracy is paid for by the necessity of increasing the bandwidth. Likewise, if one wishes to measure accurately the Doppler resulting from target motion, one must utilize a narrow frequency band W in the signal spectrum. This gain in the accuracy of doppler measurement is paid for with a long pulse. Consequently, as long as one uses simple pulse shapes for which Eq. (2.18) is valid, one cannot make simultaneous, accurate measurements of doppler and range.

The remarks of the last paragraph should be elaborated upon to avoid misunderstanding. In order to achieve accuracy in the measurement of range one must use a pulse with a broad frequency spectrum W, but this is not necessarily a pulse that has a short time duration T. Similarly, one can measure doppler accurately provided the pulse has a long time duration T. This does not mean necessarily that the signal has a narrow bandwidth W. Both of these requirements can be achieved at the same time by designing a signal for which the product WT is large, say 10^2 to 10^4. The character of such pulses will be discussed further in Section 2.5.

2.4 Hilbert Transforms

The representation of the signal by a real function $E(t)$ is not entirely satisfactory. First, the mathematical analysis of circuit theory can be carried out more readily with complex analytic functions than with real functions. Secondly, the presence of energy components in the negative band of frequencies is not entirely satisfactory from a physical point of view. Further, Eq. (2.10) shows that all of the information about the Fourier transforms of a real pulse is contained in $\hat{E}(f)$ for non-negative values of f. For these and other reasons an alternate representation of the signal has been proposed.

One may associate with the real function $E(t)$ that represents the signal a second function $E^i(t)$ such that $E(z) + iE^i(z)$ is an analytic function of the complex variable $z = t + i\tau$. Further, this association may be achieved in such a way that the complex function $E(t) + iE^i(t)$ of the real variable t has a Fourier transform which vanishes for negative frequencies. In order to show how this can be done, make use of Eq. (2.10) to rewrite Eq. (2.3) as follows:

$$E(t) = 2 \text{ Real} \int_0^\infty \hat{E}(f)\, e^{+i2\pi ft}\, df\ . \tag{2.24}$$

If one expresses $\hat{E}(f)$ in polar form, say

$$\hat{E}(f) = A(f)\, e^{i\phi(f)}\ , \tag{2.25}$$

where $A(f)$ and $\phi(f)$ are real functions, Eq. (2.24) may be written

$$E(t) = 2\int_0^{\infty} A(f) \cos\left[2\pi ft + \phi(f)\right] df . \tag{2.26}$$

One may use this representation as a guide in forming the associated signal $E^i(t)$. One may consider a hypothetical network which will shift the phase of each frequency by 90° without changing the amplitude $A(f)$. The output of this network, designated $E^i(t)$, is

$$E^i(t) = 2\int_0^{\infty} A(f) \sin\left[2\pi ft + \phi(f)\right] df . \tag{2.27}$$

Any detection system, such as the human ear, which is not sensitive to phase will respond to $E(t)$ and $E^i(t)$ in the same manner so that to this extent they are the same signal. When the two signals $E(t)$ and $E^i(t)$ are combined, one has the complex signal

$$\varepsilon(t) = E(t) + iE^i(t) = 2\int_0^{\infty} A(f)\, e^{+i2\pi ft + i\phi(f)}\, df$$

$$= 2\int_0^{\infty} \hat{E}(f)\, e^{+i2\pi ft}\, df. \tag{2.28}$$

The evaluation of the Fourier transform of $\varepsilon(t)$ will be carried out in detail since it will furnish another example of the use of the delta function. When Eq. (2.28) is substituted into Eq. (2.4), one obtains

$$\hat{\varepsilon}(f) = \int_{-\infty}^{+\infty} \varepsilon(t)\, e^{-i2\pi ft}\, dt$$

$$= 2\int_{-\infty}^{+\infty} dt \int_0^{\infty} \hat{E}(f_1)\, e^{+i2\pi f_1 t - i2\pi ft}\, df_1$$

$$= 2\int_0^{\infty} \hat{E}(f_1)\, df_1 \int_{-\infty}^{+\infty} e^{+i2\pi(f_1 - f)t}\, dt .$$

It has been assumed in the last step that the change in the order of integration is permissible. When the second integral in the last member is compared with

Eq. (2.21), one sees that this integral is $\delta(f_1 - f)$. Hence, one has

$$\hat{\varepsilon}(f) = 2 \int_0^{\infty} \hat{E}(f_1)\, \delta(f_1 - f)\, df_1 \; .$$

If f is negative, the delta function vanishes throughout the entire range of integration. On the other hand, if f is positive, the integral is readily evaluated. Thus one has

$$\hat{\varepsilon}(f) = \left. \begin{array}{ll} 2\,\hat{E}(f) & \text{if } f > 0 \\ \hat{E}(0) & \text{if } f = 0 \\ 0 & \text{if } f < 0 \; . \end{array} \right\} \tag{2.29}$$

It is not apparent from the preceding analysis, but Titchmarsh (1959) proves that the two functions $E(t)$ and $E^i(t)$ are Hilbert transforms of one another. By definition this means that

$$E^i(t) = \frac{1}{\pi} ⨍_{-\infty}^{+\infty} \frac{E(t^1)\, dt^1}{t^1 - t} \tag{2.30}$$

and

$$E(t) = -\frac{1}{\pi} ⨍_{-\infty}^{+\infty} \frac{E^i(t^1)\, dt^1}{t^1 - t} \; . \tag{2.31}$$

The bar through the integral sign indicates that Cauchy's principal value is understood. This means that the improper integrals are evaluated as

$$⨍_{-\infty}^{+\infty} = \lim_{\epsilon \to 0} \left\{ \int_{-\infty}^{t-\epsilon} + \int_{t+\epsilon}^{+\infty} \right\} .$$

A brief table of Hilbert transforms is given in Appendix 2.2.

Born and Wolf (1959) and others refer to $E(t) + iE^i(t)$ as "the analytic signal belonging to $E(t)$." It is well known that if $E(t)$ is composed of a narrow band of frequencies centered about f_0 (and, of course, a similar band centered about $-f_0$), it is useful to represent it in the form

$$E(t) = E_0(t) \cos \left[2\pi f_0 t + \Phi(t) \right] ,$$

where $E_o(t)$ ($\geqslant 0$) is referred to as the envelope of the signal. Born and Wolf show that

$$E_o(t) = \left[E^2(t) + [E^i(t)]^2\right]^{1/2} .$$

An interesting paper by Cron and Nuttall (1965) shows how one may use the Hilbert transform to calculate the distortion of a wave reflected from an acoustic bottom at incident angles more grazing than the critical angle. The examples in their paper are an excellent supplement to the material presented here.

The importance of Hilbert transforms in analysis is not generally realized. As an example it might be mentioned that they are also used in the theory of dispersion relations of quantum mechanics (see pp. 6-11 of Screaton, 1961).

In summary it might be well to point out some of the advantages and disadvantages of the Hilbert transform. On the credit side is the fact that there is an elegant expression for the envelope of a narrow-band signal. Also, if one wishes to discuss doppler shifts, there is a great advantage in having only positive frequency components in the analytic signal. On the debit side is the fact that a second function, $E^i(t)$, is introduced in the analysis which in many cases must be generated internally in the signal processing equipment. It is at this point that an extensive knowledge of Hilbert transform theory on the part of the designer may lead to significant simplifications in the circuitry. It must be remembered that if one carries out an analysis of a system by transforming to analytic signals, one must also transform the expression for the background noise to the equivalent analytic representation.

2.5 The Ambiguity Function

It was pointed out above that simple pulses could be designed to give good range resolution or good doppler resolution, but not both. However, it is possible to introduce complications into the pulse structure so that range and doppler can be detected simultaneously. The suitability of a given pulse for the resolution of both range and doppler can be discussed with the aid of a function called the ambiguity function. The motivation for this definition cannot be appreciated fully until the concept of a matched filter is discussed in Chapter VII.

The significance of the ambiguity function for echo ranging was first pointed out by Woodward (1953). The motivation behind the definition of the ambiguity is discussed in some detail by Price and Green (1960). The present discussion will be limited to a definition and a brief statement of a few of the properties of the ambiguity function. Since doppler shifts will be introduced, the analysis will be slightly easier if one utilizes the analytic function $\varepsilon(t)$ rather than the real signal $E(t)$ in order to avoid the complication of negative frequencies. Suppose that the amplitude of the signal $E(t)$ is adjusted so that

$$\int_{0}^{+\infty} |\hat{\varepsilon}(f)|^2 \, df = 1 . \tag{2.32}$$

It might be noted that this integral gives twice the energy associated with the real signal. The reason for this is that the addition of a second signal in quadrature doubles the energy.

When the signal $E(t)$ is reflected from a moving object, there will be a doppler shift f_d in the frequency components, and since one is not certain of the exact time of return for the signal, one should introduce a delay in the time of arrival of the signal of amount τ_d. When these two shifts are introduced, the spectrum of the analytic signal becomes

$$\hat{\varepsilon}\,(f + f_d)\, e^{-i2\pi f \tau_d} .$$

Suppose now that this shifted and delayed signal is detected with a filter whose frequency response is $\hat{\varepsilon}^*(f)$, the complex conjugate of $\hat{\varepsilon}(f)$. It will be shown in Section 7.2 that this is the response of a filter which maximizes the signal-to-noise ratio when the background is a white noise. The output of the filter is a function of time but attention will be fixed on the value at $t = 0$, since, as shown below in Section 7.2, the maximum value of the signal-to-noise ratio occurs at $t = 0$. The output of the filter is given by Eq. (2.13) when $t = 0$. Since we are concerned with an analytic function, the output will be a complex number. Hence, the ambiguity function is defined as the square of the absolute value of the output of the filter, i.e., the ambiguity function ψ^2 is

$$\psi^2(\tau_d, f_d) = \left| \int_{0}^{\infty} \hat{\varepsilon}^*(f)\, \hat{\varepsilon}(f + f_d)\, e^{-i2\pi f \tau_d} \, df \right|^2 . \tag{2.33}$$

It is not difficult to show that this integral in the frequency domain can be replaced by an integral in the time domain to give the equivalent definition

$$\psi^2(\tau_d, f_d) = \left| \int_{-\infty}^{+\infty} \varepsilon\,(\tau)\, \varepsilon^*(\tau + \tau_d)\, e^{-i2\pi f_d \tau} \, d\tau \right|^2 . \tag{2.34}$$

The ambiguity function is a measure of the spread of the pulse $\varepsilon(t)$ in frequency and time. In fact, the width of the ambiguity function considered as a function of τ_d when $f_d = 0$ is approximately the reciprocal of the bandwidth of the signal, and the width as a function of f_d when $\tau_d = 0$ is approximately the reciprocal of the signal duration. If the signal $\hat{\varepsilon}(t)$ is normalized so that the total energy is unity, one can easily show that

$$\psi^2(0, 0) = 1 \tag{2.35}$$

and

$$\iint_{-\infty}^{+\infty} \psi^2(\tau_d, f_d)\, d\tau_d df_d = 1\,. \tag{2.36}$$

Hence, when one represents the ambiguity function by a surface over the τ_d, f_d-plane, the total volume under the surface is a constant independent of the shape of the signal.

Figure 2.2, which is reproduced from Fig. 10 of the report by Green (1963), shows the characteristic functions of a few pulse shapes. In the first three figures the values of TW are near unity and there is a single maximum in the surface ψ^2. The first two figures are self explanatory. The third pulse, which is a pulse shape similar to $E(t) = \exp(-at^2)\cos(\omega_0 t + bt^2)$, can be used to measure either doppler or range provided the other quantity is known. A pulse shape like this is frequently used in measurements of range on stationary targets.

If one wishes to make an accurate, simultaneous measurement of range and doppler, it is necessary to devise a signal shape which has an ambiguity function that is concentrated near the origin. Unfortunately, Eq. (2.36) in conjunction with Eq. (2.35) insures that this cannot be done unless one pays the price of having wide skirts on the ambiguity function, secondary maximum in the ambiguity function, or both. An example of the latter difficulty is shown in Fig. 2.2(d). In this case, which was analyzed by Woodward (1953), the short pulses of Fig. 2.2(b) are repeated at regular intervals. The envelope of the pattern is gaussian. The resulting ambiguity function has a beautifully sharp peak at the origin so that range and doppler can be measured simultaneously with great accuracy. Unfortunately, there are many secondary peaks whose amplitudes are not negligible. This pulse shape can be used only when one knows approximately the range and the doppler and is able, consequently, to gate out all but the primary peak.

Figure 2.2(e) is an example in which a pseudorandom noise of long duration is used to achieve a single, sharp peak in the ambiguity function. In this case there is a single maximum but this peak is surrounded by a high level skirt. This skirt will not cause serious trouble if the target has a well defined range and doppler. It will be noted that the signals (d) and (e) both have a large TW product and that the accuracy of measurement increases as the TW product increases.

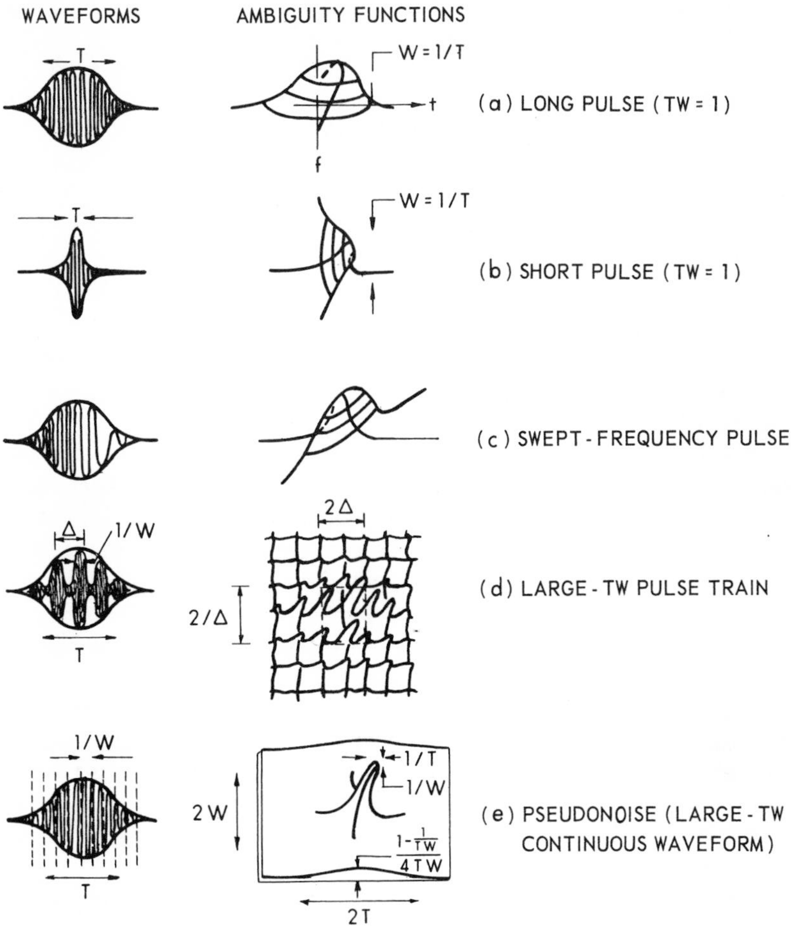

Figure 2.2–Ambiguity functions of typical gaussian-shaped pulse waveforms reproduced by courtesy of Lincoln Laboratory.

When a target is broad in range and doppler, the skirts of pulse (e) and secondary lobes of pulse (d) lead to a form of self noise. Price and Green define a scattering function which in effect resolves the echo into range and doppler increments and show that the total signal received is the convolution of the ambiguity function and this scattering function. When the scattering function is spread in range and doppler, the unwanted features in the ambiguity function contribute significantly and undesirably to the received signal. An example of a target spread in range is a complex target which is large compared to wavelength and which may be considered as an assemblage of discrete scatterers. If, as the target changes aspect, target strengths of the individual scatterers change rapidly, one has a target that is spread in range and doppler.

The nature of the ambiguity function is important in the study of volume and surface reverberation. The source of reverberation is scattering from objects which are distributed in range, and which, especially in the case of volume reverberation, may be distributed in velocity.

An interesting paper by Lerner (1958) discusses the question of designing pulses with large value of *TW* which have desirable ambiguity functions. He discusses also the use of a binary shift register to produce pseudorandum noise pulses.

2.6 Suggestions for Further Reading

A working knowledge of the simple properties of the Fourier transforms will be necessary for many of the topics discussed below. This material is available in many places. The books by Guillemin (1956) and Titchmarsh (1959) provide excellent accounts both of Fourier and Hilbert transforms at two very different levels of mathematical sophistication. An extensive table of Fourier transforms was compiled by Campbell and Foster (1931). Tables of Fourier, Hilbert, and other transforms are given by Erdélyi (1954).

Good accounts of the Hilbert transforms are not very common. In addition to the references of the last paragraph one can refer to Born and Wolf (1959) and Beran and Parrent (1964). These two accounts are concerned with electromagnetic waves but the reader can apply their comments and formulas to the acoustic case. The importance of Hilbert transforms in the field of acoustics is certain to increase. The paper by Gabor (1946) is fundamental and should be read carefully. The reader is also referred to a report by van Schooneveld (1963).

The ambiguity function is another topic whose importance for underwater acoustics will increase steadily. In addition to the writings of Woodward (1953), Lerner (1958), and Price and Green (1960) already mentioned, the reader should also refer to a paper by Siebert (1956), a paper by Stewart and Westerfield (1959), and a report by Green (1963).

Appendix 2.1

Fourier Transforms

$$E(t) = \int_{-\infty}^{+\infty} \hat{E}(f)\, e^{+i2\pi ft}\, df \qquad\qquad \hat{E}(f) = \int_{-\infty}^{+\infty} E(t)\, e^{-i2\pi ft} dt$$

General Formulas

(1) $E(t)$	$\hat{E}(f)$
(2) $a E_1(t) + bE_2(t)$	$a \hat{E}_1(f) + b\hat{E}_2(f)$
(3) $E_1(t)\, E_2(t)$	$E_1(f) * E_2(f) = \int_{-\infty}^{+\infty} \hat{E}_1(f_1)\, \hat{E}_2(f-f_1)\, df_1$
(4) $E_1(t) * E_2(t) = \int_{-\infty}^{+\infty} E_1(t_1)\, E_2(t-t_1)\, dt_1$	$\hat{E}_1(f)\, \hat{E}_2(f)$
(5) $E(at)$ $\quad a > 0$	$\frac{1}{a} \hat{E}\left(\frac{f}{a}\right)$
(6) $E(-t)$	$\hat{E}(-f)$

Functions

(7)	$e^{+i2\pi f_o t}$	$\delta(f-f_o)$
(8)	$\delta(t-t_o)$	$e^{-i2\pi f t_o}$
(9)	$\delta(t+\Delta t)+\delta(t-\Delta t)$	$2\cos 2\pi f\Delta t$
(10)	$\cos 2\pi f_o t$	$\frac{1}{2}\left[\delta(f+f_o)+\delta(f-f_o)\right]$
(11)	$\frac{1}{\sqrt{\lvert t\rvert}}$	$\frac{1}{\sqrt{\lvert f\rvert}}$
(12)	$\frac{\sin 2\pi a t}{2\pi t}$	$\begin{cases} \frac{1}{2}, & \lvert f\rvert < a \\ 0, & \lvert f\rvert > a \end{cases}$
(13)	$\begin{cases} \pi/a, & \lvert t\rvert < \frac{a}{2\pi} \\ 0, & \lvert t\rvert > \frac{a}{2\pi} \end{cases}$	$\frac{\sin af}{af}$
(14)	$\begin{cases} e^{i\mu 2\pi t}, & p < t < q \\ 0, & t < p \\ & t > q \end{cases}$	$\frac{i}{2\pi} \quad \frac{e^{ip(\mu+f)} - e^{iq(\mu+f)}}{\mu+f}$
(15)	$e^{-\lambda(2\pi t)^2}, \quad Re\lambda > 0$	$\frac{1}{2\sqrt{\pi\lambda}} e^{-f^2/4\lambda}, \quad Re\lambda > 0 \; . \; Re\sqrt{\lambda} > 0$
(15a)	$\frac{e^{-t^2/2\sigma^2}}{\sqrt{2\pi}\sigma}$	$e^{-\frac{1}{2}(2\pi f\sigma)^2}$
(16)	$\frac{1}{\sqrt{a^2+(2\pi t)^2}}$	$\frac{1}{\pi} K_o(a\lvert f\rvert)$
(17)	$2K_o(a\lvert 2\pi t\rvert)$	$\frac{1}{\sqrt{a^2+f^2}}$

(18)	$\dfrac{1}{(2\pi t)^2 + a^2}$	$\dfrac{1}{2a} e^{-a\,\lvert f \rvert}$
(19)	$\dfrac{\pi}{a} e^{-a\,\lvert 2\pi t \rvert}$	$\dfrac{1}{a^2 + f^2}$
(20)	$\dfrac{1}{\sqrt{a^2 - (2\pi t)^2}}, \quad \lvert t \rvert < a$	$\dfrac{1}{2} J_0(af)$
	$0 \qquad , \quad \lvert t \rvert > a$	

Appendix 2.2

Hilbert Transforms

$$E(t) = -\frac{1}{\pi} \int_{-\infty}^{+\infty} \frac{E^i(t^1)\, dt^1}{t^1 - t} \qquad E^i(t) = \frac{1}{\pi} \int_{-\infty}^{+\infty} \frac{E(t^1)\, dt^1}{t^1 - t}$$

General Formulas

(1)	$E(a + t)$	a real	$E^i(a + t)$
(2)	$E(at)$	$a > 0$	$E^i(at)$
		$a < 0$	$-E^i(at)$
(3)	$(a + t)\; E(t)$		$(a + t)\; E^i(t) + \frac{1}{\pi} \int_{-\infty}^{\infty} E(t)\, dt$
(4)	$E'(t)$		$[E^i(t)]'$

Functions

(5)	1		0
(6)	0	$-\infty < t < a$	$\frac{1}{\pi}\log\left\|\frac{b-t}{a-t}\right\|$
	1	$a < t < b$	
	0	$b < t < \infty$	
(7)	0	$-\infty < t < a$	$\frac{1}{\pi t}\log\left\|\frac{a}{a-t}\right\|$ $\quad t \neq 0$
	t^{-1}	$a < t < \infty$	$t \neq a$
		$a > 0$	
(8)	0	$-\infty < t < a$	$\frac{1}{\pi t^2}\log\left\|\frac{a}{a-t}\right\| - \frac{1}{\pi a t}$
	t^{-2}	$a < t < \infty$	$t \neq 0$
		$a > 0$	$t \neq a$
(9)	$(t+a)^{-1}$	$Im\, a > 0$	$i(t+a)^{-1}$
		$Im\, a < 0$	$-i(t+a)^{-1}$
(10)	$\frac{\lambda t + \mu a}{t^2 + a^2}$	$\mathrm{Re}\ a > 0$	$\frac{\lambda a - \mu t}{t^2 + a^2}$
(11)	0	$-\infty < t < 0$	$\csc(\nu\pi)\,(-t)^{\nu-1}$ $\quad -\infty < t < 0$
	$t^{\nu-1}$	$0 < t < \infty$	$\mathrm{ctn}(\nu\pi)\, t^{\nu-1}$ $\quad 0 < t < \infty$
		$0 < \mathrm{Re}\nu < 1$	
(12)	$\|t\|^{\nu-1}$	$0 < \mathrm{Re}\,\nu < 1$	$-\mathrm{ctn}(\frac{1}{2}\nu\pi)\ \mathrm{sgn}\, t\, \|t\|^{\nu-1}$
(13)	$\mathrm{sgn}\, t\, \|t\|^{\nu-1}$	$0 < \mathrm{Re}\,\nu < 1$	$\tan(\frac{1}{2}\nu\pi)\, \|t\|^{\nu-1}$
(14)	e^{iat}	$a > 0$	$i\, e^{iat}$

(15)	$e^{-a^2 t^2}$		$\frac{2}{\sqrt{\pi}} e^{-a^2 t^2} \int_0^{at} e^{\tau^2} \, d\tau$
(16)	$\sin(at)$	$a > 0$	$\cos(at)$
(17)	$\cos(at)$	$a > 0$	$-\sin(at)$
(18)	$\frac{\sin(at)}{t}$	$a > 0$	$\frac{\cos(at)-1}{t}$

PROBLEMS

2.1 Evaluate the transfer function $\hat{Y}(f)$ and the impulse response $h(t)$ for the three circuits in Fig. 2.3. Simplify your answers by introducing the time constant T = RC in circuits *a* and *b*, and $\omega_o^2 = 1/LC$ and $Q = R/\omega_o L$ in circuit *c*.

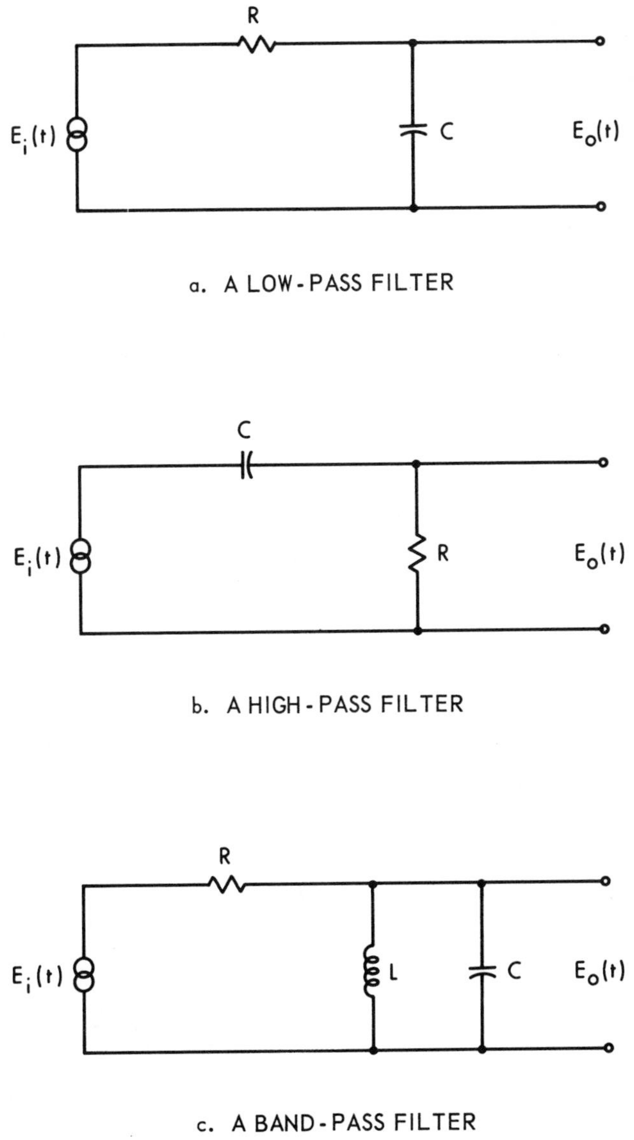

Figure 2.3–Illustrations for the problems.

2.2 A dc pulse $E_0(t)$ defined by

$$E_0(t) = 0,\ t < 0,\ t > T_1$$
$$= E_0 \quad 0 < t < T_1$$

is applied to the low-pass filter of Fig. 2.3a.

(a) Derive an analytic expression for the output.

(b) What is the ratio of the total energy of the output to the total energy of the input if T_1 = RC/2? For the purpose of this question interpret total energy as the integral of the square of the voltage.

2.3 In order to specify the frequency response of a narrow-band filter of bandwidth W it is tempting to assume

$$\hat{Y}(f) = 1\ ,\quad |f - f_0| < W/2$$
$$= 0\ ,\quad |f - f_0| > W/2\ ,$$

where f_0 is the center of the passband.

(a) Give two reasons why this definition for $\hat{Y}(f)$ is not physically acceptable.

(b) Show how one of these objections can be overcome by a change in the definition of $\hat{Y}(f)$.

2.4 Cauchy's theorem states that if $f(z)$ is an analytic function in the interior of and on a simply connected curve C,

$$f(\zeta) = \frac{1}{2\pi i} \oint_C \frac{f(z)dz}{z-\zeta}$$

where the closed contour integral is evaluated on the path C in the counter-clockwise direction. Show how one may utilize this theorem to find the shape of the pulse $E(t)$ whose Fourier transform is defined by

$$\hat{E}(f) = \frac{1}{a + i2\pi(f - f_0)} + \frac{1}{a + i2\pi(f + f_0)}$$

where a and f_0 are positive, real constants.

Hint. Let C be a semicircle with diameter on the real axis and let the radius become infinite. There are two cases according as the semicircle is above or below the real axis.

2.5 Calculate the Fourier transform of the unit step function $H(t)$ defined by $H(t) \equiv 0,\ t < 0$, and $H(t) \equiv 1,\ t > 0$.

Hint. First evaluate the transform of the approximation $H_a(t) \equiv 0,\ t < 0$, and $H_a(t) = \exp(-at),\ t > 0$ and take the limit as $a \to 0$.

2.6 The limiting process described in the last problem produces a singularity at $f = 0$ for the function $\hat{H}(f)$. Can one obtain a correct value $H(t)$ for the transform by using Cauchy's principal value defined in Eq. (2.31)? If not, how must one interpret the Fourier integral in order to obtain a correct answer?

2.7 Evaluate the integral

$$I = \int_0^1\int_0^1 (6-2x-2y)\ \delta\ (y-x^2)\, dx\, dy\ .$$

2.8 Show that the Fourier transform No. 13 of Appendix 2.1 is a special case of No. 14.

2.9 Derive the Hilbert transform No. 9 of Appendix 2.2.

2.10 Compute the ambiguity function ψ^2 for the pulse

$$E(t) = \exp\left\{-(at)^2\right\} \cos 2\pi f_o t.$$

Construct a model or plot contours for the special values $a = 1{,}000\ \text{sec}^{-1}$ and $a = 10\ \text{sec}^{-1}$.
Hint. Introduce approximations in the integrals by neglecting the "tails" of the integrals of the error functions.

2.11 Compute the ambiguity function ψ^2 for the pulse

$$E(t) = \exp\left\{-(at)^2\right\} \cdot \left[\ \cos 2\pi \left(f_o - \frac{W}{2}\right) t + \cos 2\pi \left(f_o + \frac{W}{2}\right) t\right].$$

Compare your answer with Fig. 2.2d.
Hint. Use the same approximations described in Problem 2.10.

2.12 A filter response $\hat{E}^*(f)$ is associated with a real signal $E(t)$. Similarly, one can define a second filter response $\hat{\varepsilon}^*(f)$ corresponding to the analytic signal $\hat{\varepsilon}(t)$ associated with $E(t)$. Show that the real part of the output of $\hat{\varepsilon}^*(f)$ is equal to the output of $\hat{E}^*$ when the inputs to the two filters are each equal to $E(t)$.

Chapter III

ELEMENTS OF THE THEORY OF STOCHASTIC PROCESSES

3.1 Description of a Random Process

Modern workers in probability theory make extensive use of the theory of real variables so that one cannot read their contributions without at least a working knowledge of this theory. For this reason a formal definition of a stochastic or random process will not be attempted until Sec. 3.3. Rather it will be assumed for the moment that the reader has an intuitive idea of what is meant by a random process and this intuitive concept will be delineated and sharpened through examples and discussion. When a physical process yields a quantity $x(t)$ such as pressure or voltage which changes with time, one can speak of the resulting function as a time series. When the nature of this time series is such that one cannot predict with exactness the future values of $x(t)$ from a knowledge of the past values, one may speak of a stochastic time series. There are two cases that are of special interest in the present study. One may observe the function $x(t)$ for a continuous interval of time, say $0 \leqslant t \leqslant T$, or one may observe $x(t)$ at a regularly spaced sequence of values $n\Delta T$, $n = 0, 1, 2, \ldots, N$. Both of these cases are important, but they differ sufficiently that parallel analyses will be carried out frequently for each case. They will be referred to as continuous and discrete time series, respectively.

In principle one may observe a time series $x(t)$ for $-\infty < t < +\infty$, but in practice a finite sample is all that one has for study. One may form the average of $x(t)$ and of various functions of $x(t)$ over the largest available sample. This type of average will be called a time average and denoted with a bar. Thus[1]

$$\overline{x(t)} = \frac{1}{T}\int_{t_o}^{t_o+T} x(t)\ dt \tag{3.1}$$

is the time average of $x(t)$ over the interval $t_o \leqslant t \leqslant t_o + T$. It is clear that $\overline{x(t)}$ will depend on both the value of t_o and of T. If values of $x(t)$ are available for a time interval large compared with T, one can compute many values of $x(t)$ for non-overlapping intervals of length T corresponding to different

[1] This notation is inadequate since the duration T of the sample should be specified in the left. This omission will be remedied in Eq. (3.10).

values of t_o. In this way one can obtain some idea of the evolution in time of the series $x(t)$. Time averages of any function of $x(t)$ can be defined in a manner analogous to Eq. (3.1).

There is an alternate approach to the analysis of $x(t)$. One can suppose that the experimental conditions which gave rise to $x(t)$ are repeated in a large number of almost identical experiments. The variability of the experimental conditions are chosen to reflect the statistics of the process. For example, if one wishes to analyze the thermal noise developed by a resistor, one can observe the potential difference across one resistor for a long time or one can imagine a very large number of similar resistors each at the same temperature and measure at one instant the potential difference across each resistor. There is no assurance that the average values obtained in these two manners will be the same, since one may have, for example, a resistor whose temperature is changing monotonically with the time.

An analogous situation arises in the case of reflection of sound from a rough sea bottom. To simplify the discussion it is assumed that the water is homogeneous and does not change with time, and that the average depth of the water is constant. Suppose that an acoustic signal is transmitted from a fixed receiver, reflected from the bottom, received at a detector, and the amplitude of the signal is measured at a fixed time delay relative to the transmitted signal. One would expect that no matter how many times the experiment was performed, the received signal would have the same value as long as the conditions did not change. In other words, this is a completely deterministic experiment in which cause and effect should apply without variation. However, if the source and receiver were moving over an irregular bottom, the sequence of received amplitudes would constitute a discrete time series. On the other hand, one could ignore the fact that the series of measurements was a time sequence and look upon the amplitudes as samples from a large number of similar experiments. In this case the distinction between a time series and an ensemble is almost a matter of definition.

The question of the precise conditions that must be placed on a stochastic process so that one can be assured of the equivalence of time averages and ensemble averages is one of the fundamental problems in the theory of stochastic processes. This hypothesis of the equivalence between time averages and ensemble averages, which is known as the ergodic hypothesis, was introduced into the scientific literature by Gibbs in his work on statistical mechanics. This hypothesis will be stated with more precision after some preliminary concepts have been defined.

3.2 Distribution Functions and Probability Densities

In a careful analysis of statistical theory it is necessary to distinguish between a random variable x and a particular sample value X of the random variable. This distinction will be made in the first part of the discussion. It is a distinction that the reader should bear in mind even when the notation is simplified by its omission.

Suppose that one has a random variable x whose behavior one wishes to study. For convenience it is assumed that the range of possible values of x is $(-\infty, +\infty)$ and that from *a priori* considerations or from observation, one can establish the probability of x having a value less than X. Thus it is assumed that one has a knowledge of a function[2] $F(\cdot)$ such that

$$\left.\begin{aligned} F(X-0) &= \text{probability that } x < X,\ -\infty < X < +\infty\,, \\ F(X+0) &= \text{probability that } x \leqslant X,\ -\infty < X < +\infty\,. \end{aligned}\right\} \tag{3.2}$$

The function $F(X)$ is defined to have the following properties:

$$\left.\begin{aligned} \lim_{X\to-\infty} F(X) = 0, \qquad \lim_{X\to+\infty} F(X) = +1\,, \\ F(X_2) - F(X_1) \geqslant 0 \text{ if } X_2 \geqslant X_1\,. \end{aligned}\right\} \tag{3.3}$$

The first two equations of Eq. (3.3) are an assertion of the scale of values assigned to $F(\cdot)$. Unity is adopted as the measure of a certain event. The third equation is an assertion that as the range of "acceptable" values of x is increased, one cannot have a decrease in the probability of obtaining an "acceptable" value.

The function $F(\cdot)$ is called a *distribution function*. This function has interesting mathematical properties, since it need not be continuous nor have a derivative at every point of its range of definition. For example, suppose that the value of x is determined by the flip of a bent coin by the rule that $x = -1$ if a tail turns up and $x = +1$ if a head turns up. The results of this experiment can be described by a distribution function $F(X)$ with the following properties. $F(X) \equiv 0$ for $X < -1$ since it is impossible for x to have a value less than -1. $F(X) \equiv 1$ for $X \geqslant 1$ since x is certain to have either the value -1 or $+1$ in each experiment. If the probability of a tail occurring on any flip is p, the distribution function, in accordance with Eq. (3.2), will be defined by $F(X) \equiv p$ for $-1 \leqslant X < +1$. It will be noted that the values of $F(X)$ are assigned so that $F(X)$ is continuous from the right. Thus by definition $F(-1) = p$ and $F(+1) = 1$. This distribution function is illustrated in Fig. 3.1.

[2] In careful mathematical usage one distinguishes between a specific value of a function $f(x)$ and the function itself $f(\cdot)$. This notation will be followed when the emphasis is on the function rather than on the argument of the function.

If the range of values that x may have is continuous and there are no isolated values having a probability different from zero, i.e., if it be assumed that $F(X)$ is absolutely continuous, one may take the derivation of $F(X)$, $F'(X) = f(X)$ to get a *probability density* or *frequency function* associated with the distribution. The probability density is related to the distribution function by

$$F(X) = \int_{-\infty}^{X} f(y)\, dy \; . \tag{3.4}$$

It is evident that the distribution function is a more general concept than the frequency function. In general the distribution function can be represented uniquely as the sum of three distribution functions

$$F(X) = F_a(X) + F_d(X) + F_s(X) \; , \tag{3.5}$$

where

$F_a(X)$ = the absolutely continuous part

$F_d(X)$ = a step function with a countable number of discontinuities. This is a function that is constant everywhere except at these steps. An example of such a function is shown in Fig. 3.1.

$F_s(X)$ = a singular function, i.e., a function that is everywhere continuous and has almost everywhere a derivative equal to zero.

In the examples considered in this book the distribution functions will not contain a singular part.

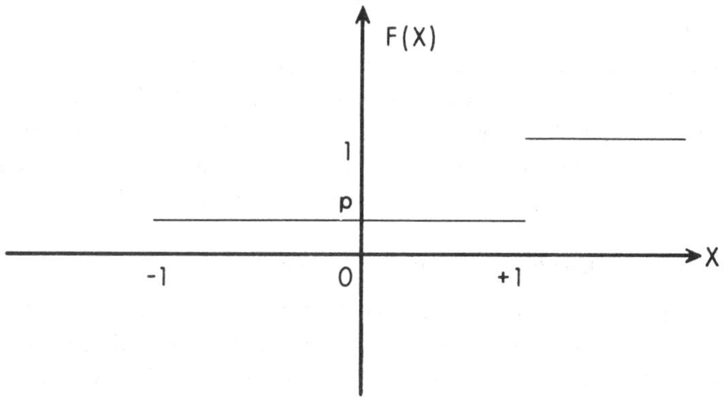

Figure 3.1–An example of a distribution function $F(X)$.

The reader is aware from the discussion of the delta function that the function $F_d(X)$ can be described by a frequency function composed of a sum of delta functions. Thus in the case of the coin flipping described by Fig. 3.1 one could write formally

$$f(y) = p\delta(y+1) + (1-p)\,\delta(y-1) \ .$$

These ideas can be repeated for a pair of random variables and extended readily to a large finite number of variables. The distribution function $F_2(X, Y)$ for a pair of random variables (x, y) is a function such that

$$\begin{aligned} F_2\,(X-0, Y-0) &= \text{probability that } x < X \text{ and } y < Y, \\ &\quad -\infty < X < +\infty, -\infty < Y < +\infty \\ F_2\,(X+0, Y+0) &= \text{probability that } x \leqslant X \text{ and } y \leqslant Y, \\ &\quad -\infty < X < +\infty, -\infty < Y < +\infty. \end{aligned} \tag{3.6}$$

It is required that

$$\lim_{X,\,Y \to -\infty} F_2(X, Y) = 0 \ , \qquad \lim_{X,\,Y \to +\infty} F_2(X, Y) = +1 \ .$$

The function $F_2(X, Y)$ should contain the distribution function $F_1(X)$ and $G_1(Y)$ of X and Y in the sense that

$$F_2(X,+\infty) = F_1(X), \ F_2(+\infty, Y) = G_1(Y) \ . \tag{3.7}$$

The functions $F_1(X)$ and $G_1(Y)$ are called the marginal distributions associated with $F_2(X, Y)$. The reader should note that this is not a reciprocal relation since, in general, $F_2(X, Y)$ cannot be determined from a knowledge of $F_1(X)$ and $G_1(Y)$.

When one considers N simultaneous random variables X_i $(i = 1, 2, \ldots, N)$, one will have an Nth order distribution function $F_N(X_1, X_2, \ldots, X_N)$ which contains all of the lower order distribution functions as marginal distributions. If the function $F_N(\cdot)$ is absolutely continuous in each variable, one can take partial derivatives to get the corresponding probability densities.

3.3 Random Variables and Stochastic Processes

It was mentioned earlier that the modern theory of probability is firmly rooted in the theory of real variables, but, unfortunately, this body of mathematics is not familiar to most physicists and engineers. Consequently, if one endeavors to make statements using this terminology which are simple enough in form to be understandable intuitively, it is most probable that no one will be pleased. The mathematical reader will object that the statements are inaccurate while the physical reader will think they are incomprehensible. Even so, this difficult path will be attempted. The reader who wishes to pursue the theory with some rigor is advised to read Cramer's (1946) excellent introduction to real variable theory.

In the examples of the last section the intuitive concept of the set of points on the real axis was used to define the distribution function of a single variable. Actually, this concept can be extended to a general set of points. The totality of points under consideration constitute a space Λ[3]. A set of points of this space will be denoted L, and any point will be denoted λ. Without entering into the details, since this involves measure theory, it is sufficient to say that (with suitable restrictions) a probability measure can be assigned to each set L of points contained in Λ. This is actually the procedure indicated in Eq. (3.3), since Λ is the real line, L is the interval $x_o < X \leqslant x_o + x$, and λ is any point of the line.

This brief description may enable the reader to understand the following definition of a random variable which is taken from Doob (1953, p. 5).

"A (real) function x, defined on a space of points λ, will be called a (real) *random variable* if there is a probability measure defined on λ sets, and if for every real number a the inequality $x(\lambda) \leqslant a$ delimits a λ set whose probability is defined, that is, a measurable λ set. Thus

$$F(a) = \text{probability that } x(\lambda) \leqslant a$$

is defined for all real a. In mathematical language a (real) random variable is thus simply a (real) measurable function."

This approach may be generalized significantly. Suppose we consider a function of the time $x(t)$ where t may be confined to an interval $0 \leqslant t \leqslant T$. These functions can be interpreted as the points λ of the space Λ so that the space Λ will be the set of all functions $x(t)$ which satisfy suitable restrictions. This leads to the concept of a family of functions $\{x(t, \lambda)\}$ where each λ determines the function and a probability measure is associated with each set L of points λ. If one restricts the discussion to N sample values $x(n\Delta t, \lambda)$, $n = 1, 2, \ldots, N$, the space Λ will have a finite number of dimensions.

Following Doob again, one can define a *stochastic process* as any family of random variables or functions $\{x(t, \lambda), t\epsilon T, \lambda\epsilon\Lambda\}$. Here we shall think of x as the random variable; t is the time at which x is observed, T is the range of values of t open to observation, and λ is a point of the space Λ on which a probability distribution has been defined. If T, the range of the parameter, is finite or denumerably infinite, $x(t, \lambda)$ is called a sample sequence rather than a sample function.

[3] In the mathematical literature, such as Doob (1953), the Greek letter ω is regularly used for this purpose. It is desirable to reserve ω for angular frequency, $2\pi f$.

These ideas can be generalized in either or both of two ways. One may replace t by several parameters, $t_1, t_2, \ldots, t_n$, each of which has its range T_i ($i = 1, 2, \ldots, n$). For example, in discussions of the topography of the ocean bottom $x(t_1, t_2, \lambda)$ would be a sample function describing the depth x as a function of horizontal position (t_1, t_2). Similarly, in discussion of random inhomogeneities in the water $\theta(t_1, t_2, t_3, \lambda)$ could be the temperature of the water at the point (t_1, t_2, t_3).

The other way of generalizing the function $x(t, \lambda)$ is to consider a set of functions $x_1(t, \lambda), x_2(t, \lambda), \ldots, x_n(t, \lambda)$. For example, these could be the simultaneous outputs of n hydrophones. A special case frequently encountered in the literature is that of two functions $x(t, \lambda)$ and $y(t, \lambda)$ which are combined to form a complex random variable $z(t, \lambda) = x(t, \lambda) + iy(t, \lambda)$.

If these definitions are unsatisfactory to the reader for any reason, he may prefer to consider probability distributions that refer to a single sample $x(t)$. One may say that a stochastic process is any process running along in time that is governed by probabilistic laws. The probability laws in this approach are stated in the form of the distribution function $F_n(\cdot)$ for n observation of the process. Thus if one observes the values $x_1, x_2, \ldots, x_n$ of the process at the times $t_1, t_2, \ldots, t_n$, respectively, these values are governed by a distribution function

$$\left.\begin{aligned} F_n(X_1 - 0, t_1; X_2 - 0, t_2; \ldots; X_n - 0, t_n) = {} & \text{probability that} \\ & x_i < X_i,\ i = 1, 2, \ldots, n. \end{aligned}\right\} \quad (3.8)$$

The stochastic process will be completely defined only if the infinite set of functions $F_n(\cdot)$, $n = 1, 2, 3, \ldots$ is known. Often the experimental evidence is limited so that only the first two or three functions are known. Any function $F_n(\cdot)$ contains all lower order distributions as marginal distributions as in Eq. (3.8).

The two points of view set forth in this section may appear at first glance to be completely different, but fortunately, they have a great deal in common for many statistical processes. Historically the two points of view arose in the development of statistical mechanics. If one has a liter of hydrogen molecules, for example, at standard conditions, one can, in principle, follow the evolution in time of the system and attempt to evaluate the probability density of position and velocities of the molecules. Alternately, one can conceive of an infinite number of vessels, each containing one liter of hydrogen molecules at standard conditions. One can attempt to find the probability density by determining the position and velocity of each molecule in each sample at any one instant of time.

The American physicist Gibbs introduced the hypothesis that these two points of view are equivalent and that time averages over one sample are completely equivalent to ensemble averages over all samples at one instant of time.

This hypothesis, known as the ergodic hypothesis, has given rise to an extensive mathematical theory. Unfortunately, the mathematical statements and proofs of the theorem are not easy to apply to physical situations, and one's physical intuition is not always a safe guide. This point will be discussed further as the need arises.

A readable but brief discussion of these ideas is given in Chapter II of Cybernetics (Wiener, 1948). A good account that is a happy balance of physics and mathematics is given by Khinchin (1949).

3.4 The Concepts of Stationarity and Ergodicity

One's everyday experience assures one that the first order distribution function $F_1(X, t_o)$ may depend on t_o. For example, suppose that a signal is emitted by a transducer and $x(t, \lambda)$ is the instantaneous pressure at some point produced by the returning reverberation in a single experiment. The range of values of $x(\cdot)$ that one may expect decreases with increasing time. In many cases this decrease follows a simple law so that by introducing some type of time varied gain, one can remove this trend and convert the time series to a new one which is free of this variation. There are other time series, for example the number of families of cephalopods in existence in any geological time, which are evolutive and which would lose most of their significance if the time variation were removed. The distinction between these two cases is not entirely clear cut, because, for example, even with the addition of suitable time varied gain, the reverberation will finally vanish. However, it seems reasonable to suppose that samples of the reverberation can be analyzed successfully as though they were samples of a stochastic process that continued forever.

The time series $x(t, \lambda)$ will be said to be *stationary in the strict sense* when all of the distribution functions $F_n(X_1, t_1; X_2, t_2; \ldots; X_n, t_n)$ are invariant under the time shift $t \to t + t_o$ for any value t_o. It will be seen later that this definition can be weakened and still lead to useful results. This is the reason for the qualification "strict." The example of reverberation given above makes it clear that real stochastic processes only approximate to mathematical definitions of stationarity, and part of the skill of the statistician is the ability to judge when the assumption can be applied to the data under analysis.

One is now in a position to discuss more quantitatively the concepts introduced in Sec. 3.1. If one has a family of time series $\{x(t, \lambda)\}$ where t is the time parameter and λ indicates the sample, one has the choice of forming a time average of one sample over some finite time interval T or of fixing the time t and averaging over the ensemble parameter λ. The latter can be achieved readily by utilizing the distribution function $F(X)$ to define the ensemble average of $x(t, \lambda)$ as

$$\langle x(t,\lambda)\rangle \equiv E\{x(t,\lambda)\} \equiv \int_{-\infty}^{+\infty} X\, dF(X) \ . \tag{3.9}$$

In general, this integral must be interpreted as a Stieltjes integral discussed in Sec. 4.2.2. However, if $F(X)$ is absolutely continuous, one can replace $dF(X)$ by $f(X)\,dX$, where $f(X)$ is the probability density, and interpret the integral as a Riemann integral. A brief discussion of the Stieltjes integral is given in Sec. 4.2.2. If the process $\{x(t,\lambda)\}$ is stationary in the strict sense, the distribution function $F(\cdot)$ is invariant under the translations $t \rightarrow t + t_o$ and the value of the integral in Eq. (3.9) is independent of the time, t.

The second member of Eq. (3.9) is referred to as the expectation of the random variable $x(t,\lambda)$ at time t. The angular braces in the first member will be used in the present account to denote the ensemble average, although many authors use this notation for the time average and use $E\{\cdot\}$ exclusively to denote ensemble average. Occasionally an expression will contain two distinct ensemble averages, as it seems better to have two notations available for this kind of average.

The time average over an interval T is defined as

$$\overline{x_T(t,\lambda)} = \frac{1}{T}\int_{-T/2}^{+T/2} x(t,\lambda)\, dt \ . \tag{3.10}$$

If the time series is not continuous but consists of a discrete sequence of samples $x(n\Delta t,\lambda)$, one replaces this definition by

$$\overline{x_N(t,\lambda)} = \frac{1}{N}\sum_{n=1}^{N} x(n\Delta t,\lambda) \ . \tag{3.11}$$

The ergodic hypothesis mentioned above can now be stated with more precision. This hypothesis asserts that if (1) a stochastic process is stationary in the strict sense, and (2) it cannot be subdivided into two or more subensembles each with probability different from zero or one, then one may equate corresponding time averages and ensemble averages. For example, if a process is ergodic one may assert that

$$\lim_{T\rightarrow\infty} \overline{x_T(t,\lambda)} = \langle x(t,\lambda)\rangle \tag{3.12}$$

for every sample choice λ with the exception of a few pathological cases the probability of which are zero. The left member of Eq. (3.12) does not depend on t so the right member cannot depend on t. It has already been remarked that this will be the case if the process is stationary in the strict sense. Conversely, the right member does not depend on λ so the left member cannot depend on λ. Crudely speaking, this means that each sample of the process must be typical or, if one is a little more precise, any sample of the process which is not typical must have zero probability of occurrence. For example, if one half of the samples of the process has a time average of zero and the other half has a time average of unity, one could not expect that any sample chosen at random would be representative of all the samples.

The assumption of ergodicity is severe, but it is one that greatly simplifies the analysis. For example, one can interchange time and ensemble averages readily in the course of a discussion. Unfortunately, this interchange is so convenient that one tends to make use of it even when it is unnecessary. As a result one tends not to distinguish whether or not a result really requires the assumption of ergodicity.

In the earlier discussions it has been suggested that many of the processes such as reverberation which arise in sonar measurements fail to meet the assumption of stationarity only because of a variation in intensity level that could be corrected for by means of a clever automatic gain control (AGC). Unfortunately, this is not always true. Volume reverberation, for example, consists of reflections from small obstacles or inhomogeneities in the medium. The nature of and the motion of these obstacles may vary with the range so that the returning signal has changing statistical parameters over and above the simple spherical spreading losses that can be removed by AGC. In the case of passive listening the signal and noise may not be stationary because of time variations in the sources and/or the transmission medium. A discussion of signal processing will not be complete unless it faces up to these problems. In particular, one must endeavor to determine a relationship between departure from stationarity and the degradation of performance.

3.5 Variance and Correlation Functions

Ensemble and time averages of a random variable are defined in Eqs. (3.9) and (3.10), respectively. Similar definitions can be made for the average of the product of two samples of a stochastic process. These averages, which are generally called second order moments, are so important that a wide variety of names have been introduced in the literature to describe them. The nomenclature introduced below follows closely that of Bonnet (1965b). These definitions have been discussed with Professor Bonnet, who has agreed to certain extensions of the notation to include time averages.

Suppose that one has a sample $x(t, \lambda)$ of a stochastic process that is governed by the second order distribution function $F_2(X_1, t_1; X_2, t_2)$. The *covariance* $\Gamma(t_1, t_2)$ is defined by

$$\Gamma(t_1, t_2) = \langle x(t_1)\, x(t_2) \rangle = \int_{-\infty}^{+\infty}\int_{-\infty}^{+\infty} X_1\, X_2\, d\,F_2(X_1, t_1; X_2, t_2)\,. \quad \ldots. \quad (3.13)$$

If one wishes to stress the fact that the two values $x(t_1)$ and $x(t_2)$ are from the same sample function, one may speak of the autocovariance. It should be noted that no assumption has been made regarding $\langle x(t, \lambda) \rangle$. If $\langle x(t, \lambda) \rangle \equiv 0$, the process is said to be *centered.*

If the stochastic process is stationary in the strict sense, the distribution function $F_2(\cdot)$ is invariant under a time translation. Hence, the integral in Eq. (3.13) will depend only on the time difference $\tau = t_2 - t_1$. In this case one may write

$$C(\tau) = \langle x(t)\, x(t+\tau) \rangle\,. \quad (3.14)$$

The function $C(\tau)$ is called the *correlation function* whether the process is centered or not. Since the process is stationary one knows that $\langle x(t, \lambda) \rangle$ is a constant, say $\bar{x}$. Some authors, such as Middleton (1960), prefer to define the covariance function as

$$\Gamma(t_1, t_2) = \langle\, [x(t_1) - E\{x(t_1)\}]\; [x(t_2) - E\{x(t_2)\}]\, \rangle$$

which reduces to Eq. (3.14) when $\langle x \rangle = 0$. Again, one can add the prefix "auto-" if one wishes to stress the fact that $x(t)$ and $x(t+\tau)$ are from the same sample.

One can write down a time average that is similar to Eq. (3.13) by defining the *time correlation function* as

$$\overline{x(t, \lambda)\, x(t+\tau, \lambda)} = \lim_{T \to \infty} \frac{1}{T} \int_{-T/2}^{+T/2} x(t, \lambda)\, x(t+\tau, \lambda)\, dt\,. \quad (3.15)$$

When the process is ergodic, the correlation function and the time correlation function are identical functions of τ and either one may be replaced by the other.

The concept of ergodicity is not entirely satisfactory from a practical standpoint because there is no simple method of testing a sample of a stochastic process to see if the process is ergodic. Often one has only a finite section of one sample so that Eq. (3.15) can be evaluated approximately, but there is no assurance that the result is a satisfactory approximation to the correlation function.

It is obvious that strict stationarity and ergodicity are rather strong assumptions and that for many purposes a weaker set of hypotheses will suffice. For example, if one is willing to restrict a discussion to ensemble averages, the question of ergodicity can be ignored. Alternately, if one only wishes to discuss second order moments, one may be content to assume only that $\langle x(t, \lambda) \rangle$ is a constant and that the correlation function $C(\tau)$ exists. In this case one says that the stochastic process is *stationary in the wide sense*.

Whether the process is stationary in the strict or the wide sense, the correlation function $C(\tau)$ has some interesting properties. First, it is a symmetric function of τ. Secondly, $C(0)$ is the mean square value of $X(t, \lambda)$ so it is closely related to the power associated with the process.

Wiener (1953, p. 154) proves that if the time correlation function defined in Eq. (3.15) is continuous at $\tau = 0$, it is continuous for all real values of τ.

The *standard deviation* σ is a quantity that is closely related to the covariance function. One defines

$$\sigma^2 = \langle [x(t) - E\{x(t)\}]^2 \rangle \tag{3.16}$$

and σ as the non-negative square root of σ^2. The standard deviation σ does not depend on the time if the process is stationary in the wide sense. If the square on the right side of Eq. (3.16) is expanded, a moment's calculation shows that

$$\sigma^2 = C(0) - [E\{x(t)\}]^2 \tag{3.17}$$

If the process is ergodic and centered, one has

$$\sigma^2 = \lim_{T \to \infty} \frac{1}{T} \int_{-T/2}^{+T/2} x^2(t)\, dt. \tag{3.18}$$

The acoustic signals which are the inputs to the hydrophones in sonar applications will almost always have an average value $E\{x(t)\}$ that is zero. However, in the analysis of systems used in signal processing, one encounters stochastic variables whose average value is not zero.

If the random variable is a complex number, the definitions given in Eqs. (3.13) and (3.14) should be modified by replacing the second factor in each integrand by its complex conjugate. When this is done for the correlation function $C(\tau)$, one sees that $C(0)$ is still real but $C(-\tau) = C^*(+\tau)$ where the asterisk means complex conjugate. The present analysis, however, will be restricted to real variables.

The important theorem that $|C(\tau)| \leqslant C(0)$ for all τ will now be proved for an ergodic process where the covariance function is equal to the time correlation. The proof will be based on the time integral so that one may introduce the Schwartz inequality. It is left as an exercise for the reader to prove the inequality without the assumptions of ergodicity. The proof is given below in the discussion leading to Eq. (11.9).

In order to prove that $|C(\tau)| \leqslant C(0)$ for ergodic processes one may utilize an important inequality known as the Schwartz, the Cauchy-Schwartz, or the Bunyakovsky inequality, according as one reads the German, French, or Soviet literature. This inequality states that if one has two real functions $g(x)$ and $h(x)$ whose squares can be integrated over an interval (a, b), then

$$\left\{\int_a^b g(x)\,h(x)\,dx\right\}^2 \leqslant \int_a^b g^2(x)\,dx \int_a^b h^2(x)\,dx \;. \tag{3.19}$$

A proof of this inequality is given in any good book on analysis; for example, Titchmarsh (1939, p. 381).

When this inequality is applied to the integral in the right member of Eq. (3.15), omitting the factor $\lim_{T\to\infty}$, one obtains

$$\left\{\frac{1}{T}\int_{-T/2}^{T/2} x(t,\lambda)\,x(t+\tau,\lambda)\,dt\right\}^2 \leqslant$$

$$\frac{1}{T}\int_{-T/2}^{+T/2} x^2(t,\lambda)\,dt \;.\; \frac{1}{T}\int_{-T/2}^{+T/2} x^2(t+\tau,\lambda)\,dt \;.$$

This inequality holds for all values of T, and, consequently it holds in the limit as $T \to \infty$. The two integrals on the right each approach $C(0)$ while the expression in the braces on the left approaches $C(\tau)$. Hence one has the inequality

$$|C(\tau)| \leqslant C(0) \;. \tag{3.20}$$

In view of this inequality the autocorrelation function is sometimes normalized by defining

$$R(\tau) = C(\tau)\,/\,C(0) \;. \tag{3.21}$$

The function $R(\tau)$, whose magnitude is never greater than unity, is called the *normalized autocorrelation function.* It is sometimes referred to as the correlation coefficient but this is improper since $R(\tau)$ is a function and not a number.

As an illustration of the autocorrelation and the autocovariance functions, consider an oscillator whose phase is random. That is, suppose

$$x(t, \lambda) = a_o \cos(2\pi f_o t - \lambda), \tag{3.22}$$

where

$$a_o, f_o = \text{constants}$$

$$t = \{t \mid -\infty < t < +\infty\}$$

and

λ = random parameter with a probability density $1/2\pi, 0 \leqslant \lambda \leqslant 2\pi$.

It is easy to show, by means of a simple trigonometric identity, that

$$x(t, \lambda)\, x(t + \tau, \lambda) = \tfrac{1}{2} a_o^2 \cos(4\pi f_o t - 2\lambda + 2\pi f_o \tau) + \tfrac{1}{2} a_o^2 \cos(2\pi f_o \tau).$$

One may take the time average of this quantity by applying Eq. (3.15) or take the ensemble average by multiplying by the probability density of λ and integrating over the range of λ. In either case one obtains

$$C(\tau) = +\tfrac{1}{2} a_o^2 \cos(2\pi f_o \tau). \tag{3.23}$$

As a second example, consider the random variable

$$x(t, \lambda) = a_o \cos(bt^2 - \lambda) \tag{3.24}$$

where

$$a_o, b = \text{constants}$$

λ = random parameter with a probability density $1/2\pi$, $0 \leqslant \lambda \leqslant 2\pi$.

A little algebra and trigonometry will enable one to show that

$$x(t, \lambda)\, x(t+\tau, \lambda) = \tfrac{1}{2} a_0^2 \cos\left[2b(t+\tau/2)^2 + \tfrac{1}{2} b\tau^2 - 2\lambda\right] + \tfrac{1}{2} a_0^2 \cos\left(2bt\tau + b\tau^2\right) \qquad (3.25)$$

The family of random functions defined in Eq. (3.24) differs from the family defined in Eq. (3.22) in that it is not invariant under a shift in the time. Hence, the present family is not stationary and one must not expect the time average and the ensemble average to be equivalent. If one applies Eq. (3.15) to Eq. (3.25) one gets the interesting result that

$$C(\tau) = \left.\begin{aligned} &1, \tau = 0 \\ &0, \tau \neq 0 \end{aligned}\right\} . \qquad (3.26)$$

In order to evaluate the integrals one can make use of Peirce's (1929) formula No. 487. On the other hand, if one performs an ensemble average, one obtains

$$\langle x(t, \lambda)\, x(t+\tau, \lambda) \rangle = \tfrac{1}{2} a_0^2 \cos\left(2bt\tau + b\tau^2\right) . \qquad (3.27)$$

The careful reader will have noticed that in the development extending from Eqs. (3.13) to (3.20), the concept of stationarity in the strict sense was not utilized fully. The only assumption made was that $C(0)$ existed and that averages such as those in Eqs. (3.15) and (3.16) depend only on τ. These slightly weaker assumptions are referred to as stationarity in the wide sense.

3.6 The Gauss Process

Of the limitless variety of distribution functions $F_n(\cdot)$ that may be envisaged, there is one class of functions that has been used most extensively in the analysis of acoustic signal processing systems. This process has an absolutely continuous distribution function so that one may describe it uniquely by the probability density function which is the gaussian function of n variables. This process is used widely in analytical studies for two reasons. First, the integrals that arise in the analysis are relatively easy to evaluate. Secondly, the process is completely specified by the second order moments.

A stochastic process $x(t, \lambda)$ is said to be *gaussian* if every finite set of sample values $x_i = x(t_i, \lambda)$, $i = 1, 2, \ldots, N$, satisfies the frequency function

$$f(x_1, x_2, \ldots, x_N) = \frac{|a_{mn}|^{1/2}}{(2\pi)^{N/2}} \exp\left[-\frac{1}{2} \sum_{m,n=1}^{N} a_{mn} \left\{x_m - \langle x(t_m) \rangle\right\} \left\{x_n - \langle x(t_n) \rangle\right\}\right] . \qquad (3.28)$$

In this expression $|a_{mn}|$ is the $N \times N$ determinant of the coefficients a_{mn}. One may assume without loss of generality that $a_{mn} = a_{nm}$.

This definition of a gaussian process does not presume a stationary process, since the quantities $\langle x(t_m) \rangle$ and a_{mn} need not be invariant under a translation of the time. However, most of the gaussian processes that are of interest in acoustic signal processing are stationary in the wide sense, and, furthermore, have the property that the average value of each sample $\langle x(t_m) \rangle$ is zero. Consequently, it is sufficient to restrict the discussion to frequency functions of the form

$$f(x_1, x_2, \ldots x_N) = \frac{|a_{mn}|^{1/2}}{(2\pi)^{N/2}} \exp\left[-\frac{1}{2}\sum_{m,n=1}^{N} a_{mn}\, x_m x_n\right] \tag{3.29}$$

where the quantities a_{mn} are functions of $t_n - t_m$ only. If one integrates $f(\cdot)$ with respect to each variable x_i, i.e., if one applies the operator $\int_{-\infty}^{+\infty} dx_i$ for all $i = 1, 2, \ldots, N$, except $i = k$, the resulting expression is the probability density or frequency function for x_k. If the series for $x(t, \lambda)$ is stationary, the resulting frequency function for x_k is a gaussian function independent of t_k.

One can utilize the frequency function (3.29) to calculate the ensemble average of the products $x_i x_j$ which are the *second order moments*[4] μ_{ij}. That is,

$$\mu_{ij} = \langle x_i x_j \rangle \ . \tag{3.30}$$

One finds quite generally that the second order moments μ_{ij} are the cofactors A_{ij} of the determinant $A = |a_{ij}|$ divided by the determinant A, and conversely. Thus if M is the determinant $|\mu_{ij}|$

$$\mu_{ij} = A_{ij}/A \quad \text{and} \quad a_{ij} = M_{ij}/M \ . \tag{3.31}$$

These general results will be illustrated for the case $N = 2$. By virtue of Eqs. (3.28), (3.29), and (3.13), one has

$$\langle x_1 x_2 \rangle = \frac{|a_{mn}|^{1/2}}{2\pi} \iint_{-\infty}^{+\infty} x_1 x_2 \exp\left[-\tfrac{1}{2}(a_{11} x_1^2 + 2a_{12} x_1 x_2 + a_{22} x_2^2)\right] dx_1\, dx_2 \ .$$

[4] This definition of μ_{ij} will lead to Eq. (3.31) only when $\langle x(t_j) \rangle = 0$ for all t_m. Otherwise, one must introduce the *central second order moments* by

$$\mu_{ij} = E\{[x_i - \langle x(t_i) \rangle]\,[x_j - \langle x(t_j) \rangle]\} \ .$$

This integral can be evaluated readily by the following steps. First, hold x_1 constant and complete the square of x_2 in the exponent. The resulting integral with respect to x_2 can be evaluated with the aid of a table of integrals. Then the process can be completed with respect to x_1. This gives

$$\mu_{12} = \langle x_1 x_2 \rangle = \frac{-a_{12}}{A} = \frac{A_{12}}{A}, \tag{3.32}$$

as required.

As the time interval $t_2 - t_1$ becomes larger, the two samples become more independent and one would expect $\langle x_1 x_2 \rangle$, μ_{12}, and a_{12} to approach zero. In this case the frequency function $f(x_1, x_2)$ approaches the product of two independent gaussian functions of the form

$$f(x_1) = \sqrt{\frac{a_{11}}{2\pi}} \exp\left[-\frac{1}{2} a_{11} \times x_1^2\right]$$

and

$$f(x_2) = \sqrt{\frac{a_{22}}{2\pi}} \exp\left[-\frac{1}{2} a_{22} x_2^2\right].$$

Since, for a stationary process, these distributions must be the same, one concludes that $a_{11} = a_{22}$ and, in general, $a_{11} = a_{jj}$ in Eq. (3.29).

Two reasons were given above for the popularity of the gaussian process in analysis. A more cogent reason is that many processes observed experimentally approximate very closely to the gaussian process. An interesting example that leads to a gaussian process is the shot effect. When an electron impinges on the plate of a vacuum tube a discrete electrical pulse is produced in the plate circuit. If the electrons arrive at the plate in a random manner, the resulting current in the plate circuit is a stochastic process. Rice (1944, 1945) has analyzed this phenomenon and shows that as the number of electrons per second increases, the stochastic process approaches a gaussian process. This model of the shot effect can be applied to many acoustic phenomena such as the collapse of cavitation bubbles. The noise at the surface of the ocean generated by wind and waves seems to be of the same nature.

Admittedly, many experimental time series are not gaussian. For example, in the Arctic Ocean there is a low frequency noise background due to the fracturing of ice caused by thermal stresses. This noise source is like the shot effect except that the number of events per unit time is too small to yield a gaussian process. Measurements of this nongaussian noise are presented by Milne and Ganton (1964).

However, if one has information about the behavior of the second order moments only, one can represent this process by a gaussian process having the same mean and second moments. Thus, unless one has experimental evidence about the third order moments, one may as well assume that the process is gaussian.

The preceding statement is a special case of a more general result proved by Doob (1953, p. 72). In this theorem it is supposed that T, the range of t, is given and two real functions $\mu(t)$ and $r(s, t)$, $[s, t\epsilon T]$ are given. The second function is subject to the conditions

(1) $r(s, t) = r(t, s)$

(2) if $t_1, t_2, \ldots, t_N$ is any finite set from T, the matrix $\| r(t_i, t_j) \|$ is non-negative definite.

When these conditions are satisfied, there is a real gaussian process $x(t, \lambda)$, $(t\epsilon T)$ for which

$$\langle x(t, \lambda) \rangle = \mu(t)$$

$$\langle x(t_i, \lambda)\, x(t_j, \lambda) \rangle - \langle x(t_i, \lambda) \rangle \langle x(t_j, \lambda) \rangle = r(t_i, t_j) \quad .$$

If the $N \times N$ matrix $\| r(t_i, t_j) \|$ is non-singular, the probability density of the N samples $x(t_i, \lambda)$, $i = 1, 2, \ldots, N$ is given by Eq. (3.28) when the matrix $\| a_m \|$ is the inverse of $\| r(t_i, t_j) \|$.

To demonstrate the original assertion it is sufficient to point out that if $\mu(t)$ and $r(s, t)$ are determined from a real, nonstationary process, the conditions of the theorem are satisfied and the "equivalent" gaussian process is determined uniquely.

The necessity of the second condition imposed on $r(s, t)$ is easily demonstrated. Suppose that one forms the square of a real, linear combination of N samples of the process $x(t, \lambda)$. Since the quantities $x(t_i, \lambda)$ are real, one must have

$$\left(\sum_{i=1}^{N} b_i\, x(t_i, \lambda) \right)^2 \geqslant 0 \ .$$

If one now takes the ensemble average of this quantity, one finds, upon interchanging the order of summing and averaging,

$$\sum_{i,j=1}^{N} \langle x(t_i, \lambda)\; x(t_j, \lambda) \rangle\, b_i b_j \geqslant 0 \ ,$$

or

$$\sum_{i,j=1}^{N} r(t_i, t_j)\; b_i b_j \geqslant 0 \;, \tag{3.33}$$

for all possible real values b_i. This is just the condition that the matrix $\| r(t_i, t_j) \|$ be non-negative definite.

The reader should note carefully the difference between a gaussian distribution and a gaussian process. The expression gaussian distribution may be applied to any random variable whether it is a sample from a process or not. The first order probability density of a stochastic process may be a gaussian function even though the process itself is not gaussian. For this reason one sometimes hears the unjustified statement that an experimental time series was "proven" to be a gaussian process when all the speaker had demonstrated was that the first order distribution was gaussian.

3.7 The Autocovariance Function for a Clipped, Gaussian Noise

One can illustrate the ideas developed in the last few sections by calculating the autocovariance function of a perfectly clipped noise. The results of this example will be needed later. Suppose that one has a stationary, stochastic process $x(t, \lambda)$ that is gaussian and whose mean is zero. A new time series $y(t, \lambda)$ is generated from $x(t, \lambda)$ by the nonlinear function

$$\left.\begin{aligned} y(t, \lambda) &= +1 \text{ if } x(t, \lambda) \geqslant 0 \\ y(t, \lambda) &= -1 \text{ if } x(t, \lambda) < 0 \end{aligned}\right\}. \tag{3.34}$$

The problem is to calculate $\langle y(t_1, \lambda)\, y(t_2, \lambda) \rangle$ from Eq. (3.13) with the aid of Eq. (3.29) for the special case $N = 2$.

The calculation of $\langle y(t_1, \lambda)\, y(t_2, \lambda) \rangle = \langle y_1 \; y_2 \rangle$ can be facilitated by considering the two dimensional cartesian coordinate system (x_1, x_2) illustrated in Fig. 3.2, where each point Q represents a possible pair of values $x_1 = x(t, \lambda)$, $x_2 = x(t_2, \lambda)$. The probability that a sequence of two observations of the y-series is (+1, +1) is the probability that the point Q is located in the first quadrant. Similarly, the probability that the sequence of values be (-1, +1), (-1, -1), or (+1, -1) is the probability that the point Q falls in quadrants II, III, or IV, respectively. The probability that the point Q is located in quadrants I, II, III, or IV may be denoted P_1, P_2, P_3, or P_4, respectively. These four events are mutually exclusive so one may add probabilities. Thus, the probability that $y_1, y_2 = +1$ is the probability that Q is located in the first or third quadrants which is $P_1 + P_3$. Similarly, the probability that $y_1, y_2 = -1$ is $P_2 + P_4$. Since the point Q is certain to fall in one of the four quadrants, it follows that

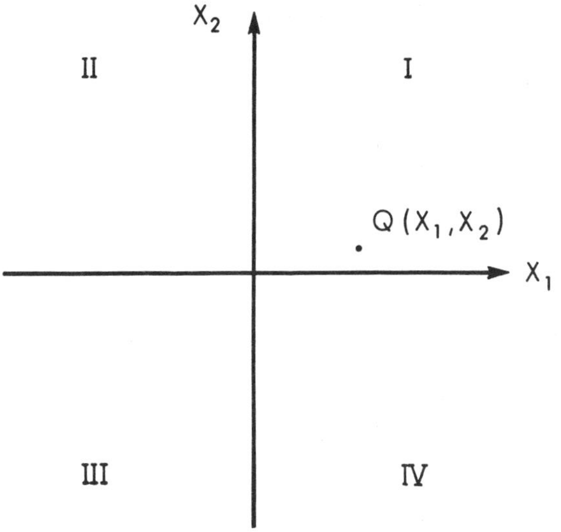

Figure 3.2–The two-dimensional space in which pairs of possible observations (x_1, x_2) can be represented by points, Q, and the four quadrants I, II, III, and IV.

$$P_1 + P_2 + P_3 + P_4 = 1 \quad . \tag{3.35}$$

In the case of two variables, Eq. (3.29) becomes

$$f(x_1, x_2) = \frac{\sqrt{A}}{2\pi} \exp\left[-\tfrac{1}{2}(a_{11} x_1^2 + 2a_{12} x_1 x_2 + a_{22} x_2^2)\right] \quad \ldots . \tag{3.36}$$

where $A = a_{11} a_{22} - a_{12}^2$ and $a_{11} = a_{22}$. The probability P_1 is given by

$$P_1 = \int_0^\infty \int_0^\infty f(x_1, x_2)\ dx_1\ dx_2 \quad . \tag{3.37}$$

The details of the evaluation of the integral for P_1 are given in Appendix 3.1 where it is shown that

$$P_1 = \frac{1}{4}\left\{1 - \frac{2}{\pi} \sin^{-1} (a_{12}/a_{11})\right\} . \tag{3.38}$$

Since $a_{11} = a_{22}$ one sees from the symmetry of Eq. (3.26) that $P_3 = P_1$. Hence the probability that $y_1 y_2 = +1$ is

$$P_1 + P_3 = \frac{1}{2}\left\{1 - \frac{2}{\pi} \sin^{-1} (a_{12}/a_{11})\right\}$$

and, by virtue of Eq. (3.35) the probability that $y_1 y_2 = -1$ is

$$P_2 + P_4 = \frac{1}{2}\left\{1 + \frac{2}{\pi} \sin^{-1}(a_{12}/a_{11})\right\}.$$

The expected value of $y_1 y_2$, $E\{y_1 y_2\} = \langle y_1 y_2 \rangle$ is $+1 \times (P_1 + P_3) + (-1) \times (P_2 + P_4)$ or

$$\langle y_1 y_2 \rangle = -\frac{2}{\pi} \sin^{-1} (a_{12}/a_{11}).$$

When the process is stationary in the wide sense, this formula can be put in a more elegant form by introducing the normalized autocovariance function $R_x(\tau)$, $\tau = t_2 - t_1$, of the process $x(t, \lambda)$. By virtue of Eq. (3.30) and a similar calculation for μ_{11}, one can show that $R_x(\tau) = -(a_{12}/a_{11})$, and so

$$\langle y_1 y_2 \rangle = \frac{2}{\pi} \sin^{-1} R_x(\tau) .$$

This is already normalized so one may write

$$R_y(\tau) = \frac{2}{\pi} \sin^{-1} R_x(\tau) . \tag{3.39}$$

The functional relationship (3.34) is invariant under a time translation. Consequently, if $x(t, \lambda)$ is an ergodic time series, $y(t, \lambda)$ is ergodic, and Eq. (3.39) is valid for ensemble averages as well as time averages.

3.8 Suggestions for Further Reading

There are a large number of books that discuss random processes at an intermediate level. Most of these are motivated by signal processing or control systems, and although they are usually excellent, they do not open the door to the mathematical literature. The best introduction to both the mathematical and the statistical developments is Cramér (1946). Two books directed towards stochastic time series are Bartlett (1956) and Hannan (1960). For the reader with considerable mathematical maturity the book by Doob (1953) is strongly recommended.

The French literature in this field is excellent. One might mention Lévy (1948), Loève (1948), Blanc-Lapierre and Fortet (1953), Blanc-Lapierre and Picinbono (1961), and Blanc-Lapierre (1963).

The material in Section 3.7 should be supplemented by an important report on clipped noise that was written during World War II. Fortunately, this report has been published recently (Van Vleck and Middleton, 1966).

Appendix 3.1

The Evaluation of Eq. (3.37)

It is required to evaluate the integral

$$I = \frac{\sqrt{A}}{2\pi} \int_0^\infty \int_0^\infty \exp\left[-\frac{1}{2}(a_{11}x_1{}^2 + 2a_{12}x_1x_2 + a_{22}x_2{}^2)\right] dx_1 dx_2 \; .$$

Transform to polar coordinates $x_1 = r \cos \phi, x_2 = r \sin \phi$. This gives

$$I = \frac{\sqrt{A}}{2\pi} \int_0^{\pi/2} d\phi \int_0^\infty \exp\left[-\frac{1}{2}(a_{11}r^2 + a_{12}r^2 \sin 2\phi)\right] rdr$$

$$= \frac{\sqrt{A}}{2\pi} \int_0^{\pi/2} \frac{d\phi}{a_{11} + a_{12} \sin 2\phi}$$

If one changes the variable by $2\phi = x$, one finds

$$I = \frac{\sqrt{A}}{4\pi} \int_0^{\pi} \frac{dx}{a_{11} + a_{12} \sin x}$$

This integral can be evaluated by means of Peirce's (1929) Eq. (298). By means of a trigonometric substitution suggested by the fact that $A = a_{11}{}^2 - a_{12}{}^2$, one obtains

$$I = \frac{1}{4}\left\{1 - \frac{2}{\pi} \sin^{-1} \frac{a_{12}}{a_{11}}\right\} .$$

PROBLEMS

3.1 Three ideal coins are tossed and the resulting number of heads that result are counted. Tabulate the probabilities for the possible cases that arise and draw the corresponding distribution function.

3.2 Illustrate the Cauchy-Schwartz inequality, Eq. (3.19), for the functions $f(x) = 1 + x^2$, $g(x) = x^3$ and the range $(a, b) = (0, 1)$.

3.3 Does clipping increase or decrease the magnitude of the normalized auto-correlation function of a gauss stochastic process? Give mathematical reasons for your answer.

3.4 A sinusoidal signal $E(t) = E_o \cos 2\pi ft$ is passed through an ideal, square law rectifier whose output is $x(t) = E^2(t)$. Compute the root-mean-square departure of $x(t)$ from its average value. If the output of the rectifier is filtered with the low-pass filter of Problem 2.1, what time constant T must the filter have in order that the root-mean-square departure be reduced by one-half?

3.5 Suppose that the water contains air bubbles the radius r of which is a random variable. The probability density governing r is such that $\ell n\, r$ (ℓn = natural logarithm) is a Gaussian function of mean $\ell n\, a$ and standard deviation σ. What is the average value of the volume of the air bubbles?

3.6 Consider Eq. (3.29) for the special case $N = 2$ and define $\sigma^2 = \mu_{11} = \mu_{22}$ and $\rho = \mu_{12}/\sigma^2 = \mu_{21}/\sigma^2$. Express the probability density $f(x_1, x_2)$ in terms of σ and ρ.

3.7 Two random variables x, y satisfy the frequency function, Eq. (3.29) where $x_1 = x$, $x_2 = y$, $M = 2$. The variable y is hard-limited as in Eq. (3.34) to give a new random variable y_c. Show that

$$\langle xy_c \rangle = \sqrt{\frac{2}{\pi}} \langle xy \rangle / \sigma_y .$$

Note that the answer is correct even if the gauss process is not stationary.

CHAPTER IV

Power Spectra

4.1 Definition of a Power Spectrum

In Section 2.1 it was shown that there is a perfectly simple way to associate an energy spectrum with a signal of finite duration or, more generally, with a signal of finite total energy. We now must consider the question of defining the equivalent of an energy spectrum for a stochastic time series. If $x(t, \lambda)$ is a sample of a stationary stochastic process

$$\lim_{T \to \infty} \int_{-T/2}^{+T/2} x^2(t, \lambda)\, dt \tag{4.1}$$

does not exist, and the energy dissipated in a one-ohm resistor by a current of magnitude $x(t, \lambda)$ amperes is unbounded. One is tempted to say that noise sources do not continue forever, so one should consider as the prototype of our noise source a time series $x_T(t, \lambda)$ of finite duration defined by

$$x_T(t, \lambda) \left. \begin{aligned} &= x(t, \lambda) \ , \ |t| \leqslant T/2 \\ &= 0 \qquad\quad , \ |t| > T/2 \end{aligned} \right\} . \tag{4.2}$$

This interpretation violates the important assumption of stationarity.

Alternately, one can give up any hope of describing a stochastic series in terms of energy and introduce in its place an average power density defined as

$$\lim_{T \to \infty} \frac{1}{T} \int_{-T/2}^{T/2} x^2(t, \lambda)\, dt \ . \tag{4.3}$$

When one compares this definition with Eq. (3.15), one sees that average power density as thus defined is nothing but the time correlation function for zero time shift. Thus $C\,(0)$ is the average power dissipated in a one-ohm resistor by a current of $x(t, \lambda)$ amperes. Theoretical progress is blocked, however, because there seems to be no way to distribute the average power $C\,(0)$

amongst the various frequency components. One cannot take the Fourier transform of $x(t, \lambda)$ since this function does not satisfy the condition given in Eq. (2.2).

Suppose that in an effort to solve this problem one takes the Fourier transform of $x_T(t, \lambda)$ to get an energy spectrum $\hat{x}_T(f, \lambda)$ and assigns an average power density $W_T(f)$

$$W_T(f) = |\hat{x}_T(f, \lambda)|^2 / T \ , \ -\infty < f < \infty \tag{4.4}$$

to the finite sample. At this point one is tempted to overlook the fact that $x(t, \lambda)$ is a sample from a stochastic process and to treat $W_T(f)$ as though it referred to a deterministic wave shape like those analyzed in Chapter II. In any discussion of the function $W_T(f)$ one must remember that two averages are implied, the time average and the ensemble average, and that every statement must be valid statistically for all samples of the process, i.e., for all $\lambda \epsilon \Lambda$, and not for the single sample from which $W_T(f)$ was obtained.

The analysis of the energy content of finite signals that was presented in Chapter II enables us to be sure that $W_T(f)$ is the correct average power density to use in connection with the signal defined by Eq. (4.2) since

$$\int_{-\infty}^{+\infty} W_T(f)\, df = \text{total energy in } x_T(t, \lambda) \ . \tag{4.5}$$

Middleton (1960, pp. 140-141) gives an excellent discussion of the reasons why one cannot take the limit of $W_T(f)$ as $T \rightarrow \infty$ and interpret this as the power density of the stochastic process. Rather, one must first perform the ensemble average on $W_T(f)$ for fixed T and then take the limit as $T \rightarrow \infty$. That is to say, one must first perform the ensemble average and then extend the time average to all time. When the question of the order of taking limits is this subtle, one cannot rely on his physical intuition, but must follow carefully the correct analytical procedures.

Although the problem of how one can assign a power spectrum to a random time series dates back to the 1890's, when Rayleigh and Schuster endeavored to analyze light waves, a mathematical solution was not available until 1930 when Wiener (1930) solved the problem. Khintchine (1934) obtained independently a solution to the problem so the relevant formula Eqs. (4.7) and (4.8) are often called the Wiener-Khintchine formulas.

Wiener and Khintchine showed that if one has a real, stationary stochastic process $x(t, \lambda)$, the function $W(f)$ defined by

$$W(f) = \lim_{T \rightarrow \infty} \langle \frac{1}{T} |\hat{x}_T(f, \lambda)|^2 \rangle , \tag{4.6}$$

where the ensemble average must be carried out before $T\to\infty$, may be properly interpreted as the power density per Hertz for $-\infty < f < +\infty$. Further, they showed the remarkable result that $C(\tau)$, the autocovariance function, see Eq. (3.14), and $W(f)$, the power spectrum, are Fourier transforms of one another. Thus

$$C(\tau) = \int_{-\infty}^{+\infty} W(f)\, e^{+i2\pi f\tau}\, df \tag{4.7}$$

$$W(f) = \int_{-\infty}^{+\infty} C(\tau)\, e^{-i2\pi f\tau}\, d\tau \, . \tag{4.8}$$

The functions $C(\tau)$ and $W(f)$ are symmetric so the Fourier transforms may be replaced by cosine transforms. In this case the power is thought of as restricted to positive frequencies. Thus one can write

$$C(\tau) = \int_{0}^{\infty} [2W(f)] \cos 2\pi f\tau\, df \tag{4.9}$$

$$[2W(f)] = \int_{0}^{\infty} C(\tau) \cos 2\pi f\tau\, d\tau \, , \tag{4.10}$$

and refer to $2W(f)$ as the power density, $0 \leqslant f < +\infty$.

The Fourier transform of $C(\tau)$ is denoted $W(f)$ instead of $\hat{C}(f)$ in accordance with the notation stated in Chapter II. This change in notation is made because the use of $W(f)$ is fairly well standardized. The letter W will also be used frequently as a bandwidth, but no confusion should arise since bandwidth is a parameter and not a function.

The reader will have noted that a numerical constant with dimensions must be added to Eqs. (4.6)–(4.10) if one wishes to assign a physical interpretation to the symbols. Thus, if x is volts, t is time in seconds, and $W(f)$ is a power density in watts per cycle per second, Eq. (4.10) needs a factor of one ohm on the left side to make the units agree. The reader can supply dimensional units in accordance with the requirements imposed by his problem, or he can treat all quantities as pure numbers. In the latter case he can follow

Titchmarsh's recommendation and assume that words like power, voltage, and cycles per second are added to give an exotic flavor to the mathematics.

The pair of formulas, Eqs. (4.7) and (4.8) are not fully satisfactory as they stand since they do not provide for a mixture of noise and steady tones. Since a pure tone represents ideally the concentration of a finite amount of power into a band of frequencies of zero width, one may enlarge the concept of the power spectrum by introducing delta functions. Alternately one can replace the power spectrum $W(f)$ by an integrated power spectrum. In order to do this one must introduce Stieltjes integrals. The details of this approach are given in the next section. The concept of the integrated power spectrum stands in the same relationship to the power spectrum $W(f)$ as the distribution function $F(X)$ does to the probability density $f(x)$.

Suppose that one wishes to introduce a steady sinusoidal signal of frequency f_o and amplitude a_o into the noise by adding a delta function to $W(f)$. One cannot add a single delta function $(a_o{}^2/2)\,\delta\,(f - f_o)$ since the power spectrum must be a symmetric function of the frequency. Hence, one is led to consider

$$w(f) = (a_o{}^2/4)\left\{\delta\,(f + f_o) + \delta\,(f - f_o)\right\}. \tag{4.11}$$

With this definition of $W(f)$, Eq. (4.7) yields

$$C(\tau) = (a_o{}^2/2)\cos\,(2\pi f_o \tau) \tag{4.12}$$

in agreement with Eq. (3.23).

Since the functions $C(\tau)$ and $W(f)$ are Fourier transforms of each other, the remarks made in Section 2.3 about the relation between the width of a function and its transform are relevant. In particular, if one has a narrow-band noise, the autocovariance function will decrease slowly with τ. Conversely, if the noise has a broadband width, the autocovariance function will approximate a delta function.

For the sake of future reference it might be pointed out if one has a stochastic process whose mean is zero, the mean square deviation of x, $\sigma_x{}^2$ is given by

$$\sigma_x{}^2 = C(0) = \int_{-\infty}^{+\infty} W(f)\;df\;. \tag{4.13}$$

4.2 The Theory of Integration

The theory of integration is a highly sophisticated branch of mathematics to which monographic books have been devoted (see, for example, Saks, 1937).

Nonetheless, it is possible to give a brief, usable introduction, provided the reader is willing to accept severe restrictions on the classes of functions that will be treated. The text of Cramér (1946) has an excellent introduction to the topics treated in this section.

4.2.1 The Riemann Integral

Consider a real function $f(x)$ defined over the closed interval $(a \leqslant x \leqslant b)$ and which is bounded over this interval. Subdivide this interval by a set of points $x_0, x_1, \ldots, x_n$ such that

$$a = x_0 < x_1 < x_2 \ldots < x_n = b \ .$$

Let m_i and M_i be the lower and upper bounds of $f(x)$ in the interval $x_i < x \leqslant x_{i+1}$, and let

$$s_n = \sum_{n=0}^{n-1} m_i \, (x_{i+1} - x_i) \ , \ S_n \sum_{n=0}^{n-1} M_i(x_{i+1} - x_i) \ . \tag{4.14}$$

Now let $n \to \infty$ in such a way that every interval $x_{i+1} - x_i$ approaches zero. The quantities s_n and S_n approach limits s and S as $n \to \infty$. If these limits are the same, their common value is by definition the *Riemann integral*

$$\int_a^b f(x)dx \ .$$

The basic problem of elementary integral calculus is the establishment of conditions on the function $f(x)$ so that the Riemann integral exists. A simple, but needlessly strict, assumption is that $f(x)$ be continuous in the closed interval $[a, b]$. A finite number of discontinuities in $f(x)$, each having a finite jump, is acceptable since the integral can be expressed as a finite sum of integrals where each of these integrals is restricted to an interval over which $f(x)$ is continuous. On the other hand it is easy to define a function for which the Riemann integral does not exist. Suppose that one defined the function $f(x)$ so that $f(x) = +1$ if x is an irrational number and $f(x) = 0$ if x is a rational number. In this case $m_i = 0$ and $M_i = +1$ no matter how the intervals $x_{i+1} - x_i$ are formed and s_n and S_n do not have a common limit.

There are so many excellent books which discuss the Riemann integral that it is not fair to single out one for reference. Nevertheless, rather than leave the reader with no reference, Chapter IV of Whittaker and Watson (1927) is mentioned.

4.2.2 The Stieltjes Integral

The Riemann integral can be generalized in the following manner. Suppose, as before that one has a bounded, real function $f(x)$ defined over the closed interval $a \leqslant x \leqslant b$. Suppose further that one has a bounded, real function $g(x)$ which is nondecreasing over the interval $[a, b]$. The two sums in Eq. (4.14) are now replaced by

$$s_n = \sum_{i=0}^{n-1} m_i \, [g(x_{i+1}) - g(x_i)] \;, \qquad S_n = \sum_{i=0}^{n-1} M_i \, [g(x_{i+1}) - g(x_i)] \;. \qquad \ldots \quad (4.15)$$

Once again n is allowed to approach infinity while the intervals $x_{i+1} - x_i$ are all required to approach zero. If the two sums approach the same limit, this common limiting value is defined to be the *Stieltjes integral* of $f(x)$ with respect to $g(x)$ and the notation is

$$\int_a^b f(x) dg(x) \;.$$

It will be noticed that in the special case $g(x) = x$, the Stieltjes integral reduces to the Riemann integral. For this reason the integral is often referred to as the Riemann-Stieltjes integral. Further, if $g(x)$ is absolutely continuous, one may write $dg(x) = g'(x)\, dx$ and again the integral reduces to a Riemann integral.

The requirement that $g(x)$ be a nondecreasing function of x assures one that the differences $g(x_{i+1}) - g(x_i)$ are never negative. One can relax this condition and require simply that $g(x)$ be of bounded variation since in this case one can always express $g(x)$ as the difference $g_1(x) - g_2(x)$ of two nondecreasing functions. An illustration of this decomposition is given in Fig. 4.1.

It is not the purpose of the present account to enter into the details of the necessary and sufficient conditions for the existence of a Stieltjes integral. The reader is referred to Widder (1946) for such details. Although the name may be new, the use of a Stieltjes integral is certainly familiar to the student of physics. Integrals such as $\int v dp$ in thermodynamics and $\int \vec{F} \cdot d\vec{r}$ in mechanics are Stieltjes integrals when p and $\vec{r}$ are functions of some parameter such as time.

The relation of the Stieltjes integral to the delta function is most interesting, and we have, already on two occasions, avoided the use of a Stieltjes integral by introducing a delta function. Consider a Heaviside unit step function $H(t)$ defined by

$$H(t) = \begin{cases} +1, & t \geqslant 0 \\ 0, & t < 0 \end{cases} \tag{4.16}$$

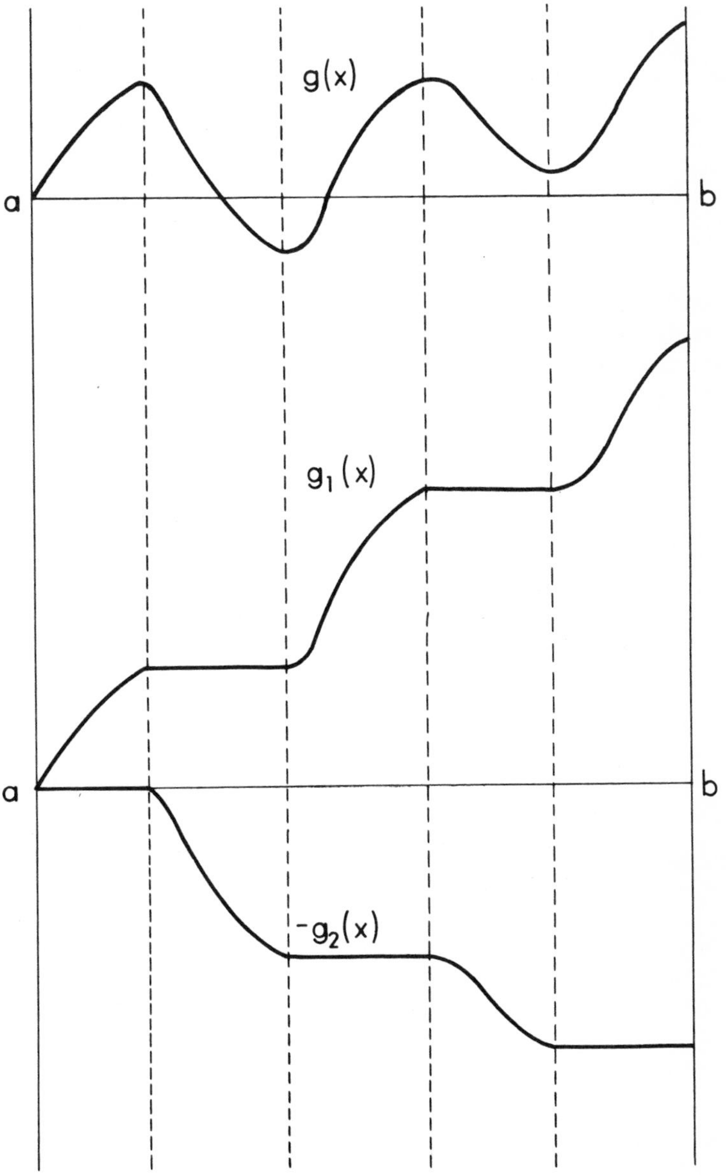

Figure 4.1–Decomposition of a function, $g(x)$, of bounded variation into the difference of two nondecreasing functions, $g_1(x)$ and $g_2(x)$.

At all points except $t = 0$ this function is continuous and has zero derivative. At $t = 0$ the function has a finite discontinuity and the derivative does not exist. The function $H(t)$ satisfies the conditions necessary for the existence of the Stieltjes integral $(a,\ b > 0)$,

$$\int_{-a}^{+b} f(t)\ dH(t)\ ,$$

provided the function $f(t)$ is continuous at $t = 0$. When one divides the interval $[-a, +b]$ into subintervals and forms the limits of the sums in Eq. (4.15), one finds the value $f(0)$ for the integral. Hence the Stieltjes integral of $f(t)$ with respect to the function $H(t)$ is precisely the same as the integral of $f(t)\ \delta(t)$ as defined in Eq. (2.20). This result is in accordance with the point of view that is prevalent among engineers and physicists, that $H(t)$ really has a derivative $H'(t)$ defined by

$$H'(t) = \delta(t)\ . \tag{4.17}$$

By this time the reader will recall the two occasions on which Stieltjes integrals have presented themselves naturally in the course of a discussion. The first instance arose when the ensemble average of a random variable x was defined in Eq. (3.9) as

$$\langle x \rangle = \int_{-\infty}^{+\infty} X dF(X)\ .$$

The distribution function $F(X)$ is a monotonically increasing function that is bounded and the integral is a Stieltjes integral. On the second occasion the Stieltjes integral was avoided by the artifice of using delta functions.

When the Wiener-Khintchine formulas, Eqs. (4.7) and (4.8) were introduced, the power spectrum was assumed to be free of line spectra. The possibility of a line spectrum was added in a heuristic manner by a pair of delta functions as in Eq. (4.11). It is now evident that instead of power density $W(f)$ one should introduce integrated power $\mathfrak{W}(f)$ defined so that $\mathfrak{W}(f)$ = total power in all frequency components less than f. With this definition Eq. (4.7) can be replaced by the Stieltjes integral

$$C(\tau) = \int_{-\infty}^{+\infty} e^{i2\pi f\tau}\ d\mathfrak{W}(f)\ . \tag{4.18}$$

In this form the presence of line spectra can be accounted for without any special terms in the formulas.

This brief introduction to the Stieltjes integral and the concept of the integrated power spectrum will enable the reader to follow an interesting discussion by Bartlett (1956, Chapter 6). Bartlett shows how one can infer the existence of the integrated spectrum $\mathfrak{P}(f)$ from the existence of the autocovariance function.

4.2.3 The Lebesgue Integral

The class of functions which have Riemann integrals is extremely limited from the viewpoint of a mathematician and many definitions of integrals have been proposed in an effort to extend the class of functions. One of the most useful of these generalizations is known as the Lebesgue integral after the discoverer. The definition of the Riemann integral given after Eq. (4.14) depends fundamentally on the idea of an interval $[x_{i+1}, x_i]$ on the real axis, so that, in a crude manner of speaking, the definition is valid only for functions which are well behaved in such an interval. On the other hand, it is easy to define the behavior of a function in terms of sets of points as in the example given above where the definition was in terms of the sets of rational and irrational points. These definitions do not lead to meaningful Riemann integrals.

The basic concept of Lebesgue integrals involves the definition of the measure of a set of points. It is highly desirable that the definition of this measure should yield the length of an interval $x_{i+1} - x_i$ when applied to the set of points $\{x | x_i < x \leqslant x_{i+1}\}$ since this will insure that the Lebesgue integral will be equal to the Riemann integral when the latter exists. In view of the fact that sets of points may be extremely complicated, the Lebesgue integral is defined not by dividing the abcissa into intervals but by dividing the ordinate scale into intervals, say $f_0 < f(x) \leqslant f_0 + \Delta f$ and asking, "What is the measure of the set of points x that satisfy this condition?" It is hardly possible to go beyond this description of a Lebesgue integral without giving much detail. There are numerous books that provide introductory accounts of these integrals. Of these only those by Cramér (1946) and Titchmarsh (1939) will be mentioned.

There is one example of a Lebesgue integral that agrees with one's intuition and which illustrates the critical features of this integral. Consider the function $f(x)$ which is defined to be +1 if x is an irrational number and 0 if x is a rational number. This function was mentioned above as an example of a function which did not admit of integration by Riemann's method. The set of points x, say in the interval [0, 1], for which x is a rational number is infinite but it is denumerable and the measure of this set, as of any denumerable set, is zero.[1] Hence these points do not contribute anything to the value of

---

[1] This statement is not self-evident. It is provided as an example of the property of measure.

the integral whether $f(x) = 0$ or is a finite number. On the other hand, there are so many irrational numbers in the interval [0, 1] that the measure of this set is one. Hence the Lebesgue integral of $f(x)$ is the product of the value of $f(x)$ which is one and the measure of the set of irrational numbers in the interval [0, 1] which is one. The Lebesgue integral in this simple example has the value one.

It is believed that this very sketchy and qualitative introduction will be helpful to the reader for three reasons. First, it should point out that readers acquainted with the theory of Riemann integration should not be intimidated by authors who state that their integrals are Lebesgue integrals. Often this statement is made for the sake of elegance rather than for physical content, so that if the reader simply thinks of the integrals as Riemann integrals he may miss some of the nuances, but no more.

Secondly, the reader will note that the events of probability bear a strong resemblance to sets of points. This means that a theory of integration based on the measure of a set of points is better suited to a discussion of probability. For example, the statement that a function has a certain property everywhere "except for a set of points of measure zero" is the analogue of a statistical statement such as no member of a family of stochastic functions $\{x(t, \lambda)\}$ is strictly periodic "except for a set of probability zero."

The third reason is the hope that this introduction might encourage the reader to learn more about the subject. The close relation between Lebesgue integrals and the foundations of probability are set forth by Kolmogorov (1933) who was the first to provide a satisfactory axiomatic basis for probability theory.

4.3 Analytic Examples of Power Spectra and Correlation Functions

If, over the band of frequencies of interest in an experiment, the power density $W(f)$ is constant, one speaks of white noise. One can approximate this situation by treating $W(f)$ as a constant W_0 over a frequency band large compared to the range of interest. Another approximation that is easier to handle in analysis is to assume

$$W(f) = W_o \exp\left\{-\frac{1}{2}(2\pi f\sigma)^2\right\} \tag{4.19}$$

where σ is very small but not zero. In this case, as may be seen from Eqs. (2.16) and (2.17),

$$C(\tau) = \frac{W_o}{\sqrt{2\pi}\sigma} \exp\left\{-\tau^2/2\sigma^2\right\} \cong W_o\ \delta(\tau)\ . \tag{4.20}$$

Suppose that this broad band noise is passed through a filter with a frequency response $\hat{Y}(f)$ so that the power spectrum of the output is $|\hat{Y}(f)|^2 W(f)$.

At this point one can let $\sigma \to 0$ with no difficulty, since the total power in the output is finite. One may calculate $C(\tau)$ for the output of the filter by computing the Fourier transform of $|\hat{Y}(f)|^2$. For example, if the filter has an ideal pass-band characteristic of width[2] W centered about f_0 and, of course, a second band centered about $-f_0$ one finds for the output

$$C(\tau) = 2WW_0 \left(\frac{\sin \pi W \tau}{\pi W \tau} \right) \cos 2\pi f_0 \tau \; . \tag{4.21}$$

The similarities between Eqs. (4.21) and (4.12) are suggestive. 2 WW_0 is the total power passed by the two pass bands centered at $\pm f_0$ and corresponds to $a_0{}^2/2$ in the first case. The finite bandwidth W yields a modulation factor $(\sin \pi W\tau)/\pi W\tau$ which approaches zero as $\tau \to \infty$.

This example is of considerable interest in that it shows how one can discuss the response of a network to noise without writing down an explicit function for the random variable $x(t, \lambda)$.

4.4 Analytic Representation of a Stochastic Process

In the last section it was seen that many results about stochastic processes could be obtained without having recourse to an analytic expression for a sample function $x(t, \lambda)$. Nonetheless, it is frequently useful to have such an expression. This problem takes two forms. One may have an experimentally recorded sample of a random process for which one desires an analytic representation. Alternately, one may wish to write down an analytic expression which can serve as a sample of a stochastic process with certain prescribed features.

Let us consider the first problem now and defer the second one until the end of Sec. 4.5. Suppose that one has recorded a function $x(t)$ over a time interval $a \leqslant t \leqslant b$ which is a sample random function. It will be assumed that this random function is a member of a stationary, ergodic stochastic process that has a zero mean and a continuous autocovariance function. There are many sequences of functions that are complete, orthogonal, and normal over the interval $[a, b]$ that may be used to represent $x(t)$. Choosing one of these sequences $\{\varphi_m(t)\}$, one may write

$$x(t) = \sum_{m=0}^{\infty} c_m \varphi_m(t) \; , \quad a \leqslant t \leqslant b \; , \tag{4.22}$$

where

---

[2] It is hoped that no confusion will result from the use of W_0 for power density and W for bandwidth. Both are standard notations.

$$c_m = \int_a^b x(t)\, \varphi_m(t)\, dt \; . \tag{4.23}$$

For any one sample $x(t)$ the coefficients are uniquely determined and there is no randomness. However, if this process is repeated for each member of the family of functions $\{x(t, \lambda)\}$, we get a new set of random variables $c_m(\lambda)$ where, as indicated, $c_m(\lambda)$ depends on the ensemble variable λ. This dependence is made explicit by writing

$$c_m(\lambda) = \int_a^b x(t, \lambda)\, \varphi_m(t)\, dt \; . \tag{4.24}$$

One may form the ensemble average of this expression and interchange the order of integration and ensemble average to give

$$\langle\, c_m(\lambda)\, \rangle = \int_a^b \langle\, x(t, \lambda)\, \rangle\, \varphi_m(t)\, dt = 0 \; . \tag{4.25}$$

The last step follows since the mean of the process vanishes.

The next question of interest is, "Are the pairs of coefficients (c_m, c_n) for any one sample, λ, statistically uncorrelated when $m \neq n$?" One can write

$$c_m(\lambda)\, c_n(\lambda) = \int_a^b \int_a^b x(t_1, \lambda)\, x(t_2, \lambda)\, \varphi_m(t_1)\, \varphi_n(t_2)\, dt_1\, dt_2 \; .$$

Taking the ensemble average, one finds

$$\langle c_m(\lambda)\, c_n(\lambda) \rangle = \int_a^b \int_a^b \langle\, x(t_1, \lambda)\, x(t_2, \lambda)\, \rangle\, \varphi_m(t_1)\, \varphi_n(t_2)\, dt_1\, dt_2 \; .$$

It has been assumed that the process is ergodic so the ensemble average in the integrand can be replaced by the time autocorrelation function $C(t_2 - t_1)$ of the process. Hence, one obtains the result

$$\langle\, c_m(\lambda)\, c_n(\lambda)\, \rangle = \int_a^b \int_a^b C(t_2 - t_1)\, \varphi_m(t_1)\, \varphi_n(t_2)\, dt_1\, dt_2 \; . \tag{4.26}$$

It seems most unlikely that this integral will vanish when $m \neq n$ for an arbitrary set of orthonormal functions. Consequently, the set of coefficients c_m of the expansion will not constitute, in general, a set of uncorrelated random numbers.

There is one case of interest that is especially simple. If the stochastic process is a white noise, i.e., if the autocorrelation function is a delta function as in Eq. (4.20) when $\sigma \to 0$, one has for Eq. (4.26)

$$\langle c_m(\lambda)\, c_n(\lambda) \rangle = W_o \int_a^b \int_a^b \delta(t_2 - t_1)\, \varphi_m(t_1)\, \varphi_n(t_2)\, dt_1\, dt_2$$

$$= W_o \int_a^b \varphi_m(t_1)\, \varphi_n(t_1)\, dt_1$$

$$= W_o\, \delta_{mn} \ .$$

Use has been made of the assumption that the set of functions $\{\varphi_m(t)\}$ is orthonormal. In this special case the coefficients are uncorrelated random variables and the mean square value of each component is W_o, the power density of the process.

It is possible, in principle, for a given autocorrelation function $C(t_2 - t_1)$ to find a set of orthonormal functions for which expansion coefficients are uncorrelated. Unfortunately, the details of this solution are rather involved and require a deep knowledge of the theory of integral equations. The interested reader is referred to Middleton (1960, pp. 383-386).

Of particular interest is the question of when can one use trigonometric functions for the orthonormal functions $\varphi_m(t)$. The answer is that trigonometric functions can be used only if the process is truly periodic. This case will be examined in detail in the next section. It is a common experimental practice to take a finite sample, say in the form of a recording on a magnetic tape, and make a periodic function by forming a closed loop. This is a practical method of getting the coefficients of the Fourier expansion, but as Eq. (4.26) shows, the resulting coefficients are not statistically uncorrelated. Nonetheless, it can be shown that if the length of the sample, $T = b - a$, is large enough so that the power density $W(f)$ does not vary appreciably over intervals of width many times $1/T$, the correlation between the Fourier coefficients is so slight that in practice one may consider them to be uncorrelated (Blackman, 1957).

A proof that the coefficients c_m of the expansion, Eq. (4.22), are uncorrelated gives a result that is weaker than one would like. A conclusion that is more useful in the analysis of signal processing is that the coefficients are statistically independent of one another. This stronger property is often introduced as a separate assumption. The reader is referred to Blackman (1957) for a discussion of this point. He says that if $x(t)$ is a gaussian process whose mean value is zero, the vanishing of the expectation $\langle c_m(\lambda)c_n(\lambda)\rangle$ implies the statistical independence of the coefficients.

4.5 The Analytic Representation of a Periodic Process

Let us suppose that the stochastic process is periodic with period T so that any sample may be written as

$$x(t, \lambda) = \sum_{n=0}^{\infty} \left\{a_n \cos(2\pi nt/T) + b_n \sin(2\pi nt/T)\right\} . \tag{4.27}$$

Note that $\langle\ \rangle$ is an ensemble average over λ so that $\langle x(t, \lambda)\rangle$ would be a function of the time were it not for the assumption of ergodicity.

Take the ensemble average of Eq. (4.27) and assume that the infinite summation and the ensemble average can be interchanged. If the stochastic process has an average value of zero, one has

$$0 \equiv \sum_{n=0}^{\infty} \left\{\langle a_n\rangle \cos(2\pi nt/T) + \langle b_n\rangle \sin(2\pi nt/T)\right\} ,$$

an identity in t. Since the sines and cosines form a set of orthogonal functions over the interval of length T, this equation will be true if and only if

$$\langle a_n\rangle = \langle b_n\rangle = 0, \quad n=0, 1, 2, \ldots \tag{4.28}$$

Next suppose one computes the autocorrelation function from the sample Eq. (4.27). By virtue of the definition,

$$C(\tau, \lambda) = \lim_{T_1 \to \infty} \frac{1}{T_1} \int_{-T_1/2}^{+T_1/2} x(t, \lambda)\, x(t + \tau, \lambda)\, dt .$$

The parameter λ is inserted in $C(\cdot)$ to remind the reader that this function is computed for a sample value λ. Now $x(t, \lambda)$ is periodic of period T so if one writes $T_1 = (2N+1)T + 2t_0$, the integral may be written as

$$C(\tau, \lambda) = \frac{1}{T} \int_{-T/2}^{+T/2} x(t, \lambda)\, x(t + \tau, \lambda)\, dt$$

$$+ \lim_{T_1 \to \infty} \frac{1}{T_1} \left\{ \int_{-NT-t_o}^{-NT} \quad dt + \int_{+NT}^{NT+t_o} \quad dt \right\} .$$

The integrand in the last two integrals is bounded and the terms approach zero in the limit so they may be dropped. This gives

$$C(\tau, \lambda) = \frac{1}{T} \int_{-T/2}^{+T/2} x(t, \lambda)\, x(t + \tau, \lambda)\, dt \tag{4.29}$$

for the periodic process. When Eq. (4.27) is substituted in Eq. (4.29) and the trigonometric terms are expanded, one gets products such as $\begin{smallmatrix}\sin\\ \cos\end{smallmatrix}(2\pi mt/T)$ $\begin{smallmatrix}\sin\\ \cos\end{smallmatrix}(2\pi nt/T)$. These are all orthogonal over the basic interval T except for $\sin^2(2\pi mt/T)$ and $\cos^2(2\pi mt/T)$. These yield integrals equal to $T/2$, if $m \neq 0$. When the details are carried through, one gets

$$C(\tau, \lambda) = a_o{}^2 + \frac{1}{2} \sum_{n=1}^{\infty} (a_n{}^2 + b_n{}^2) \cos(2\pi n\tau/T) . \tag{4.30}$$

This function is symmetric in τ, as it should be, and $C(0)$ is equal to the sum of the powers in all the components, including the dc term if it is present.

It will be remembered that this calculation has been carried out for one sample of the process corresponding to a particular value of λ, the ensemble parameters. In order to obtain an autocorrelation function that is typical of the process rather than of the sample, one must form an ensemble average on λ. This gives

$$C(\tau) = \langle C(t, \lambda) \rangle = \langle a_o{}^2 \rangle + \frac{1}{2} \sum_{n=1}^{\infty} \left\{ \langle a_n{}^2 \rangle + \langle b_n{}^2 \rangle \right\} \cos(2\pi n\tau/T).$$

$$\ldots . \tag{4.31}$$

A digression is introduced at this point by returning to the subject of the last section. If the periodic autocorrelation function, Eq. (4.31), is substituted into Eq. (4.26) and if the functions[3] $\varphi_m(t_1), \varphi_m(t_2)$ are replaced by $\genfrac{}{}{0pt}{}{\sin}{\cos}(2\pi m t_1/T)$ and $\genfrac{}{}{0pt}{}{\sin}{\cos}(2\pi n t_2/T)$, one finds that

$$\left.\begin{aligned} \langle a_m\, a_n \rangle &= \langle b_m\, b_n \rangle = 0 \text{ if } m \neq n\,, \\ \langle a_m\, b_n \rangle &= 0 \text{ for all } m, n \\ \langle a_m{}^2 \rangle &= \langle b_m{}^2 \rangle\,, m \neq 0. \end{aligned}\right\} \tag{4.32}$$

This is the proof of the statement made above that if the process is truly periodic, it can be represented by a Fourier series whose coefficients are uncorrelated.

Returning to the discussion of the periodic stochastic process, one can use the Wiener-Khintchine theorem, Eq. (4.8), to find the power spectrum associated with Eq. (4.31). When one makes use of the fact that $\langle a_n{}^2 \rangle = \langle b_n{}^2 \rangle$, one finds

$$W(f) = \frac{1}{2} \sum_{n=-\infty}^{+\infty} \epsilon_n \ \langle a_n{}^2 \rangle \ \delta\left(f + \frac{n}{T}\right), \tag{4.33}$$

where, by definition, $\langle a_n{}^2 \rangle = \langle a_{-n}{}^2 \rangle$, and ϵ_n is the Neumann factor, $\epsilon_n = 1$, $n \neq 0$, $\epsilon_0 = 2$. This formula agrees exactly with one's ideas of the distribution of power in the components of a Fourier series when it is remembered that the power has been divided between negative and positive frequencies.

When T is large, the spectral components are close together, since they are separated by a frequency of $1/T$. If one is willing to "spread out" the power into a continuous spectrum the power density at frequency $f_n = n/T$ is defined so that

$$W(f_n)\,\Delta f = W(f_n)\,\frac{1}{T} = \frac{1}{2}\langle a_n{}^2 \rangle$$

except at $n = 0$. The smoothed spectrum is

---

[3] Each constant c_m (except c_0) in Eq. (4.22) must be replaced by a pair of constants a_m, b_m. The functions $\genfrac{}{}{0pt}{}{\sin}{\cos}(2\pi mt/T)$ can be normalized, if one wishes, by multiplying by $\sqrt{2/T}$ ($\sqrt{1/T}$ if $m = 0$).

$$\begin{aligned} W(f_n) &= \frac{T}{2} \langle a_n^2 \rangle \\ W(0) &= T \langle a_0^2 \rangle . \end{aligned} \tag{4.34}$$

It will now be shown that the result of this heuristic derivation of a continuous power spectrum for a periodic process for large periods T is compatible with the Wiener-Khintchine theorem as it should be. If Eq. (4.32) is rewritten using $\langle a_n^2 \rangle = \langle b_n^2 \rangle$ and extending the sum over negative integers, one has

$$C(\tau) = \frac{T}{2} \sum_{n=-\infty}^{+\infty} \epsilon_n \langle a_n^2 \rangle \left(\cos 2\pi \frac{n}{T} \tau\right)\left(\frac{1}{T}\right) ,$$

where again, by definition, $\langle a_{-n}^2 \rangle = \langle a_n^2 \rangle$. Following the standard procedure in going from a Fourier series to an integral, set $(1/T) = \Delta f$, $(n/T) = f$, and use Eq. (4.34). In the limit as $T \to \infty$ this gives

$$C(\tau) = \int_{-\infty}^{+\infty} W(f) \cos 2\pi f \tau \, df$$

as required.

The example of the periodic process is discussed in some detail since it will help the reader to understand an artifice that is frequently used to analyze the response of a system. The reader is referred to Bryn (1962) for an example. It is assumed at the beginning of the analysis that the process is periodic and can be represented by a Fourier series. At the end of the analysis one can let $T \to \infty$ to obtain results for a non-periodic process. It is often realistic to assume that each coefficient of the series has a gaussian distribution with zero mean. That is, it is assumed that each coefficient is a random variable whose probability density is

$$f(a_n) = \frac{1}{\sqrt{2\pi \langle a_n^2 \rangle}} \exp\left\{-a_n^2/2 \langle a_n^2 \rangle\right\} . \tag{4.35}$$

By virtue of Eq. (4.34), one can choose the gaussian distribution so that the stochastic process described by Eqs. (4.27) and (4.35) approximates closely to any assigned power spectrum. The standard deviation of a_n or b_n is $\sqrt{W(f_n)\Delta f}$ where, as before, $f_n = n/T$, $\Delta f = 1/t$.

The last step in the analysis is the derivation of the probability density of the random variable $x(t, \lambda)$ defined in Eq. (4.27). In order to avoid arguments based on infinite sums, let us assume that all harmonic components of frequency greater than $f_N = N/T$ have zero amplitude. This is not a significant restriction from a practical point of view. Any constant time t the random variable is given by

$$x(t, \lambda) = \sum_{n=0}^{N} \left\{ a_n \cos(2\pi nt/T) + b_n \sin(2\pi nt/T) \right\} .$$

The a_n's and b_n's are independent, gaussian variables. The coefficients $\begin{smallmatrix}\sin\\ \cos\end{smallmatrix}(2\pi nt/T)$ are constants so the finite sum is a gaussian variable whose mean square value is the sum of the mean square values of the individual terms. Thus

$$\langle x^2 \rangle = \sum_{n=0}^{N} \left\{ \langle a_n{}^2 \rangle \cos^2(2\pi nt/T) + \langle b_n{}^2 \rangle \sin^2(2\pi nt/T) \right\}$$

but $\langle a_n{}^2 \rangle = \langle b_n{}^2 \rangle$ so

$$\langle x^2 \rangle = \frac{1}{2} \sum_{n=-N}^{+N} \epsilon_n \langle a_n{}^2 \rangle = C(0) . \tag{4.36}$$

the last step follows from Eq. (4.30). Hence, the random variable $x(t, \lambda)$ has the probability density function

$$f(x) = \frac{1}{\sqrt{2\pi c(0)}} \exp\left\{-x^2/2\, C(0)\right\} . \tag{4.37}$$

We are now in a position to answer the second question raised at the beginning of Sec. 4.4. One can write down a Fourier series representation of a sample of a random process when either the autocorrelation function or the power spectrum is specified.

PROBLEMS

4.1 The input to the low-pass filter of Problem 2.1 is a white noise with spectral density W_o volts^2 per Hz. What is the autocovariance function of output of the filter?

4.2 Repeat Problem 4.1 for the high-pass filter in Problem 2.1.

4.3 Consider a phase-modulated signal

$$E(t) = E_o \cos\left\{\omega_1 t + a \sin \omega_2 t\right\}$$

where $a \ll 1$ and $\omega_2 \ll \omega_1$. What is the integrated power density $\mathcal{W}(f)$ of this signal?

4.4 The input to the low-pass filter of Problem 2.1 is a white noise whose power density per unit Hertz is W_o. The resulting output voltage has a root-mean-square-value $E(T)$ where T is the time constant of the filter.

(a) Plot $E(T)/W_o{}^{1/2}$ versus $1/T$.

(b) Instead of assuming that the input power spectrum is constant, use the more realistic assumption given by Eq. (4.19). Derive a formula for and plot the curve of $E(T)/E_o$ versus $\sigma/\sqrt{2}\,T$, where E_o is the root-mean-square voltage of the input noise. Derive the asymptotic forms of $E(T)/E_o$ for large and small values of $\sigma/\sqrt{2}\,T$.

(c) Give a physical explanation why $E(T)/E_o$ is unbounded in part (a), but is bounded in part (b).

4.5 When an electric charge q is moved through an electric field $\vec{E}$ from a point A to a point B, the work done by the experimenter is $-\int_A^B q\vec{E} \cdot d\vec{s}$. This expression fails to give the correct answer if the path goes through a surface dipole distribution. Show that when the work is expressed as a Stieltjes integral, this difficulty is avoided.

4.6 A stochastic time series $x(t, \lambda)$ is governed by the following distribution function at time $t = t_o$.

$$F(X) \begin{cases} = 0, & X < -1, \\ = (1+X)^2, & -1 \leqslant X < -\tfrac{1}{2}, \\ = \tfrac{1}{2}, & -\tfrac{1}{2} \leqslant X < +\tfrac{1}{2}, \\ = X, & +\tfrac{1}{2} \leqslant X < 1, \\ = 1, & +1 \leqslant X. \end{cases}$$

(a) Evaluate the Stieltjes integral in Eq. (3.9) to find the expected value of x.

(b) Find the expected value of x^2.
(c) Find the probability density associated with this distribution.

4.7 A stochastic process of period T has the form

$$x(t, \lambda) = \sum_{n=1}^{N} \frac{1}{n} \cos\left(2\pi \frac{nt}{T} + \lambda\right)$$

where λ is a random variable whose probability density is constant over the interval $(0, 2\pi)$ and zero elsewhere.

(a) Show that the ensemble average $\langle x \rangle$ is zero.

(b) Show that the ensemble average $\langle x^2 \rangle$ is a function of the time t and is, in fact, unbounded at $t = 0$ as $N \to \infty$.

(c) Discuss the relevant difference between this example and the example that led to Eq. (4.36) where $\langle x^2 \rangle$ is independent of the time.

CHAPTER V

Miscellaneous Topics in Probability Theory

5.1 Conditional Probability, Likelihood, and Bayes Theorem

One of the important problems of classical probability is that of assessing the probability of a hypothesis after one or more observations have been made. This can be restated in the context of the present discussion by asking what is the probability of the hypothesis that a signal is present after the output of the detector has been sampled. Suppose that one has a physical situation about which certain information $\mathcal{I}$ is available. On the basis of this information $\mathcal{I}$ one analyzes the situation and arrives at a set of hypotheses H_0, $H_1, \ldots, H_N$ from which one would like to make a choice. The selection of the particular H_i will be made after certain further information p has been obtained. One may speak of the prior probability[1] $P(H_i \mid \mathcal{I})$ of the hypothesis H_i before the additional data p have been obtained and of the posterior probability $P(H_i \mid p\mathcal{I})$ of the hypothesis H_i after the data are available.

The standard form of conditional probability enables us to express the probability $P(H_i p \mid \mathcal{I})$ of both the hypothesis H_i and the data p as the product of the probability of p happening, given $\mathcal{I}$, times the probability of H_i happening, given both p and $\mathcal{I}$. Thus

$$P(H_i\, p \mid \mathcal{I}) = P(p \mid \mathcal{I})\; P(H_i \mid p\mathcal{I}) \; . \tag{5.1}$$

The term on the left is symmetric in H_i and p so one can write equally well

$$P(p\, H_i \mid \mathcal{I}) = P(H_i \mid \mathcal{I})\; P(p \mid H_i \mathcal{I}) \tag{5.2}$$

When the ratio of the last two equations is formed, the terms on the left cancel. This gives

$$P(H_i \mid p\, \mathcal{I}) = \frac{P(H_i \mid \mathcal{I})\, P(p \mid H_i\, \mathcal{I})}{P(p \mid \mathcal{I})} \tag{5.3}$$

The denominator of the term on the right does not depend on the ith hypothesis, so in comparing the different hypotheses one may write

[1] One frequently encounters the expression "a priori" but in this section the usage of Kendall (1948) will be followed. The expression $P(H_i \mid \mathcal{I})$ is read "the probability of the hypothesis H_i given the information $\mathcal{I}$." This notation will be used extensively here and in Chapter VIII.

$$P(p \mid H_i \mathcal{I}) \propto \frac{P(H_i \mid p \mathcal{I})}{P(H_i \mid \mathcal{I})} , \tag{5.4}$$

where the constant of proportionality does not depend on i. The term on the left is commonly called the *likelihood*. The term on the right, the ratio of the posterior probability to the prior probability, is sometimes called the surprise because it is large when the observations require a large change in one's assessment of the corresponding hypothesis.

The proportionality, Eq. (5.4), is called *Bayes' theorem* or *Bayes' principle of inverse probability*. The latter terminology results from the following interpretation. The hypothesis that yields the largest likelihood is the most probable. Thus one uses the observations to deduce conclusions about the hypotheses which is the inverse of the more customary procedure of predicting observations from the hypotheses.

In the case of signal processing the hypotheses H_i relate to the presence or absence of a signal. For example, in the simple case in which only one possible signal can occur one can let H_0 = hypothesis that no signal is present, H_1 = hypothesis that a signal is present, and let p denote the message received by the detector. The likelihood ratio in this case is the ratio $P(p \mid H_1 \mathcal{I})/P(p \mid H_0 \mathcal{I})$ of the likelihoods. If many signals S_i are present, each with some known probability, the likelihood ratio will be averaged over the signal class to form an expectation if one is concerned only with the hypothesis that any signal is present. The constant of proportionality that is not written explicitly in Eq. (5.4) cancels when one forms the likelihood ratio. The reader is referred to Woodward (1953) for an interesting discussion of likelihood and its application to radar detection.

5.2 The Characteristic Function

Most of the physical quantities that have been discussed have had Fourier transforms that were equally useful. Illustrative of this statement are the frequency response and power spectrum which were shown to be the transforms of the impulse response and the autocorrelation functions, respectively. Similarly, the Fourier transform of the probability density is of great importance and is called the *characteristic function*, customarily denoted $\varphi(t)$. The variable t does not mean time in this instance. One defines

$$\varphi(t) = E\left\{e^{itx}\right\} = \int_{-\infty}^{+\infty} e^{itx} f(x)\, dx = \int_{-\infty}^{+\infty} e^{itx}\, dF(x) \ . \tag{5.5}$$

The last form is more fundamental since it is based on the distribution function.

It should be noted that this form differs from the other Fourier transforms in that a factor 2π does not occur in the exponent. In order to correct for this change one must write the inverse transform for the probability (when one exists) as

$$f(x) = \frac{1}{2\pi} \int_{-\infty}^{+\infty} e^{-itx} \varphi(t) \, dt \; . \tag{5.6}$$

Unfortunately, this means that in order to use the Fourier transforms listed in Appendix 2.1, a change of variable must be made.

If one differentiates Eq. (5.5) successively with respect to t and sets $t = 0$, one finds

$$-i\varphi'(0) = \int_{-\infty}^{+\infty} x dF(x) = \langle x \rangle \tag{5.7}$$

$$-\varphi''(0) = \int_{-\infty}^{+\infty} x^2 \, dF(x) = \langle x^2 \rangle \; , \tag{5.8}$$

$$\vdots \qquad\qquad \vdots$$

provided, of course, the integrals exist. Thus a Maclaurin expansion of the characteristic function yields the moments of the distribution functions of the random variable. This suggests immediately the mathematical question, "What restrictions must be placed on an arbitrary function $\varphi(t)$ in order that it will be the Fourier transform of a probability function?" For an answer to this question the reader is referred to Kendall (1948) or Cramér (1946).

Chandrasekhar (1943, p. 9) has remarked that there is "a very general principle" that the characteristic function has a more direct relationship to the physical situation than the probability density. A trivial example of this general principle arises in the calculation of the probability density of the sum of two independent, random variables. If, instead of computing the probability density of the sum, one computes the characteristic function of the sum, one finds

$$\varphi_z(t) = E\left\{ e^{itz} \right\} = E\left\{ e^{it(x+y)} \right\}$$

$$= \iint_{-\infty}^{+\infty} e^{it(x+y)}\, f(x, y)\, dx\, dy \tag{5.9}$$

where $f(x, y)$ is the probability density of the pair of random variables (x, y). If x and y are independent, random variables, $f(x, y) = f_1(x)\, f_2(y)$, and one has

$$\varphi_z(t) = \iint_{-\infty}^{+\infty} e^{it(x+y)}\, f_1(x)\, f_2(y)\, dx\, dy$$

$$= \int_{-\infty}^{+\infty} e^{itx}\, f_1(x)\, dx \int_{-\infty}^{+\infty} e^{ity}\, f_2(y)\, dy$$

$$= E\left\{ e^{itx} \right\} E\left\{ e^{ity} \right\} = \varphi_x(t)\, \varphi_y(t) \ . \tag{5.10}$$

Thus the characteristic function of the sum of two independent, random variables is the product of the characteristic functions.

It was stated in Eq. (2.7) that the Fourier transform of a product is the convolution of the individual transforms. This enables one to assert immediately that the probability density of z is given by

$$f(z) = f_1(z) * f_2(z) \ . \tag{5.11}$$

These arguments regarding two independent, random variables can be extended readily to the sum of N independent, random variables.

Another example that will be needed later is the characteristic function associated with a cosinusoidal surface $z = a \cos(2\pi\, x/\lambda)$ where λ is the wavelength and a the waveheight. If the elevation z is sampled at random positions x and all values of x are equally probable, one may restrict the range of x to $0 \leqslant x \leqslant \lambda$ and write $p(x) = 1/\lambda$. In this example Eq. (5.5) becomes

$$\varphi(t) = E\{ e^{itz} \} = E\{ e^{ita \cos(2\pi x/\lambda)} \}$$

$$= \frac{1}{\lambda} \int_0^{\lambda} e^{ita \cos(2\pi x/\lambda)}\, dx \ .$$

By using a simple change of variables one can reduce this integral to

$$\varphi(t) = \frac{1}{2\pi}\int_0^{2\pi} e^{iat\cos\theta}\, d\theta = J_0(at) , \qquad (5.12)$$

by substituting this function in Eq. (5.6) and using Fourier transform No. 20 in Appendix 2.1, one finds

$$p(z) \begin{cases} = \dfrac{1}{\pi\sqrt{a^2 - z^2}} , & |z| < a \\ = 0 , & |z| > a . \end{cases} \qquad (5.13)$$

It is evident that $p(z)$ must vanish for $|z| > a$ since a is the peak amplitude of the surface. At first glance it might be surprising that $\lim_{|z| \to a^-} p(z) = \infty$, but this is related to the fact that the slope of the surface vanishes at $z = \pm a$. The factor π^{-1} is the required normalization factor for a probability density.

5.3 The Probability Density for Functions of and Sums and Products of Random Variables

Every detection system requires the performance of mathematical operations on random variables. It is the purpose of this section to show how one can compute the probability densities of the results of these various operations.

As a simple beginning, suppose that one has a device such that the output y is a known function $y = y(x)$ when the input has the value x. If x is a random variable with a probability density $f(x)$, y is also a random variable with a probability density $g(y)$, say. The relationship between these two densities can be found readily by considering the graph in Fig. 5.1. If x falls in the interval dx, y falls in the interval dy, so the probability of these two events are equal. Hence

$$g(y)\ dy = f(x)\ dx \qquad (5.14)$$

or

$$g(y) = f(x)\ \frac{dx}{dy} . \qquad (5.15)$$

In applying this formula it must be remembered that the inverse function $x = x(y)$ may not be single valued so that more than one interval dx corresponds to a given interval dy.

Consider, for example, the square law device $y = ax^2$ illustrated in Fig. 5.2. For any given interval dy there are two intervals dx located at $+x$ and $-x$. Now there is no necessity that $f(+x) = f(-x)$ so one must write

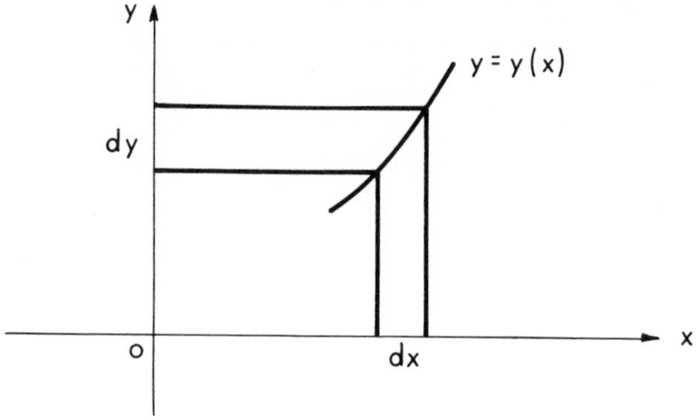

Figure 5.1–The relationship between two probability densities.

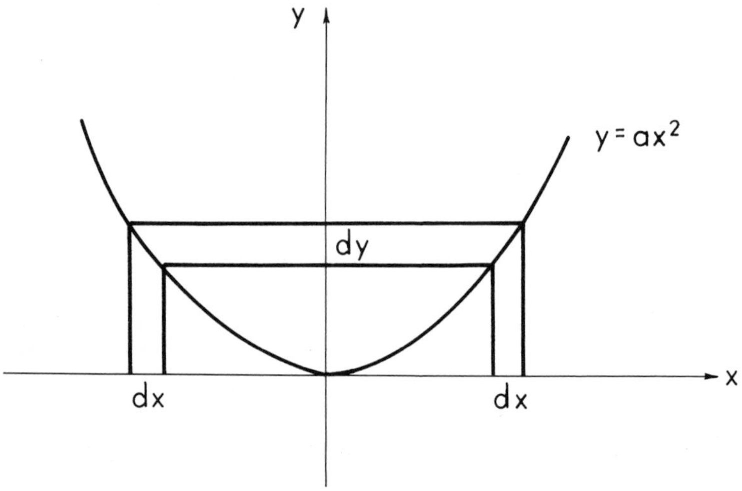

Figure 5.2–The response of a square-law device, $y = ax^2$.

$$g(y)\,dy = [f(+x) + f(-x)]\,dx\,,\ 0 \leqslant x < \infty\,,\ 0 \leqslant y < \infty. \tag{5.16}$$

As a special but interesting case, suppose that

$$f(x) = \frac{1}{\sqrt{2\pi}\sigma} e^{-x^2/2\sigma^2}\ ,$$

i.e., that x has a gaussian distribution with mean zero and standard deviation σ. Now if $y = ax^2$, $dx/dy = ½ax$, so from Eq. (5.16),

$$g[y(x)] = \frac{1}{\sqrt{2\pi}\sigma a x} e^{-x^2/2\sigma^2}$$

or

$$g(y) = \frac{e^{-y/2a\sigma^2}}{\sqrt{2\pi a y}\ \sigma} . \tag{5.17}$$

This distribution is a special case of a more general distribution known as the chi-square distribution that is of great importance in statistics.

One has a ready check on his algebra since $\int g(y)\,dy$ must equal one as can be seen from Eq. (5.14). One notices that $g(0)$ is unbounded although it can be integrated.

Another example of interest is the sinusoid $y(x) = a \sin(2\pi x/\lambda)$ shown in Fig. 5.3. Since all values of x are equally probable, one may take advantage of the symmetry of the curve and consider only the range of $x\{-\lambda/4 \leqslant x \leqslant +\lambda/4\}$ and let $f(x) = 2/\lambda$, a constant. From Eq. (5.14)

$$g(y) = f(x)\frac{dx}{dy} = \frac{2/\lambda}{(2\pi a/\lambda)\cos(2\pi x/\lambda)} \quad \text{(as a function of } y\text{)}$$

or

$$g(y) = \frac{1}{\pi\sqrt{a^2 - y^2}}, \quad |y| \leqslant a$$

in agreement with Eq. (5.13) which was derived from a consideration of characteristic functions.

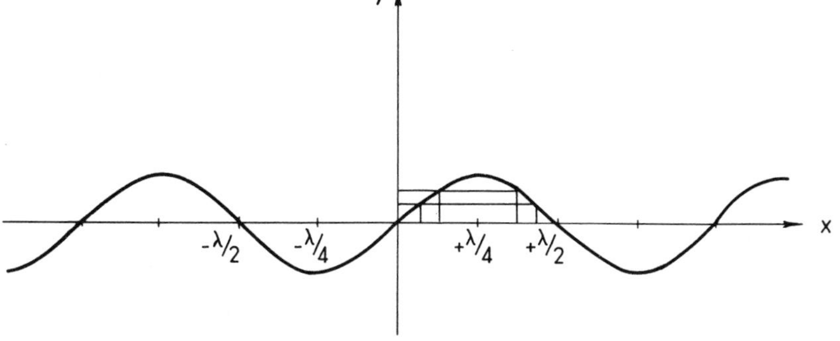

Figure 5.3–The sinusoid, $y(x) = a \sin(2\pi x/\lambda)$.

Equation (5.14) was derived from intuitive considerations based on Fig. 5.1. It can be derived more formally from mathematical considerations based on a function of a function. This approach is desirable since it enables us to extend the development to two dimensions more readily. One has formally

$$f(x)\,dx = f[x(y)]\,\frac{dx}{dy}\,dy = g(y)\,dy \;, \tag{5.18}$$

where

$$g(y) = f[x(y)]\,\frac{dx}{dy} \;. \tag{5.19}$$

In order to interpret $g(y)$ as a probability density it may be necessary to take the absolute value of dx/dy. There is one complication that must be watched since the inverse function $x(y)$ may not be single valued. In this case the range of x must be divided into regions in which $x(y)$ is single valued. The values of x are independent so one can sum the values of $g(y)$ for each of these regions as in Eq. (5.16).

If one has two random variables x, y which have a joint probability density $f(x, y)$, and if one computes a new pair of variables r, s from x, y, the joint probability density $g(r, s)$ can be obtained from a generalization of Eq. (5.18). One has the identity

$$f(x, y)\,dxdy = f[x(r, s), y(r, s)] \cdot \frac{\partial(x, y)}{\partial(r, s)}\,drds$$

where a standard notation for the Jacobian of the transformation has been used. Hence, the probability densities are related by

$$g(r, s) = f[x(r, s), y(r, s)] \cdot \left|\frac{\partial(x, y)}{\partial(r, s)}\right| \;. \tag{5.20}$$

Since the inverse functions are involved, the (x, y) plane must be divided into regions in which the inverse functions are single valued whenever this is necessary.

Webb (1956, 1962) has applied this transformation to find the probability density of a product. For this purpose one can set

$$\left.\begin{aligned} s &= x\,y \\ r &= x \;. \end{aligned}\right\} \tag{5.21}$$

The Jacobian of this transformation is l/r, so

$$g(r, s) = f(r, s/r)\,/r \;,\; r \geqslant 0.$$

The joint distribution can be integrated with respect to r to get the marginal distribution which is the probability density $p(s)$ of the product s. This yields

$$p(s) = \int_0^{+\infty} g(r, s)\, dr = \int_0^{+\infty} f(r, s/r)\, d(\ln r) .$$

These integrals can be extended to negative r by adding a term $f(-r, -s/r)$ to the integrand. As an example, suppose that x and y are independent random variables each of which have a gaussian distribution with mean zero and variance σ. The inverse of the function s is not single valued since the values of s in quadrant I of the (x, y) plane are repeated in quadrant III. If we restrict the integration to the first quadrant, one has since $r = x$,

$$p_1(s) = \frac{1}{2\pi\sigma^2} \int_0^{\infty} \exp\left[\frac{-x^2}{2\sigma^2} - \frac{s^2}{2\sigma^2 x^2}\right] d(\ln x) .$$

This integral has the value

$$\frac{1}{2\pi\sigma^2} K_o\left(\frac{|s|}{\sigma^2}\right),$$

where $K_o(\cdot)$ is the modified Bessel function of the second kind. Integration over the third quadrant gives the same distribution of s so the value $p_I(s)$ should be doubled. Finally, the symmetry of the probability densities for x and y demands that $p(s)$ be symmetric in s. Hence, $p_I(s)$ is applicable in the second and fourth quadrants, and one has

$$p(s) = \frac{1}{\pi\sigma^2} K_o\left(\frac{|s|}{\sigma^2}\right), \quad -\infty < s < +\infty . \tag{5.22}$$

One can certify that

$$\int_{-\infty}^{+\infty} p(s)\, ds = 1 .$$

It is left as an exercise for the reader to show that if $f(x, y)$ is the bivariate gaussian distribution of Eq. (3.33), the probability density of the product is

$$p(s) = \frac{\sqrt{A}}{\pi} e^{-a_{12}s}\ K_o(a_{11}\, |s|) . \tag{5.23}$$

Equation (5.23) contains (5.22) as a special case when $a_{12} = 0$. The asymptotic form of $K_0(\cdot)$ contains the factor $\exp(-a_{11} \mid s \mid)$ which always dominates the factor $\exp(-a_{12}\ s)$ since $\mid a_{12} \mid \leqslant a_{11}$. The probability density depends on the sign of the product $a_{12}\ s$ as one would expect.

When one is concerned with the sum, product, or quotient of only two variables, there is an alternate method of deducing the probability. This is the method used in Sec. 3.7 to discuss the limiter.[1] The random variables x and y are portrayed on a two-dimensional graph and lines of constant sum, product, or quotient are drawn as in Fig. 5.4a, b, c. In each of these cases the probability that the sum, product, or quotient, z, of the two variables be less than Z is

$$P(z < Z) = \iint\limits_{\text{(shaded area)}} f(x, y)\, dx dy \ , \tag{5.24}$$

where the shaded area is portrayed in Fig. 5.4a, b, c, respectively. If the probability density $f(x, y)$ contains two dimensional delta functions, one must exercise care in defining the shaded area to exclude these points if they fall on the boundary. The integral in Eq. (5.24) yields the cumulative distribution[2] $F_1(Z)$ which can be differentiated to give probability density.

5.4 The Rayleigh Distribution

There are many physical situations that yield a probability density known as the *Rayleigh distribution.* Baron Rayleigh (1937) obtained this distribution by considering the amplitude of the sum of a large number of sinusoidal pressures having equal amplitudes and random phases. Alternately, one can obtain this distribution by considering random walks in two dimensions. The displacement of a particle in a plane is the result of a large number of separate displacements, each having the same magnitude but with arbitrary orientation. A moment's reflection shows that these two processes are equivalent.

Another method of obtaining a Rayleigh distribution is to consider the probability density of the magnitude R of the distance $\overline{OP}$ where the coordinates of the point (x, y) are independent of one another and each is governed by the gaussian distribution

$$p(x) = \frac{1}{\sqrt{2\pi}\sigma} \exp(-x^2/2\sigma^2) \ . \tag{5.25}$$

The easiest way of obtaining the answer is to calculate the cumulative distribution for R from an area integral as in Eq. (5.24). In this case one has

---

[2] At this point the distribution between the random variable z and the value of this variable Z has been introduced again.

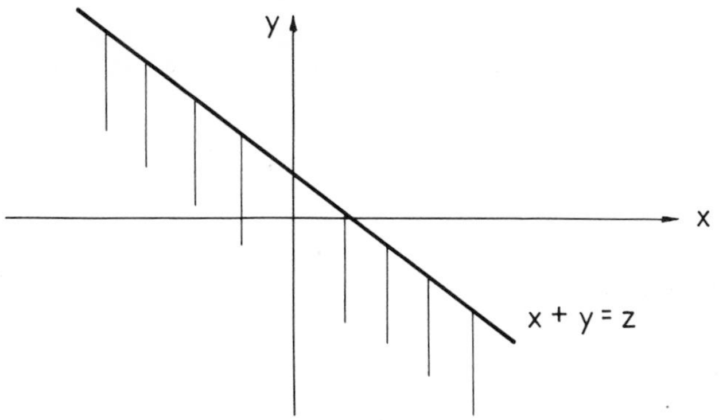

(a) DOMAIN WHERE THE SUM OF TWO VARIABLES IS LESS THAN Z

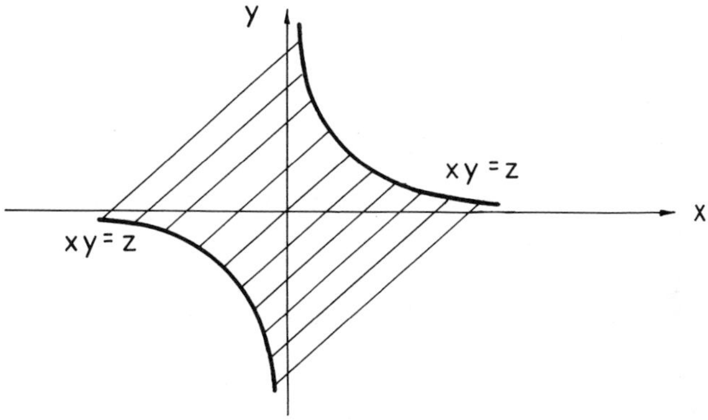

(b) DOMAIN WHERE THE PRODUCT OF TWO VARIABLES IS LESS THAN Z

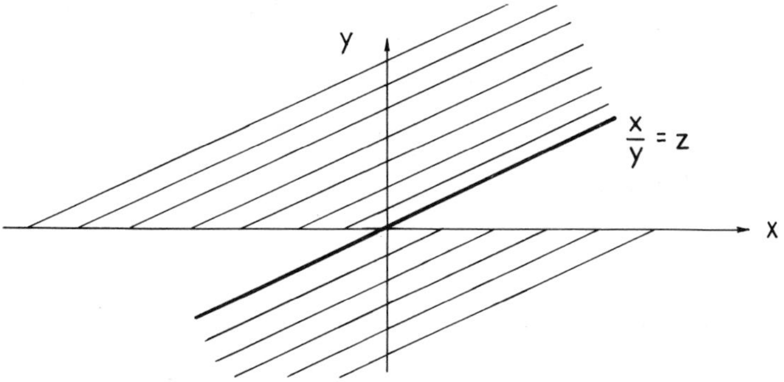

(c) DOMAIN WHERE THE QUOTIENT OF TWO VARIABLES IS LESS THAN Z, A POSITIVE NUMBER

Figure 5.4

$$P(R < a) = \int_0^a r dr \int_0^{2\pi} \frac{1}{2\pi\sigma^2} \exp(-r^2/2\sigma^2)\ d\theta$$

where

$$\begin{aligned} x^2 + y^2 &= r^2 \\ \tan^{-1}(y/x) &= \theta \end{aligned}$$

This integral is easily evaluated to give

$$P(R < a) = [1 - \exp(-a^2/2\sigma^2)]$$

or

$$p(R) = \frac{R}{\sigma^2} \exp(-R^2/2\sigma^2)\ . \tag{5.26}$$

By virtue of the definition of R, $p(R) = 0$ if R is negative.

The probability density Eq. (5.26) is known as the Rayleigh distribution. The mean square value of R is $2\sigma^2$ which is what one would expect from the Pythagorean theorem.

5.5 The Envelope of a Narrow-Band Gaussian Noise

Suppose that one has a linear filter which passes a narrow-band of frequencies of width W centered about a frequency f_o. If the input to this filter is white, gaussian noise, the output may be described as narrow-band gaussian noise. When the output is viewed on an oscilloscope, one sees a signal that looks like a sinusoidal wave except that amplitude and phase are changing steadily. When the filter response is narrow, one may represent the output realistically as

$$y(t) = R(t) \cos[\omega_o t + \Phi(t)] \tag{5.27}$$

or

$$y(t) = \alpha(t) \cos \omega_o t + \beta(t) \sin \omega_o t \tag{5.28}$$

where

$$\left.\begin{aligned} \alpha(t) &= R(t) \cos \Phi(t) \\ \beta(t) &= -R(t) \sin \Phi(t)\ . \end{aligned}\right\} \tag{5.29}$$

Since the signals cos $\omega_0 t$ and sin $\omega_0 t$ are in quadrature, one would conclude from the arguments of the preceding section that if $\alpha(t)$ and $\beta(t)$ are independent gaussian variables of zero mean, $R(t)$ is a random variable governed by a Rayleigh distribution. This demonstration can be carried out rather simply by using the Fourier representation of Sec. 4.5. The details are given in many places, of which one might mention Rice (1944, pp. 81-84) and Davenport and Root (1958, pp. 158-165). The latter authors show that the frequency components of $R(t)$, $\Phi(t)$, $\alpha(t)$, and $\beta(t)$ are contained in a band of width W centered on zero frequency.

The analysis of the behavior of the envelope $R(t)$ of a narrow-band gaussian function shows the following results. The probability density of $R(t)$ is the Rayleigh distribution, Eq. (5.26). The successive values of the envelope are correlated, but one can say roughly that the period of fluctuation of the envelope is $1/W$. These properties of the narrow-band gaussian noise have been used to simulate reverberation.

When CW pulses are used in sonar transmission, the returning reverberation often can be explained as the superposition of a large number of sinusoidal pulses of equal amplitude but random phase. This is exactly the model that led Rayleigh to consider his distribution in the first place, and, as mentioned above, it is the distribution that results from a narrow-band gaussian noise. The nature of the fluctuations can be regulated by selecting the bandwidth W. The reader is referred to Eckart (no date, approximately 1946, pp. 91-95) for an example of the use of narrow-band noise to simulate reverberation.

5.6 Suggestions for Further Reading

The classical approach to probability theory can be found in the books by Kendall (1948) and Jeffreys (1961). Both of these books are well written, interesting, and contain many illustrations based on experimental data. The modern approach to probability theory is described in the excellent book by Cramér (1946). There are many excellent books on this subject but it would be invidious to name a few without naming all of them.

The reader who is interested in the Bayes theorem should consult Woodward (1953) and the interesting historical survey by Fisher (1956).

PROBLEMS

5.1 Evaluate the mode, the mean, and the root-mean-square value associated with the Rayleigh distribution, Eq. (5.26).

5.2 A sum, $w = x + y + z$, of three independent, random variables x, y, and z is observed. It is known that

$$P(x{=}0) = 0.5 \,, \quad P(y{=}0) = 0.3 \,, \quad P(z{=}0) = 0.5 \,,$$
$$P(x{=}1) = 0.5 \,, \quad P(y{=}1) = 0.4 \,, \quad P(z{=}1) = 0.5 \,,$$
$$P(y{=}2) = 0.3 \,,$$

(a) Prepare a table of the prior probabilities of the possible values of the sum w.

(b) Prepare a table of the posteriori probability that $z = 0$ for each possible value of w.

5.3 Each of the two independent, random variables x and y are governed by the probability density $P(u) = 1, 0 \leqslant u \leqslant 1$. $P(u) = 0$ for all other values of u.

(a) Calculate the distribution functions for the sum $x + y$, the product xy, and the quotient x/y.

(b) Calculate the probability density for the sum $z = x + y$ from the convolution $P(z) * P(z)$ and from the Fourier transform of the characteristic function.

5.4 Random values (y_1, y_2) are formed from pairs of samples (x_1, x_2) of a gaussian process, Eq. (3.29) by means of the linear combination

$$y_1 = x_1 \cos\theta + x_2 \sin\theta$$
$$y_2 = -x_1 \sin\theta + x_2 \cos\theta \ .$$

The time interval $t_2 - t_1$ between the samples x_1 and x_2 is held constant.

(a) Find the values of θ for which y_1 and y_2 are uncorrelated.

(b) What is the joint probability density of (y_1, y_2) for the value of θ obtained in (a)?

5.5 Is it possible to generalize the results of the last example to N samples? That is, is it possible to find an orthogonal rotation matrix $\beta = (b_{ij})$ such that the N variables

$$y_i = \sum_{j=1}^{N} b_{ij}\, x_j \ , \ i = 1, 2, \ldots, N$$

are uncorrelated? Again the time intervals $t_i - t_j$ associated with the samples x_i and x_j of the gaussian process are held constant.

5.6 Equation (5.1) is sometimes written as follows for two random variables x and y:

$$P(x, y) = P(x)\, P_x(y)$$

where $P_x(y)$ is read "the probability density of the variable y for the given value of x." Apply this form of the equation to the following problem. A sinusoidal function

$$z = z_0 \cos 2\pi t$$

is sampled twice. The first sample, z_1, is at the random time $t = \lambda$ where $P(\lambda) = 1, 0 \leqslant \lambda \leqslant 1$, and $P(\lambda) = 0$, otherwise. The second sample, z_2, is at the time $t = \lambda + a$ where a is a fixed constant. What is the joint probability density $P(z_1, z_2)$?

5.7 Use Eq. (5.20) to calculate the joint probability density of the variables y_1, y_2 defined by

$$y_1 = \frac{1}{\sqrt{2}}(x_1 + x_2)$$

$$y_2 = \frac{1}{\sqrt{2}}(-x_1 + x_2)$$

where x_1 and x_2 are governed by the gaussian process, see Eq. (3.2a), with $N = 2$. Compare the answer with that of Problem 5.4.

5.8 What is the characteristic function of the gaussian probability density of mean zero and standard deviation σ?

5.9 What is the probability density of the sum

$$z = \sum_{i-1}^{N} x_i$$

of N independent, random variables x_i? Each variable x_i has a gaussian probability density of mean zero and standard deviation σ_i.

5.10 What is the characteristic function of the Rayleigh distribution of mean square value $2\sigma^2$?

5.11 Frequently integrals containing the Bessel function $J_0(x)$ can be approximated by setting $J_0(x) \cong \exp(-x^2/4)$ for $|x| \ll 1$. Use this approximation to derive Eq. (5.25).

Hint. The projection on the x-axis of any one random walk is governed by the characteristic function Eq. (5.12). The sum of the x-components of N independent random walks has a characteristic function

$$\varphi_N(t) = [J_0(at)]^N \cong \exp(-Na^2 t^2/4)$$

where a is the amplitude of any one walk.

5.12 Derive an expression for the probability density for the ratio of two random variables x, y by transforming to new variables $s = x/y$ and $r = x$ and integrating with respect to r to find the marginal distribution.

5.13 (a) Apply the result of Problem 5.12 to the bivariate gaussian density

$$f(x, y) = \frac{|a_{ij}|^{1/2}}{2\pi} \exp\left[-\tfrac{1}{2}(a_{11}x^2 + 2a_{12}xy + a_{22}y^2)\right] .$$

Here $|a_{ij}| = a_{11}a_{22} - a_{12}{}^2$.

(b) What is the expected value of the ratio x/y?

5.14 If a noise source moves by a stationary receiver, the root-mean-square amplitude of the output of the receiver varies in time because of the variation in range. This amplitude variation is sometimes removed by forming the ratio of the time derivative of the signal and the instantaneous value of the signal. The resulting ratio, which is sometimes referred to as the logarithmic derivative, can be approximated by a new time series

$$y(t, \lambda) = \frac{x(t + \Delta t, \lambda) - x(t, \lambda)}{x(t, \lambda)\, \Delta t} = \frac{1}{\Delta t}\left[\frac{x(t + \Delta t, \lambda)}{x(t, \lambda)} - 1\right]$$

where Δt is a constant. Discuss the statistics of $y(t, \lambda)$ when $x(t, \lambda)$ is a gauss process.

(a) What is the probability density of y?

(b) Does the mean square value of y exist?

5.15 Show that the analytic signal $\mathcal{Y}(t)$ belonging to the narrow-band message $y(t)$ defined in Eq. (5.28) can be approximated by

$$\mathcal{Y}(t) \cong e^{i2\pi f_o t} \int_{-\infty}^{+\infty} [\hat{\alpha}(f) - i\hat{\beta}(f)]\, e^{i2\pi f t}\, df$$

when $W \ll f_o$.

5.16 In an experiment the observed pressure, p, was converted to an intensity level, I, by the formula $\mathrm{I} = 20 \log(p/p_o)$, where p_o is a constant reference pressure. It was found that the experimental values of I satisfied a gaussian distribution with mean I_o and standard deviation σ.

(a) What is the probability density satisfied by p?

(b) Show that the probability density found in part (a) approaches a gaussian density as σ becomes small. What are the values of the mean and the standard deviation?

5.17 Consider Eq. (3.29) for the special case $N = 2$ but suppose that the second order moments μ_{ii} are not constant but have the form $\mu_{ii} = \sigma^2 s(t_i)$ where $s(t)$ is a nonvanishing, positive function of t. What must be the functional dependence of μ_{12} on the time in order that the stochastic variable $x/\sqrt{s(t)}$ be stationary?

CHAPTER VI

Measurements of Random Processes

6.1 Effects of the Finite Length of the Sample

In all of the preceding discussion it has been assumed tacitly that a sample $x(t, \lambda)$ of a stochastic process was available for all $t(-\infty < t < \infty)$. In practice one can only sample a finite portion of $x(t, \lambda)$. Sometimes, even, the experimental function with which one is concerned exists only for a finite time and the extrapolation to infinite duration is an idealization. An example of the latter situation is the reverberation that follows the production of the sound signal.

Since one always has available only a finite portion of a signal, any parameters that are calculated from this sample are themselves random variables and will have a distribution about a true value. As an example, suppose one has a sample $x(t, \lambda)$ of an ergodic, stochastic process which as a mean value zero and a standard deviation σ, i.e.,

$$\langle x(t, \lambda) \rangle = \overline{x(t, \lambda)} = \lim_{T \to \infty} \frac{1}{T} \int_{-T/2}^{+T/2} x(t, \lambda)\, dt = 0 \tag{6.1}$$

and

$$\langle x^2(t, \lambda) \rangle = \overline{x^2(t, \lambda)} = \lim_{T \to \infty} \frac{1}{T} \int_{-T/2}^{+T/2} x^2(t, \lambda)\, dt = \sigma^2 \ . \qquad \ldots . \tag{6.2}$$

On the other hand, if one has available only a finite sample of length T, one can compute a quantity, see Eq. (3.10),

$$\overline{x_T(t, \lambda)} = \frac{1}{T} \int_{-T/2}^{+T/2} x(t, \lambda)\, dt \tag{6.3}$$

which by definition is the time average of $x(\cdot)$ over the time interval T. This quantity will not be zero in general, although one would expect that if many values of $\overline{x_T(t, \lambda)}$ were determined for non-overlapping samples these in turn would have an average of zero.

The average value of $\overline{x_T(t, \lambda)}$ can be determined most readily by taking the ensemble average of each member of Eq. (6.3) and interchanging the order of integration and averaging. This gives

$$\langle \overline{x_T(t, \lambda)} \rangle = \frac{1}{T} \int_{-T/2}^{+T/2} \langle x(t, \lambda) \rangle \, dt = 0 \, . \tag{6.4}$$

The last step follows from Eq. (6.1).

The mean square value of $\overline{x_T(t, \lambda)}$ can be calculated from the following series of equations which are almost self-evident.

$$\langle [\overline{x_T(t, \lambda)}]^2 \rangle = \left\langle \frac{1}{T} \int_{-T/2}^{+T/2} x(t_1, \lambda) \, dt_1 \cdot \frac{1}{T} \int_{-T/2}^{+T/2} x(t_2, \lambda) \, dt_2 \right\rangle$$

$$= \left\langle \frac{1}{T^2} \int_{-T/2}^{+T/2} \int_{-T/2}^{+T/2} x(t_1, \lambda) \, x(t_2, \lambda) \, dt_1 \, dt_2 \right\rangle$$

$$= \frac{1}{T^2} \int_{-T/2}^{+T/2} \int_{-T/2}^{+T/2} \langle x(t_1, \lambda) \, x(t_2, \lambda) \rangle \, dt_1 \, dt_2$$

$$= \frac{1}{T^2} \int_{-T/2}^{+T/2} \int_{-T/2}^{+T/2} C(t_2 - t_1) \, dt_1 \, dt_2 \, . \tag{6.5}$$

It is not necessary to assume in the last step that the process is ergodic; only that it is stationary in the wide sense.

The iterated integral can be simplified by rotating the coordinate axes 45° by the following change of variables:

$$\sqrt{2} \, u_1 = t_2 + t_1 \, , \quad \sqrt{2} u_2 = t_2 - t_1 \, . \tag{6.6}$$

The two coordinate systems and the corresponding areas of integration are illustrated in Fig. 6.1. Since $C(\cdot)$ is a symmetric function, Eq. (6.5) becomes

$$\langle [\overline{x_T(t, \lambda)}]^2 \rangle = \frac{2}{T^2} \int_0^{T/\sqrt{2}} C(\sqrt{2} u_2) \, du_2 \int_{-[(T/\sqrt{2}) - u_2]}^{+[(T/\sqrt{2}) - u_2]} du_1 \, .$$

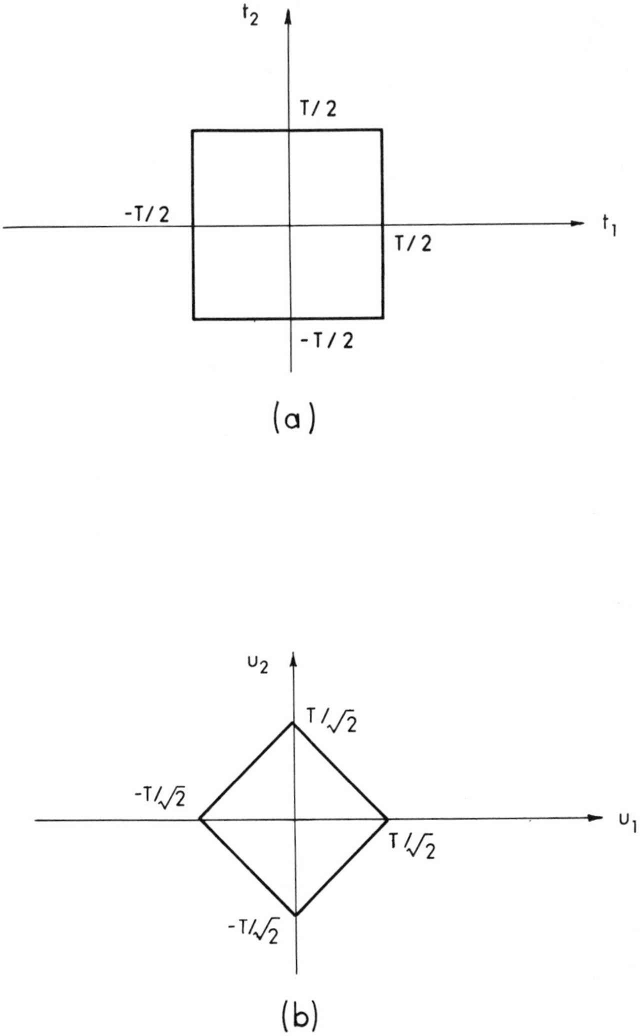

Figure 6.1–Coordinate systems for evaluating $\langle\, \overline{[X_T(t,\lambda)]^2}\,\rangle$ and corresponding areas of integration.

The factor two results from the symmetry of $C(\cdot)$ and not from the change of variables. The last integral can be evaluated readily. Upon introducing the change of variable, $\sqrt{2}\,u_2 = \tau$, one has

$$\langle\, \overline{[x_T(t,\lambda)]^2}\,\rangle = \frac{2}{T}\int_0^T \left(1 - \frac{\tau}{T}\right) C(\tau)\, d\tau \quad . \tag{6.7}$$

This formula enables one to choose the sample length T necessary to achieve prescribed limits on the fluctuations of the average value.

If T is large compared to the values of τ for which $C(\tau)$ is significantly different from zero, the second term in the parenthesis is negligible. This is rigorously true, for example, in white noise. When this approximation is valid, see Eq. (4.20),

$$\langle [\overline{x_T(t, \lambda)}]^2 \rangle \cong \frac{W_o}{T} \quad , \tag{6.8}$$

where W_o is the power density of the process at $f = 0$. On the other hand as $T \to 0$, the right member of Eq. (6.7) approaches $C(0)$ which is the mean square value of the unfiltered noise.

This simple example illustrates a characteristic of noise studies that is generally true. In order to calculate the average value of the random variable $\overline{x_T(t, \lambda)}$ one needs only the distribution function of $x(\cdot)$. However, in order to calculate the mean square value in order to estimate the fluctuations in $\overline{x_T(t, \lambda)}$ one needs the second order function $C(\tau)$ for the process. Similarly, if one wants to study the fluctuations in the random variable $\overline{x_T(t, \lambda)}^2$ or in $\overline{x_T^2(t, \lambda)}$, one must know the higher order distribution functions defined in Eq. (3.7) for $n = 1, 2, 3, 4$.

It is frequently convenient in experimental measurements to generate the average of $x(\cdot)$ with a simple RC-circuit as in Fig. 6.2. In this case Eq. (6.3) is replaced by

$$e_o(t, \lambda) = \frac{1}{RC} \int_{-\infty}^{0+} e^{(u/RC)} \, x(u + t, \lambda) \, du \ . \tag{6.9}$$

The parameter λ has been introduced in $e_o(\cdot)$ to remind the reader that $e_o(t, \lambda)$ is a stochastic process which depends on the sample parameter λ. If one takes the ensemble average of both sides of Eq. (6.9), one establishes that $\langle e_o(t, \lambda) \rangle = 0$.

Proceeding exactly as in Eq. (6.5), one can show that

$$\langle e_o^2 \rangle = \frac{1}{(RC)^2} \int_{-\infty}^{0+} \int_{-\infty}^{0+} e^{[(t_2 + t_1)/RC]} \, C(t_2 - t_1) \, dt_1 \, dt_2 \ .$$

When the coordinates are transformed as in Eq. (6.6), one gets, after a little manipulation,

$$\langle e_o^2 \rangle = \frac{1}{2RC} \int_{-\infty}^{+\infty} \exp(-|\tau|/RC) \, C(\tau) \, d\tau \ . \tag{6.10}$$

If RC is large enough, this may be approximated by

$$\langle e_o{}^2 \rangle \cong \frac{1}{2\,RC} \int_{-\infty}^{+\infty} C(\tau)\, d\tau \,. \qquad (6.11)$$

This last result can be given a physical interpretation since, by Eq. (4.8), the integral is the power density, W_o, of the input at zero frequency. The response of the low-pass RC-filter is down 3 dB at $f = 1/2\pi RC$. Hence,

$$\langle e_o{}^2 \rangle \cong \text{noise power passed by filter.}$$

Since long integrating times, i.e., large RC, yield narrow band widths, long integrating times lead to small fluctuations in the output of the filter.

One should note that the preceding analysis is not an analysis of a square law detector, but is rather the analysis of the fluctuation of the output of a low-pass RC-filter when the input is noise. The analysis is applicable to the following situation.

Suppose that one has a sensor such as a depth gauge whose output is a d.c. signal s_o, but that the output is contaminated by an additive noise $n(t)$ whose origin may be in the medium or in the electronic equipment associated with the sensor. Thus the output of the instrument is a time series

$$x(t) = s_o + n(t) \qquad (6.12)$$

where s_o is the desired value and $n(t)$ is the obscuring noise. In order to improve the determination of s_o one can filter $x(t)$ with the RC-filter of Fig. 6.2. If $n(t)$ has a mean value of zero, one can reduce the fluctuations in the output to as small a value as desired by increasing the time constant, RC. On the other hand, there is a limit to how long one is willing to integrate since s_o itself is usually a slowly varying quantity. Equation (6.11) shows the trade-off between instrument sensitivity and time response.

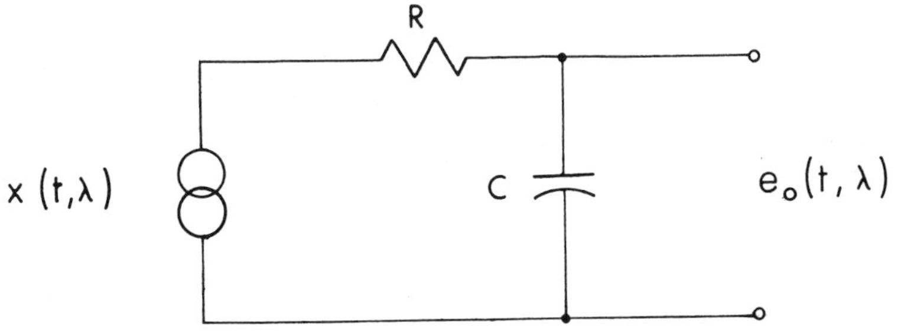

Figure 6.2–A simple RC-circuit.

6.2 Filtering the Square-Law Rectifier

One of the standard methods of describing a noise level is the specification of the mean square value of the time series. When the average is carried out over an infinitely long sample, the result is $C(0)$ as we have seen. A common experimental arrangement for this purpose is shown in Fig. 6.3. The first filter will be omitted in the initial discussion.

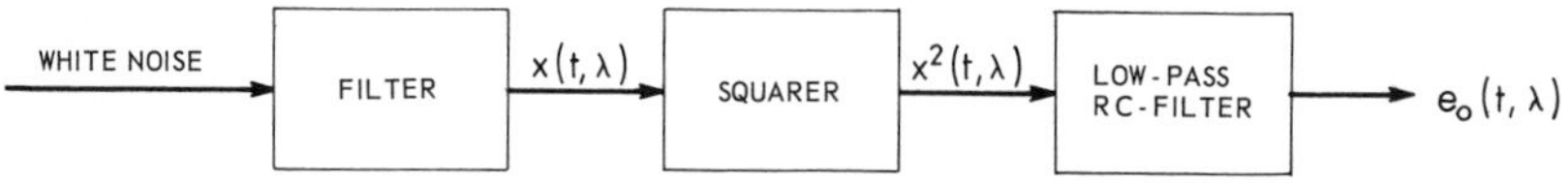

Figure 6.3–Illustration of the square-law rectifier and its filter.

The output of the system is given by Eq. (6.9) if the $x(\cdot)$ in the integrand is replaced by $x^2(\cdot)$. This gives

$$e_o(t,\ \lambda) = \frac{1}{RC} \int_{-\infty}^{0+} e^{u/RC}\, x^2(t+u,\ \lambda)\, du\ . \tag{6.13}$$

Upon taking ensemble averages, one finds

$$\langle\, e_o(t,\ \lambda)\,\rangle = \frac{1}{RC} \int_{-\infty}^{0+} e^{u/RC}\, \langle\, x^2(t+u,\ \lambda)\,\rangle\, du$$

$$= \sigma^2 \int_{-\infty}^{0+} e^{u/RC}\, d\left(\frac{u}{RC}\right)$$

provided the process is stationary. Hence

$$\langle\, e_o(t,\ \lambda)\,\rangle = \sigma^2 \tag{6.14}$$

as it should. Thus, one concludes that on the average the RC-filter gives the correct answer no matter what the value of RC. Some instruments, described as True RMS voltmeters, form the square root of $< e_o >$ and thus provide directly a value of σ.

The output $e_o(t,\ \lambda)$ will fluctuate about its average value so one would like to have a measure of this fluctuation. The root-mean-square value of this fluctuation sets a limit to the sensitivity since one cannot hope to detect a change in the output if it is masked by fluctuations. By definition the mean-square departure from the average value is

$$\langle [e_o(t,\lambda) - \sigma^2]^2 \rangle = \langle e_o^2 \rangle - 2\langle e_o \rangle \sigma^2 + \sigma^4$$
$$= \langle e_o^2 \rangle - \sigma^4 \quad . \tag{6.15}$$

In order to calculate e_o^2 one may write

$$\langle e_o^2(t,\lambda) \rangle = \frac{1}{(RC)^2} \left\langle \int_{-\infty}^{0+}\int_{-\infty}^{0+} e[(u_1+u_2)/RC] \; [x(t+u_1,\lambda)x(t+u_2,\lambda)]^2 \, du_1 \, du_2 \right\rangle$$

$$= \frac{1}{(RC)^2} \int_{-\infty}^{0+}\int_{-\infty}^{0+} e[(u_1+u_2)/RC] \, \langle [x(t+u_1,\lambda)x(t+u_2,\lambda)]^2 \rangle \, du_1 \, du_2 .$$

In order to evaluate this integral it is necessary to know the fourth order moments of the process. This information is not usually available. One of the reasons for the popularity of the gaussian statistics is that the fourth order moments can be expressed in terms of the second order moments. The reader is referred to Bendat (1958, pp. 288-294) or Freeman (1958, pp. 245-247) for the details of the evaluation.

Bendat shows that if $\langle x(t,\lambda) \rangle = 0$, i.e., if the process is centered,

$$\langle [x(t+u_1,\lambda)x(t+u_2,\lambda)]^2 \rangle = C^2(0) + 2C^2(u_2-u_1) \quad . \tag{6.16}$$

This enables one to use again the change of variable given in Eq. (6.6) to simplify the integral. One finds

$$\langle e_o^2(t,\lambda) \rangle = C^2(0) + \frac{1}{2RC} \int_0^{+\infty} e^{-\tau/RC} \, C^2(\tau) \, d\tau \quad . \tag{6.17}$$

Consequently, the mean square deviation of the output about its mean value, σ^2, is, from Eqs. (6.15) and (6.17),

$$\langle [e_o(t,\lambda) - \sigma^2]^2 \rangle = \frac{1}{RC} \int_{-\infty}^{+\infty} \exp(-|\tau|/RC) \, C^2(\tau) \, d\tau \quad .$$

Thus the longer the time constant, the smaller the fluctuations in the output. Again if RC is large enough, one has

$$\langle [e_o(t, \lambda) - \sigma^2]^2 \rangle \cong \frac{1}{RC} \int_{-\infty}^{+\infty} C^2(\tau)\, d\tau \ . \tag{6.18}$$

It is profitable to compare Eqs. (6.11) and (6.18) for the case of a narrow-band noise. In this case $C(\tau)$ is oscillatory and the integral in Eq. (6.11) can be small even though $C(\tau)$ does not approach zero rapidly. This is not true for Eq. (6.18). Suppose this behavior is examined in more detail.

If the first filter in Fig. 6.3 is a band-pass LRC filter, either parallel or series, the autocorrelation function of the output, $x(t, \lambda)$, is

$$C(\tau) = \frac{W_o \pi f_o}{Q}\, e^{-u/2Q}\, [\cos u\sqrt{1-1/4Q^2} - 1/\sqrt{4Q^2-1}\, \sin u\sqrt{1-1/4Q^2}\,],$$

$$u \geqslant 0 \ \ldots \tag{6.19}$$

where

u = $2\pi f_o \tau$
Q = Q of tuned circuit
W_o = power spectral density of white noise input.

The derivation of Eq. (6.19) is left as an exercise for the reader. If we restrict the discussion to filters with a narrow band-pass, i.e., high-Q circuits, this equation may be approximated by

$$C(\tau) = \frac{W_o \pi f_o}{Q}\, e^{-u/2Q} \cos u \ , \quad u \geqslant 0 \ .$$

Values of $C(\tau)$ for negative τ can be obtained by symmetry. It is easy to show that for the latter approximation

$$\int_{-\infty}^{+\infty} C(\tau)\, d\tau = \frac{W_o}{2Q^2}$$

and

$$\int_{-\infty}^{+\infty} C^2(\tau)\, d\tau = \frac{W_o^{\,2} \pi f_o}{2Q} = \sigma^2/2 \tag{6.20}$$

since $W_o \pi f_o/Q = C(0) = \sigma^2$ and $Q \gg 1$.

One sees that the output of a low-pass RC averaging filter falls off as $1/Q^2$ when narrow-band noise is applied to it, but the output of the square law rectifier followed by a low-pass RC filter falls off as $1/Q$. If Eq. (6.20) is substituted into Eq. (6.18), one finds

$$\langle [e_o(t, \lambda) - \sigma^2]^2 \rangle = \frac{\sigma^2}{4RC}$$

or the root-mean-square fluctuation in the output about the mean value σ^2 is $\sigma/\sqrt{4RC}$ provided $RC \gg Q/\pi f_o$.

6.3 The Effect of Sampling in Time

The operations described in the last section can be carried out with analog devices. Frequently, however, one wishes to sample the time series at discrete instants of time and carry out all calculations with these samples. One may use (in principle) the exact ordinate values or quantize the sample values into two or more levels. There is also a question of the time interval between samples. Under some circumstances it may be desirable to use random time intervals between the samples, but it is customary to use a constant interval, Δt, between samples. This practice will be followed here.

Suppose that one has a sample $x(t, \lambda)$ of a stochastic process and that it is desired to replace this continuous sample by an infinite set of discrete values

$$x(n\Delta t, \lambda) \ , \ n = \ldots . -2, -1, 0, +1, +2, \ldots \tag{6.21}$$

One can obtain some guide to the best choice for Δt from a theorem known as the *sampling theorem* (Shannon, 1949). This theorem states that if the power spectrum $W(f)$ of the process is limited so that $W(f) \equiv 0$ for $|f| > W$, no information about $x(t, \lambda)$ will be lost if $\Delta t \leqslant 1/2W$. Since one is interested in making Δt as large as possible, the sampling theorem is usually stated in the form that the time series $x(t, \lambda)$ should be sampled at $\Delta t = 1/2W$.

The sampling theorem was stated in the last paragraph for a stochastic process. A derivation will be given, however, only for a deterministic signal which has a Fourier transform. This enables one to simplify the proof and emphasize the physical aspects. The reader is referred to Middleton (1960, pp. 212-215) for the extension to stochastic processes. Suppose that one has a signal $E(t)$ with a Fourier transform $\hat{E}(f)$ such that $\hat{E}(f) \equiv 0$ for $|f| > W$. The function $\hat{E}(f)$ can be represented exactly over the frequency range $-W < f < +W$ by the complex Fourier series

$$\hat{E}(f) = \sum_{n=-\infty}^{+\infty} A_n \, e^{-in\pi f/W} \tag{6.22}$$

where

$$A_n = \frac{1}{2W} \int_{-W}^{+W} \hat{E}(f)\; e^{+in\pi f/W}\, df, \quad n = 0, \pm 1, \pm 2, \ldots \tag{6.23}$$

The infinite set of coefficients A_n determines $\hat{E}(f)$ uniquely.

It has been assumed that $E(t)$ has $\hat{E}(f)$ for a Fourier transform so one may write, see Eq. (2.3),

$$E(t) = \int_{-\infty}^{+\infty} \hat{E}(f)\; e^{+i2\pi ft}\, df = \int_{-W}^{+W} \hat{E}(f)\; e^{+i2\pi ft}\, df\ . \tag{6.24}$$

Upon comparing Eqs. (6.23) and (6.24) one sees that

$$A_n = \frac{1}{2W}\, E\left(\frac{n}{2W}\right). \tag{6.25}$$

Therefore, one only needs to sample the wave form at a time interval $\Delta t = 1/2W$ in order to determine all of the information contained in the signal.

The sampling theorem is exact but one is left a little unhappy about the assumptions placed on the spectrum. Most real processes have a spectrum that falls off rapidly at higher frequencies but there is not a sudden cut-off as postulated. Perhaps a more realistic assumption would be to introduce the sampling of Eq. (6.21) and determine what effect it has on the power spectrum of $x(t, \lambda)$. The mathematical details of the answer to this question can be found in Blackman and Tukey (1958).

If one samples a time series at a regular interval Δt, and a sinusoidal wave of frequency $f(f > 1/2\Delta t)$ is present, the sampled values plot smoothly as though they were representative of a wave of frequency lower than $1/2\Delta t$. This phenomenon, which is well known, is illustrated in Fig. 6.4. As a result when a stochastic process is sampled at regular intervals Δt, and a power spectrum is computed, the power at frequencies greater than $1/2\Delta t$ appears in the computed power spectrum at the frequency between zero and $1/2\Delta t$. The relationship between the true frequency of a spectral component and the apparent frequency can be illustrated graphically as in Fig. 6.5. The frequency f_N in this figure,

$$f_N = 1/2\Delta t, \tag{6.26}$$

is referred to as the *folding frequency* or, more frequently, the *Nyquist frequency*.

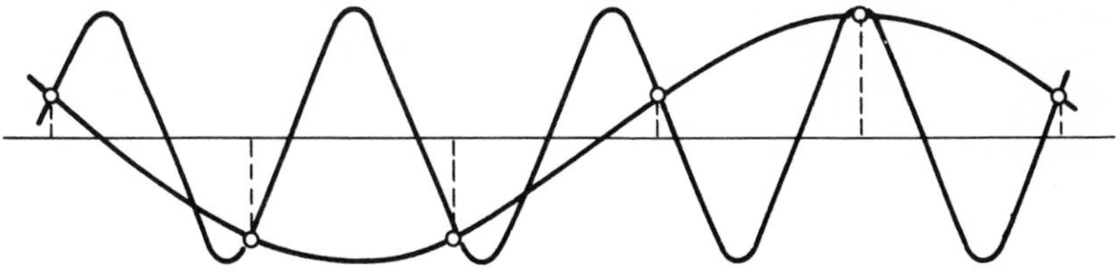

Figure 6.4–Sine waves of different frequencies with the same set of equally spaced sample values.

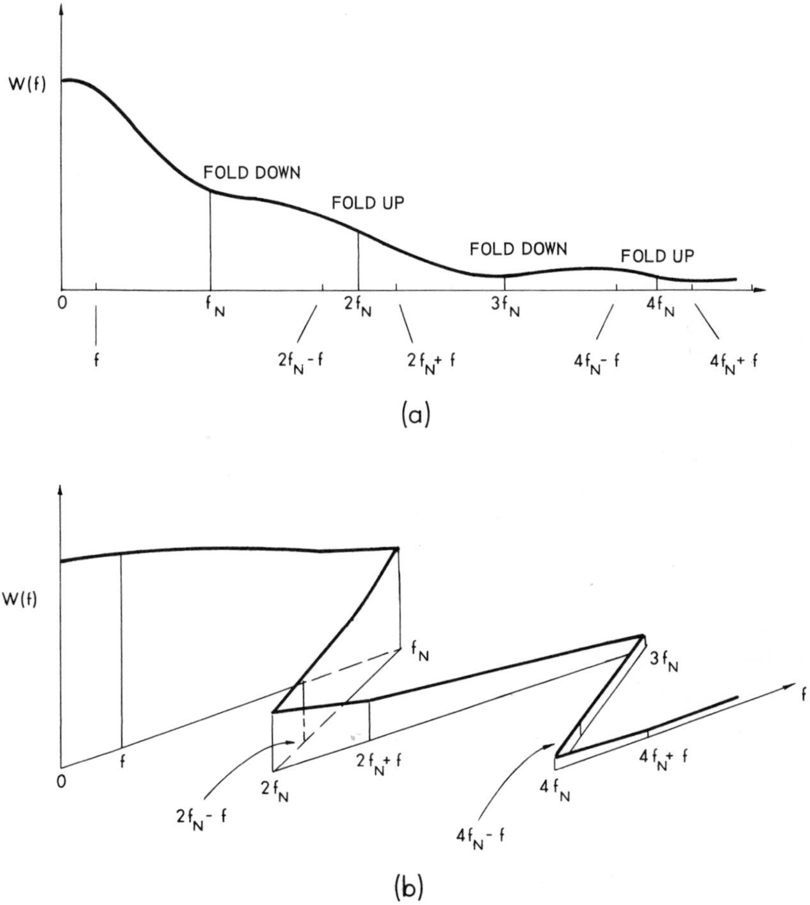

Figure 6.5–Pictorial description of a folded spectrum.

As illustrated in Fig. 6.5, the power density $W_s(f)$ at frequency f of the sampled process, is related to the power density $W(f)$ of the unsampled process by

$$W_s(f) = W(f) + \sum_{n=1}^{\infty} [W(2nf_N + f) + W(2nf_N - f)] \quad . \tag{6.27}$$

In order to enhance the physical interpretation of the folding concept, Eq. (6.27) and the illustration in Fig. 6.5 are given for a power spectrum that is restricted to positive frequencies.

The illustration of Fig. 6.5 offers a new way in which to view the sampling theorem stated above. If the power spectrum $W(f)$ is identically zero for $|f| > f_N$, there is no power "folded back" into the interval $0 \leqslant |f| \leqslant f_N$ and no distortion results from the sampling. This may be phrased in another manner in order to provide emphasis. When a time series is sampled by an infinite set of equally spaced values, as in Eq. (6.21), there is *no* loss of information if $W(f) \equiv 0$ for $|f| > 1/2\Delta t$. Further, it can be shown that the original signal can be reconstituted exactly from the sample values (Goldman, 1953, pp. 67-69).

In the extreme case where the sample interval Δt is much too large for the process being sampled, each sample value is independent of the others and a smooth curve drawn through the sample values will not bear any resemblance to the original data. Figure 6.6 gives an example[1] of this error. The top curve is a graph based on sample values with $\Delta t = 100$ minutes. The second pair of curves shows curves based on a sample interval of 10 minutes, while the third curve shows the results of decreasing the sampling interval to one minute. All of these curves are essentially similar since the adjacent samples are uncorrelated. It is only when the sampling interval was reduced to six seconds that a meaningful sample was obtained from which the original data could be reconstructed.

In the discussion of sampling it has been tacitly assumed that the noise was a broad-band noise as illustrated in Fig. 6.5. In most cases of interest in sonar applications, the noise is a narrow band of width W centered about a frequency f_o. A blind application of the sampling theorem stated above would lead one to assert that the time series must be sampled with $\Delta t = 1/2(f_o + W/2)$. Clearly this seems in error since the narrow band noise can be looked upon as a sinusoidal signal of frequency f_o which has both amplitude and phase modulation. The frequency spectra of the amplitude and the phase are restricted essentially to the frequency band $|f| \leqslant W/2$. Hence, there should be no loss

---

[1] This figure is reproduced from Fig. 4 of a paper by Webster (1964) who very kindly gave permission for the reproduction. The ordinate is the bearing in degrees of a velocity vector.

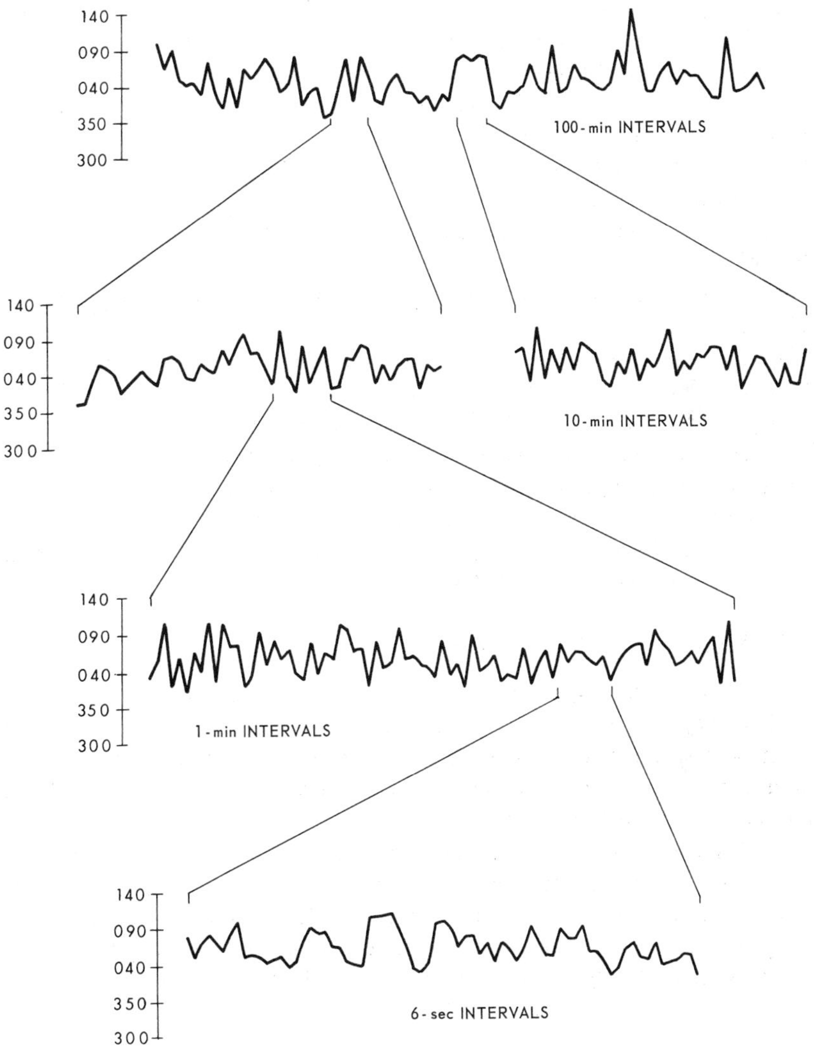

Figure 6.6–An example of the effect of sampling a time series with too large a sampling interval.

of the information contained in the modulation if each of these modulation functions were sampled at a time interval of $1/W$, making a total of $2W$ samples per second. A proof of this assertion is given by Kohlenberg (1953).

A large number of papers have been published in which the problem of analyzing narrow-band noise samples is discussed. In the argument above regarding the necessity of $2W$ samples per second to represent a narrow-band signal, appeal was made to the amplitude and phase modulation functions. This is equivalent to using the analytic representation of the real signal and sampling the real and the imaginary parts of the analytic signal each at a rate of W samples per second. In fact, one of the practical schemes of sampling narrow-band signals requires the construction of the Hilbert transform, i.e., the imaginary part of the analytic signals.

Normally the sampling of a time series is not an end in itself, but the sample values will be used for some purpose. One may wish to reconstruct the original signal at some later date or one may wish to approximate a calculation of a cross-correlation integral by a sum of products of sample values. The first problem is referred to as interpolation and has an extensive literature. The reader can refer to a paper by Kohlenberg (1953) and one by Bonnet (1965a). The second problem, which is of immediate interest in signal processing has been considered by Duflos (1964) and van Schooneveld (1965).

It is obvious to the reader that the sampling theorem is valid whether the independent variable is time or distance and that the theorem can readily be extended to a wavefield in three dimensions. In the latter case one can use a three-dimensional grid of sample points. The details of this generalization have been given by Stocklin (1963a, b).

6.4 Suggestions for Further Reading

A fundamental paper on the effect of sampling and one that is easy to read is Davenport, *et al.* (1952). The book by Goldman (1953) has numerous formulas pertaining to sampling in the frequency and the time domain. This book contains many references to the literature and some interesting material on the Hilbert transform.

A recent development in computer programming called the fast Fourier transform (FFT) provides an alternate method for computing power spectra. In this program the Fourier transform is computed directly from the sampled data points and the power spectrum is obtained from Eq. (2.9). The reader is referred to the paper by Cooley and Tukey (1965) for details.

PROBLEMS

6.1 The bandwidth of a filter is sometimes measured by using a wide-band noise generator whose output power density is a constant equal to W_0 from a few Hertz to, say, one megaHertz. This noise is passed through the filter and the total integrated power $\mathcal{W}$ is measured at the output of the filter. The bandwidth of the filter is defined as $\Delta f = \mathcal{W}/W_o$. Apply this definition to the bandpass filter of Problem 2.1 and compare the resulting value of Δf with the bandwidth between the 3 dB points of the frequency response.

6.2 A stationary, stochastic time series $x(t, \lambda)$ with autocovariance function $C_x(\tau)$ is smoothed by forming an average

$$y(t, \lambda) = \frac{1}{N} \sum_{n=1}^{N} x(t + \tau_n, \lambda)$$

where the τ_n are constants such that $\tau_m \neq \tau_n$, $m \neq n$.

(a) What is autocovariance function $C_y(\tau)$ of the new time series $y(t, \lambda)$?

(b) Specialize your answer to the case $\tau_n = n\Delta t$ and $N = 4$.

6.3 A stationary stochastic time series $x(t, \lambda)$ is used to construct a new time series

$$y(t, \lambda) = \frac{x(t + \Delta t, \lambda) - x(t)}{\Delta t}$$

which may be thought of as an approximation to the derivative of $x(t, \lambda)$ provided Δt is small.

(a) Show that

$$C_y(\tau) \cong \partial^2 C_x(\tau)/\partial \tau^2$$

(b) Relate the power spectrum of $y(t, \lambda)$ with the power spectrum of $x(t, \lambda)$ by partial integration of Eq. (4.8). State any assumptions regarding $C_x(\tau)$ that are necessary to justify your development.

6.4 The relationship between the power spectrum of $x(t, \lambda)$ and the spectrum of its derivative was obtained in an approximate manner in the preceding problem. This relationship can also be obtained by differentiating Eq. (4.27) term by term whenever this is justifiable. Carry through the formal details of this argument and obtain the power spectrum of the derivative.

6.5 Evaluate exactly the integrals

$$\int_{-\infty}^{+\infty} C(\tau)\, d\tau \text{ and } \int_{-\infty}^{+\infty} C^2(\tau)\, d\tau$$

when $C(\tau)$ is given by Eq. (6.19).

CHAPTER VII

The Detection of a Known Signal in a Noise Background–Single Channel

Part A. The Matched Filter

7.1 Intuitive Methods

The problem of detecting a signal of known shape in a noise background will be discussed at some length for the case of a single channel, since the mathematical methods are relatively simple. Further, the problems that arise in the multiple channel systems are generalizations that can be understood better after a discussion of the single channel case.

It has been seen that the noise output of any device can be characterized partially by the power spectrum $W(f)$ whose Fourier transform is the covariance function $C(\tau)$. Equation (4.7) yields, for the special case $\tau = 0$,

$$C(0) = \int_{-\infty}^{+\infty} W(f)\, df\,. \tag{7.1}$$

Now the value of the covariance function for zero lag, $C(0)$, is the mean square value of the noise. Hence, an assertion about the root-mean-square amplitude of a stationary, stochastic time series is really an assertion about the total power in the series. Therefore, since $W(f)$ is a non-negative function, Eq. (7.1) shows that *any* filtering that is applied to the noise will reduce the mean-square amplitude of the noise. Also, as shown by Eq. (4.37), *any* filtering will reduce the probability that a sample value of a gaussian noise will exceed any preassigned value. Consequently, the first step in processing a signal contaminated by noise is to filter it with a band-pass filter centered about the dominant frequency associated with the signal.

One can give a qualitative, intuitive answer to the question of how wide the pass-band should be. On the basis of the argument presented in the preceding paragraph one would expect that the pass-band should be as small as possible compatible with a minimal distortion of the signal shape and loss of energy content. For example, if the signal were a sinusoidal pulse of long duration, one could use a filter with an extremely narrow pass-band centered about the signal frequency and reduce $C(0)$ to an acceptable level. The price that one would pay for this reduction in $C(0)$ is increased detection time since, as the Q of the filter becomes larger, the time required for the signal level in the output to build up becomes longer. However, as one works out various examples, one will discover that this intuitive answer is not always the optimum answer.

When the peak amplitude of the signal is comparable to the square root of $C(0)$, one becomes most hesitant about decisions regarding the presence or absence of a signal. This hesitancy will exist whether the output of the detector is presented on a paper recording, a cathode ray oscilloscope, or as an audible signal. Often one has the feeling that if one could look or listen a second or third time one could arrive at a better decision. When the signal is presented on an oscilloscope tube or aurally, one begins to rely on the human memory to compare successive signals in an effort to increase the reliability of detection. This is a form of time averaging over and above the filter mentioned above and it could be built into the system. For the present, however, the discussion will be restricted to the possibility of only one "look."

7.2 Analytical Solution

It was argued above from qualitative considerations that one should use a band-pass filter as narrow as possible compatible with the energy spectrum of the signal whose detection is sought. Fortunately, this statement can be made more explicit by virtue of a paper by Dwork (1950)[1]. The following analysis follows parts of this paper rather closely, and the reader is referred to it for more details.

Suppose that one has a linear, passive device whose frequency response is $\hat{Y}(f)$ as described in Fig. 2.1 and Eq. (2.12). The input to this filter is the linear sum of a noise signal $x(t, \lambda)$ with power spectrum $W(f)$ and a signal $E_i(t)$ whose wave shape is known. The output signal, $E_o(f)$ in the absence of noise is given by (see Eq. (2.5))

$$\frac{1}{2}\{ E_o(t-)+E_o(t+)\} = \int_{-\infty}^{+\infty} \hat{Y}(f)\, \hat{E}_i(f)\, e^{+i2\pi ft}\, df. \tag{7.2}$$

It seems likely that one could replace the term on the left by $E_o(t)$ for all transfer functions $\hat{Y}(f)$ that correspond to experimental equipment. However, since the unknown function $\hat{Y}(f)$ will be determined so as to maximize a signal-to-noise ratio, it is well not to restrict the class of functions by requiring a continuous output.

Denote by S the maximum value of $|E_o(t)|$ considered as a function of time.

---

[1] This is not the earliest paper on the subject. Solutions for special cases date back to World War II.

The total power in the noise at the output of the network is denoted N^2 and is given by

$$N^2 = \int_{-\infty}^{+\infty} W(f) \mid \hat{Y}(f) \mid^2 df \ . \tag{7.3}$$

As pointed out in the discussion following Eq. (7.1), N is the root-mean-square of the output signal when noise alone is present. Therefore it appears quite reasonable to take the ratio S/N as the measure of the signal-to-noise ratio and to search for the function $\hat{Y}(f)$ that maximizes this ratio. The reader will note that S is defined in the absence of noise and N is defined in the absence of signal.

Dwork asserts and proves the following theorem:

The maximum possible value for S/N at the output will be obtained if, and only if, we set[2]

$$\hat{Y}(f) = \frac{\hat{E}_i^*(f)}{W(f)} \, e^{-i2\pi fT} \tag{7.4}$$

(T any real number), and the maximum value of S/N so obtained is

$$M = \left[\int_{-\infty}^{+\infty} \mid \hat{E}_i(f) \mid^2 [W(f)]^{-1} \, df \right]^{1/2} \tag{7.5}$$

Since the proof of the theorem presents an interesting example of the mathematical techniques of analysis of the response of a system to noise, the proof of the first part of the theorem will be given in detail. The reader is referred to the original paper for a proof of the "only if." It will first be shown that the maximum value S/N may have for any filter response is M. Secondly, it will be shown that if the filter response $\hat{Y}(f)$ is of the form given in Eq. (7.4), the resulting value of S/N is greater than or equal to M. These two demonstrations guarantee that the prescribed filter yields the maximum value of S/N.

In order to allow generality in the class of filters considered in the analysis, it has been assumed that the output $E_o(t)$ of the filter may have a finite set of discontinuities. Consequently, a statement about the maximum value of $\mid E_o(t) \mid$ must be phrased as the maximum of the pair of values $\mid E_o(t-) \mid$ and $\mid E_o(t+) \mid$ since the maximum might occur at a point of discontinuity if one exists. For all values of t

[2] If one wishes to preserve physical dimensions, a factor of one ampere must be inserted on the right.

$|E_o(t)| \leqslant$ larger of the numbers $|E_o(t-)|$, $|E_o(t+)|$

$$\leqslant \int_{-\infty}^{+\infty} |\hat{Y}(f)\,\hat{E}_i(f)|\,df\ . \tag{7.6}$$

By virtue of the definitions of S and N one has

$$\left(\frac{S}{N}\right)^2 \leqslant \frac{\left[\int_{-\infty}^{+\infty} |\hat{Y}(f)\,\hat{E}_i(f)|\,df\right]^2}{\int_{-\infty}^{+\infty} W(f)\,|\hat{Y}(f)|^2\,df}\ . \tag{7.7}$$

Schwartz' inequality, Eq. (3.19), will be applied to the numerator. It is desirable to write the integrand in the following form:

$$|\hat{Y}(f)\,\hat{E}_i(f)| = \sqrt{W(f)}\;|\hat{Y}(f)|\cdot\frac{|\hat{E}_i(f)|}{\sqrt{W(f)}} = g(f)h(f)\ .$$

This enables one to write the following inequality:

$$\left[\int_{-\infty}^{+\infty} |\hat{Y}(f)\,\hat{E}_i(f)|\,df\right]^2$$

$$\leqslant \left[\int_{-\infty}^{+\infty} W(f)\,|\hat{Y}(f)|^2\,df\right]\cdot\left[\int_{-\infty}^{+\infty}\frac{|\hat{E}_i(f)|^2}{W(f)}\,df\right],$$

so that Eq. (7.7) becomes

$$\left(\frac{S}{N}\right)^2 \leqslant \int_{-\infty}^{+\infty} |\hat{E}_i(f)|^2\,[W(f)]^{-1}\,df = M^2 \tag{7.8}$$

for *any* filter response. There remains only the task of showing that the equality is achieved for the filter response defined in Eq. (7.4).

Now, by definition, S is the maximum value of $|E_o(t)|$ for all t, so that for the particular value of $t = T$.

$$S \geqslant \text{maximum of } |E_o(T-)|, |E_o(T+)|$$
$$\geqslant \tfrac{1}{2}[E_o(T-) + E_o(T+)] \ .$$

The last term on the right is given by Eq. (7.2) for $t = T$, so

$$S \geqslant \int_{-\infty}^{+\infty} \hat{Y}(f)\, \hat{E}_i(f)\, e^{+i2\pi fT}\, df \ . \qquad (7.9)$$

If $\hat{Y}(f)$ is given by Eq. (7.4), the integral on the right becomes equal to M^2 as seen from Eq. (7.5) and also, in this case, to N^2 as seen from Eq. (7.3). Consequently,

$$S \geqslant M^2 = N^2 = MN$$

so

$$S/N \geqslant M. \qquad (7.10)$$

Equations (7.8) and (7.10) are compatible only if $S/N = M$ as asserted in the theorem. The meaning of the hitherto unspecified parameter T is now understood. It is the time at which the output of the filter achieves its maximum value. If one is not concerned with physical realizability, T may be any real number.

This is an extremely important theorem but one must be careful to understand what it does not say as well as what it does say. For example, a system designed by this theorem is not a detection system in the strict meaning of this expression since no judgement is offered regarding the presence or absence of a signal. The theorem only says that if one plans to build a detection system which will operate on the instantaneous values of the output, the filter response given by Eq. (7.4) will produce a maximum value of S/N. Detection rules must be added to the system based on other criteria. Similarly, the system does not provide a signal extraction system since one has no assurance that $E_o(t)$ will resemble $E_i(t)$ or represent a value of any parameter associated with it.

The system design has been restricted in its generality by the assumption of linearity. This assumption was implicit in Eq. (7.2). An example of one of the effects of this restriction is pointed out by Mermoz (1964). He remarks that the nature of the noise enters into the solution only through the power spectrum $W(f)$. This function depends only on the second order moments of the process $x(t, \lambda)$. It has been pointed out that the process is completely determined by the second order moment only if the process is gaussian. Two processes may have identical autocovariance functions and still differ in the higher order moments. It seems unlikely that the same filter response would be optimum for both of these processes.

7.3 Physical Realizability of the Solution

The parameter T is arbitrary unless one wishes to specify the instant of time at which the output of the filter is observed, but it is evident that the factor $\exp(-i2\pi fT)$ provides a distortionless time delay T in the output. One would like to minimize this time delay as much as possible, but one is constrained by the necessity of examining a certain amount of input signal in order to provide the maximum value of S. Since a realizable filter can provide memory, but not anticipation, the energy of the pulse cannot be fully utilized before its termination. Another way of stating this is that there may be a minimum value of T that is permissible in order to assure physical realizability of the filter.

There is no assurance that the operator prescribed by the transfer function $\hat{Y}(f)$ can be realized easily by a physical mechanism. However, in the special case that the input noise power spectrum is a constant, W_o, one can make more explicit statements. One can demonstrate a specific method of achieving the desired filter and with the aid of this embodiment demonstrate that the response satisfies the conditions of physical realizability.

A specific method of processing the data will be prescribed and it will be shown that this method is equivalent to the filter response of Eq. (7.4) when the noise power $W(f)$ is a constant W_o. The known signal $E_i(t)$ is used as a pattern for the construction of an image signal $E_i^i(t) = E_i(-t)$. The incoming message $y(t)$ which is the sum of the noise $x(t, \lambda)$ and the signal $E_i(t)$ is multiplied by the known signal $E_i(\cdot)$ and the product is integrated over all time. As the position of the known signal $E_i(\cdot)$ is shifted relative to $y(t)$, one obtains a new time series $z(t)$ defined by

$$z(t) = \int_{-\infty}^{+\infty} y(\tau)\, E_i(\tau - t + T)\, d\tau \ . \tag{7.11}$$

The translation of $E_i(\tau - t)$ along the time scale by an amount T is clearly arbitrary and will vary according as one is processing data in real time or is processing data that have been stored either temporarily or permanently.

In order to utilize the techniques of Fourier analysis, it is necessary to introduce the customary notation

$$Y_{T_o}(\tau) \left. \begin{aligned} &= y(\tau)\,, \ |\tau| \leqslant T_o/2 \\ &= \ 0\,, \ |\tau| > T_o/2\ . \end{aligned} \right\} \tag{7.12}$$

Since

$$y_{T_o}(\tau) = \int_{-\infty}^{+\infty} \hat{y}_{T_o}(f_1)\, e^{+i2\pi f_1 \tau}\, df_1 \tag{7.13}$$

and

$$E_i(\tau\text{-}t+T) = \int_{-\infty}^{+\infty} \hat{E}_i(f_2)\, e^{+i2\pi f_2(\tau-t+T)}\, df_2, \tag{7.14}$$

Equation (7.11) may be written, after changing the order of the integrals,

$$z_{T_o}(t) = \int_{-\infty}^{+\infty} \hat{y}_{T_o}(f_1) df_1 \int_{-\infty}^{+\infty} \hat{E}_i(f_2)\, e^{-i2\pi f_2(t-T)}\, df_2 \times \int_{-\infty}^{+\infty} e^{+i2\pi(f_1+f_2)\,\tau}\, d\tau\ . \tag{7.15}$$

The last integral is the delta function, $\delta(f_1 + f_2)$. This enables one to evaluate readily the integral with respect to f_2 to give

$$z_{T_o}(t) = \int_{-\infty}^{+\infty} \hat{y}_{T_o}(f_1)\, \hat{E}_i(-f_1)\, e^{+i2\pi f_1(t-T)}\, df_1\ . \tag{7.16}$$

Now $E_i(t)$ is a real function of time, so by virtue of Eq. (2.10),

$$\hat{E}_i(-f_1) = \hat{E}_i{}^*(f_1)\ , \tag{7.17}$$

and one sees that the operation described by Eq. (7.11) or, equivalently, Eq. (7.16) is equivalent to processing the data with a filter whose response is

$$\hat{E}_i{}^*(f)\, e^{-i2\pi fT}\ . \tag{7.18}$$

The parameter T_o has served its purpose and may now be allowed to approach infinity.

The response given by Eq. (7.18) is identical, except for a constant factor, with the response given by Eq. (7.4) when $W(f)$ is a constant. The ratio

S/N is unchanged when the filter response is changed by a constant factor so the goal has been achieved; that is, the goal of describing a specific embodiment of the filter.

The operation of multiplication and integration described by Eq. (7.11) is commonly referred to as a correlation detector. On the other hand, if $E_i(\tau - t + T)$ is replaced by the image signal, the integral on the right becomes a convolution between the signal $y(\tau)$ and the image signal. For example, in the special case that $T = 0$, $z(t) = y(t) * E_i^i(t)$. The discussion of Eq. (2.14) can be applied to show that if a filter can be designed whose impulse response is the image signal, the output of this filter will be $z(t)$ when the input is $y(t)$ for some value of T.

When the power density $W(f)$ of the input is white noise, the filter designed by the present procedure is physically realizable in accordance with the requirements set forth in Sec. 2.2 provided a modest limitation is placed on the class of signal functions $E_i(t)$. Since $\hat{E}_i(f)$ is the transform of a real signal $E_i(t)$, the magnitude and phase of $\hat{E}_i(f)$ are even and odd functions of f, respectively. The product $\hat{E}_i(f) \exp(-i2\pi fT)$ has the same property. Therefore condition number (2) is satisfied. One can see readily from Eq. (7.11) that if the input $y(\tau)$ is the delta function $\delta(\tau)$, the output is given by

$$z(t) = E_i(-t+T) = E_i^i(t-T) \tag{7.19}$$

One can select T so that this output will be zero for $t < 0$ provided there exists a time t_o such that the signal $E_i(t)$, which serves as the basis for the design, vanishes for all $t > t_o$. Further details of this argument are given by Dwork.

7.4 Further Discussion of the Filter (Matched Filters)

Let us drop the assumption of white noise and return to the optimum filter response defined by Eq. (7.4). In order to simplify the discussion the parameter T, which is at our disposal, will be set equal to zero. If the input to the filter is signal alone, the output will have an amplitude spectrum $|\hat{E}_i(f)|^2/W(f)$. On the other hand, if the input is noise alone, the power spectrum of the output is $W(f)\,|\hat{Y}(f)|^2 = |\hat{E}_i(f)|^2/W(f)$. Thus the design leads to a filter response for which the shape of the output spectrum is the same whether the input is signal alone or noise alone. At first glance this seems paradoxical, since one might think that the best filter would be one that produces a maximum separation between the output for noise alone and the output for signal alone. A more careful consideration enables one to see the explanation.

The clue to the apparent paradox is that an *amplitude* spectrum for the signal was found to be the same[3] as the *power* spectrum for the noise. These

[3] These statements sound wrong from the viewpoint of dimensions since dimensional constants of unit magnitude have been omitted.

two spectra respond differently to changes in the filter response. When the power density of the noise exceeds the energy density of the signal, it is clear that the filter should reduce the response of the system in this band of frequency. There is a limit to how much one should reduce this response, a limit that is reached when the amplitude spectrum of the output signal is equal to the power spectrum of the output noise. Similarly, when the signal energy spectrum exceeds the power spectrum of the noise at the input, one should increase the response of the filter, but not indefinitely.

It is customary in the literature to denote the filter developed in Sec. 7.2 as a "matched filter." This term was first introduced by Van Vleck and Middleton (1946), but Middleton (1960, p. 717) now prefers to call it a "matched (S/N) filter" to distinguish it from filters matched on the basis of other criteria. It is customary now to define a matched filter with respect to signal shapes rather than detection criterion. For example, Turin (1960) gives the following definition. "If $E(t)$ is any physical wave form, then a filter which is matched to $E(t)$ is, by definition, one with impulse response

$$h(t) = kE(T_o - t) \tag{7.20}$$

where k and T_o are arbitrary constants. A brief calculation will show that the S/N matched filter described in Sec. 7.2 is matched to $E(t)$ in the sense of Turin if $W(f)$ is constant.

Frequently, the matched filter is thought of as a device for pulse compression so that a long pulse can be transmitted at low peak power. The effect of the correlator is to shorten the pulse and increase the peak power correspondingly. As a consequence of this viewpoint, the output of the correlator is often squared and integrated with a circuit whose time constant is equal to the width of the correlation function of the transmitted pulse. This approach is of value when the power output of the transducer is limited by cavitation.

7.5 An Application of Matched Filters to Narrow-Band Signals

It is desirable to give a few details of the application of a matched filter to a narrow-band signal since this will illustrate the distinction between coherent and incoherent detection that will be discussed in more detail in Sec. 8.4. The following illustration is applicable to any type of matched filter and is not restricted to the specific matched filter that maximizes the signal-to-noise ratio.

Suppose that one transmits a narrow-band signal centered about a frequency f_o. It was pointed out in Sec. 5.5 that this kind of signal can be represented by

$$E(t) = A(t) \cos \omega_o t + B(t) \sin \omega_o t \tag{7.21}$$

where $A(t)$ and $B(t)$ are functions restricted to a frequency range $|f| \leqslant W/2 \ll f_o = \omega_o/2\pi$. As long as the doppler shifts due to the motion of the target and the volume and surface scatterers are small compared to W, a filter may be used in the receiving system to reject all noise signals whose frequencies fall outside the bands $\pm (f_o \pm W/2)$. Consequently, the received message may be expressed as

$$x(t) = \alpha(t) \cos \omega_o t + \beta(t) \sin \omega_o t \ . \tag{7.22}$$

If one wishes to form a cross-correlation between a stored replica of the transmitted signal $E(t)$ and a finite sample of duration T of the received message, one calculates

$$C_{Ex}(\tau) = \int_{-T/2}^{+T/2} E(t)\, x(t+\tau)\, dt \ . \tag{7.23}$$

When the product is expanded with the aid of trigonometric identities, one has (omitting terms of frequency $2\omega_o$)

$$C_{Ex}(\tau) = \alpha(\tau) \cos \omega_o \tau + \beta(\tau) \sin \omega_o \tau \ , \tag{7.24}$$

where

$$\mathcal{A}(\tau) = \frac{1}{2} \int_{-T/2}^{+T/2} [A(t)\ \alpha(t\text{-}\tau) + B(t)\ \beta(t+\tau)]\ dt \tag{7.25}$$

and

$$\mathcal{B}(\tau) = \frac{1}{2} \int_{-T/2}^{+T/2} [A(t)\ \beta(t+\tau) - B(t)\ \alpha(t+\tau)]\ dt \ . \tag{7.26}$$

It is evident from Eq. (7.24) that, after the frequency components in the vicinity of $2\omega_o$ are removed by filtering, the output of the cross-correlator is a narrow-band signal centered about ω_o. If one knows the carrier phase of the transmitted signal relative to the signal modulation, the detection process can be based solely on the function $\alpha(\tau)$ defined in Eq. (7.25). However, if the phase of the carrier is unknown, one must work with the envelope of $C_{Ex}(\tau)$: Equation (7.24) may be written

$$C_{Ex}(\tau) = R(\tau) \cos [\omega_o \tau - \Phi(\tau)] \ , \tag{7.27}$$

where

$$R^2(\tau) = \mathcal{A}^2(\tau) + \mathcal{B}^2(\tau) \ , \tag{7.28}$$

and

$$\Phi(\tau) = \tan^{-1} [\mathcal{B}(\tau)/\mathcal{A}(\tau)] \ . \tag{7.29}$$

The significance of these operations for the signal-to-noise ratio can be understood by assuming that the received signal is obscured by an additive gaussian noise. After narrow-band filtering centered about the frequency $f_0(= \omega_0/2\pi)$, the noise can be represented by an equation like (7.21), say

$$E_N(t) = A_N(t) \cos \omega_0 t + B_N(t) \sin \omega_0 t \ , \tag{7.30}$$

where $A_N(t)$ and $B_N(t)$ are independent gaussian variables (Davenport and Root, 1958, p. 160). The noise contributes to each of the terms in the right members of Eqs. (7.25) and (7.26). In coherent detection where one knows the phase of the carrier and can work with $\mathcal{A}(\tau)$ only, the two terms on the right side of Eq. (7.25) will yield a coherent addition for the in-phase and the quadrature components of the signal. The phase and quadrature components of the noise, however, will be dependent so it is the sum of their intensities rather than of their amplitudes that is important. This argument shows that when the phase of the carrier relative to the signal modulation is known, one can enhance the signal-to-noise ratio 3 dB by using both the in-phase and the quadrature components.

If the carrier phase of the returning signal is not known, one must work with the envelope $R(\tau)$ of the output of the cross-correlator. This means in turn that one must calculate $\mathcal{B}(\tau)$ defined by Eq. (7.26). The computation of $\mathcal{B}(\tau)$ does not add any further information about the signal $E(t)$ but it does double the effective noise in the output since the noise power contributes as much to $\mathcal{B}(\tau)$ as it does to $\mathcal{A}(\tau)$. Therefore, the signal-to-noise ratio for the case of no knowledge of the carrier phase is 3 dB less than the value when the carrier phase is known, all other variables being the same. This difference is significant, of course, only when the signal-to-noise ratio is low.

It is evident from this discussion that the shape of the signal which is used to modulate the carrier should be synchronized with the carrier for optimum performance. In echo ranging one will not know the carrier phase of the returning signal so that one will not know the instant of time, τ, at which $\mathcal{A}(\tau)$ or $R(\tau)$ should be sampled.

Nevertheless, there will be situations such as in a closed communication system or in a laboratory instrument where one has a knowledge of the carrier phase relative to an external, stable clock so that one can know the time at which the output of the cross-correlator should be sampled.

7.6 Maximum Signal-to-Noise Ratio for a Finite Number of Sample Values

The careful reader will have noted that in the solution of the optimum filter developed above, it was assumed that the experimenter had an infinite sample of signal on which to operate. This assumption was disguised since most of the operations were carried out in the frequency domain. However, the solution of Problem 7.1 will show that, in general, all of the signal $y(t)$, $-\infty < t < +\infty$, is necessary for the computation of the output, $z(t)$, of the ideal processor which maximizes signal-to-noise ratio. In practice, operations are restricted to a finite sample of data so the question should be restated as follows: "What filter response will yield the maximum signal-to-noise ratio when the length of the data sample is finite?" Since the answer to this question requires a knowledge of integral equations, the reader is referred to Helstrom (1960, pp. 95-121) and Middleton (1960, pp. 714-717) for the solution.

If sampled data are used in the processing of the acoustic signal, the integral equation mentioned in the last paragraph is replaced by a set of simultaneous, linear equations which can be inverted by matrix algebra. In view of the widespread use of time samples in signal processing, it seems desirable to carry out the design of a processor that maximizes the signal-to-noise ratio for a set of M sample values.

Suppose that M values of the received message $y_i = y(t_i)$ $(i = 1, 2, \ldots, M)$ are formed. Each sample value y_i is the sum of a noise component, $N_i = N(t_i, \lambda)$, and a known signal component, S_i. Normally, the message samples are equally spaced in time. Although this assumption is not necessary for the present analysis, it will be introduced to facilitate the discussion. The received message is processed by a linear operator of the form

$$z_i = \sum_{j=1}^{M} b_j y_{i+j} \,, \quad i = \ldots, -1, 0, +1, \ldots \tag{7.31}$$

This linear function of message samples may be looked upon as an approximation to the convolution obtained in Problem 7.1 or to the integral in Eq. (7.11).

It is assumed in the present analysis that the shape of the signal and the arrival time are known. The first assumption shows that the number of terms in the operator (b_i) are such that $t_M - t_1$ is equal to the duration of the signal, since the use of fewer terms in the operator would mean that not all of the signal contributes to the output while the use of more terms would only increase the contribution of the noise. Consequently, the output signal, S, in the absence of noise may be defined as

$$S = \sum_{j=1}^{M} b_j S_j \,. \tag{7.32}$$

The noise level, N, in the absence of the signal is defined in terms of the average of the square of the output. Thus N is the positive square root of

$$N^2 = \left\langle \left(\sum_{j=1}^{M} b_j N_{i+j} \right)^2 \right\rangle = \sum_{j,k=1}^{M} b_j b_k \langle N_{i+j} N_{i+k} \rangle . \quad (7.33)$$

If the noise is stationary in the wide sense, this ensemble average is independent of the subscript i. If the noise process has an average value of zero, the ensemble averages on the right are the central second order moments, Eq. (3.30), of the process, and one may write

$$N^2 = \sum_{j,k=1}^{M} b_j b_k \mu_{jk} . \quad (7.34)$$

The design of a linear operator (b_j) that will maximize the signal-to-noise ratio will be achieved when the ratio

$$\left(\frac{S}{N}\right)^2 = \frac{\left(\sum_{j=1}^{M} b_j S_j \right)^2}{\sum_{j,k=1}^{M} b_j b_k \mu_{jk}} \quad (7.35)$$

is maximized. This general problem of maximization will be restricted, however, by holding the numerator constant and minimizing the denominator. This restriction is justifiable in view of the limited dynamic range of the sonar system. The restriction is equivalent to fixing the output level that is desired for the signal and minimizing the background noise that obscures it.

The problem of minimizing the denominator of the right member of Eq. (7.35) while the numerator is held constant can be solved by introducing a small variation in the operator coefficients. Let

$$b_j \to b_j + \epsilon c_j$$

where ϵ is a small, real number. The numerator will remain constant if the coefficients (c_j) are subjected to the condition

$$\sum_{j=1}^{M} c_j S_j = 0 . \quad (7.36)$$

The denominator will have an extreme value (which can be shown to be a minimum) if

$$\frac{\partial}{\partial \epsilon} \sum_{j,k=1}^{M} (b_j + \epsilon c_j)(b_k + \epsilon c_k)\, \mu_{jk} \Big|_{\epsilon=0} = 0 .$$

When this expression is evaluated and the symmetry of the second order moments, μ_{jk}, is utilized, one obtains

$$\sum_{j,k=1}^{M} c_j\, b_k\, \mu_{jk} = 0 . \tag{7.37}$$

Equations (7.36) and (7.37) are mutually consistent provided

$$\sum_{k=1}^{M} \mu_{jk}\, b_k = S_j, \quad j = 1, 2, \ldots, M . \tag{7.38}$$

The desired set of operator coefficients is found by solving this set of linear equations.

If the source of the noise is a gauss process defined in Sec. 3.6, the matrix (a_{jk}) appearing in the probability density function, Eq. (3.29), is the inverse of the matrix (μ_{jk}) of the second order moments. In this case the solution of Eq. (7.38) is

$$b_j = \sum_{k=1}^{M} a_{jk}\, S_k . \tag{7.39}$$

In summary, if a known signal is obscured by gaussian noise and the processing system consists of the formation of a linear combination of M samples, the signal-to-noise ratio will be maximized when the coefficients of the operator are determined by Eq. (7.39). If the noise is white, the matrix (a_{jk}) is diagonal, $a_{jk} = a\, \delta_{jk}$, and Eq. (7.31) represents a finite approximation to the matched filter.

Part B. The Likelihood Ratio

7.7 Signal Detection as a Problem of Hypothesis Testing

It was shown in Part A of this chapter how one may develop methods for maximizing the signal-to-noise ratio, but this process, useful though it is, does not solve the problem of signal detection. Some criterion for the decision, "Yes, a signal is present." must be introduced. Presumably, one can introduce a threshold, or limiting value, and decide that a signal is present whenever the output exceeds this threshold. Unfortunately, this approach is empirical and does not appear to offer a sufficiently broad foundation on which a theory of signal detection may be developed.

A more fundamental approach to the problem of signal detection can be achieved by considering it as a question of hypothesis testing. It was pointed out in Sec. 5.1 that two hypotheses may be considered: H_0, no signal is present, and H_1, a signal is present. It is assumed that these two hypotheses are mutually exclusive and that one hypothesis is correct. In theory it is possible to assess the prior probabilities of these two hypotheses before any measurements have been made, although in practice this assessment may be extremely difficult to justify. After the available measurements are analyzed, one can assess the posterior probabilities of the two hypotheses. It is reasonable to assume that in some sense the best decision is made when one selects that hypothesis which has the greater posterior probability. It may be desirable to depart from this decision rule in order to allow for other considerations such as the false alarm rate or changes in the assumed values of the prior probabilities.

These ideas can be expressed more concisely by using the formulas of Sec. 5.1. In Sec. 5.1 the parameter $\mathcal{I}$ was introduced in the equations to designate fundamental information such as depth of water, roughness of the bottom, and the nature of the sea surface. This kind of information is still relevant but the parameter $\mathcal{I}$ will be suppressed in order to simplify the form of the equations.

The observation was denoted simply by the parameter p in Sec. 5.1, but for the present discussion it is desirable to delineate more carefully what is meant by an observation. In the case of a single channel the observation may be a recording of a time series $x(t, \lambda)$ over a finite time interval, $0 \leqslant t \leqslant T$, but it is often convenient to form discrete, equally spaced sample values of $x(t, \lambda)$. In the latter case one has a set of sample values as in Eq. (6.21) with $n = 1, 2, \ldots, M$, and the observation may be represented as a vector $\vec{V}$ in an M-dimensional space. In keeping with this point of view the scaler parameter p will be replaced by a vector $\vec{V}$ whose components are the M observations.

When these changes in notation are introduced and the number of hypotheses is restricted to two, Eq. (5.3) becomes

$$P(H_0 \mid \vec{V}) = \frac{P(H_0)\, P(\vec{V} \mid H_0)}{P(\vec{V})} \tag{7.40}$$

and

$$P(H_1 \mid \vec{V}) = \frac{P(H_1)\, P(\vec{V} \mid H_1)}{P(\vec{V})} \tag{7.41}$$

As mentioned above, the prior probabilities are related by

$$P(H_0) + P(H_1) = 1 \ . \tag{7.42}$$

Similarly, the posterior probabilities are related by

$$P(H_0 \mid \vec{V}) + P(H_1 \mid \vec{V}) = 1 \ . \tag{7.43}$$

The unknown probability $P(\vec{V})$ can be eliminated by forming the ratio of Eqs. (7.40) and (7.41). The resulting equation and Eq. (7.43) can be solved for the posterior probabilities. This yields

$$P(H_0 \mid \vec{V}) = \left[1 + \frac{P(H_1)}{P(H_0)}\, \ell(\vec{V})\right]^{-1} \tag{7.44}$$

and

$$P(H_1 \mid \vec{V}) = \left[1 + \frac{P(H_0)}{P(H_1)}\, \frac{1}{\ell(\vec{V})}\right]^{-1} , \tag{7.45}$$

where the *likelihood ratio,* $\ell(\vec{V})$, is defined by

$$\ell(\vec{V}) = \frac{P(\vec{V} \mid H_1)}{P(\vec{V} \mid H_0)} \ . \tag{7.46}$$

The form of Eqs. (7.44) and (7.45) can be made simpler if the likelihood ratio is generalized to

$$L(\vec{V}) = \frac{P(\vec{V} \mid H_1)\, P(H_1)}{P(\vec{V} \mid H_0)\, P(H_0)} \ . \tag{7.47}$$

Further, it will be seen that this extended definition of the likelihood ratio arises naturally in the development of Eq. (8.28). However, in order to calculate $L(\vec{V})$ one must endeavor to assess realistically the probabilities $P(H_1)$ and $P(H_0)$. This is extremely difficult to do since it involves answering subjective questions such as, "What is the probability that a submarine is in the sonar beam?" For this reason the discussion of signal detection often is based on the function $\ell(\vec{V})$.

7.8 Thresholds for the Likelihood Ratio

The simplest solution of the problem of threshold selection would be a comparison of the two posterior probabilities $P(H_0 \mid \vec{V})$ and $P(H_1 \mid \vec{V})$ followed by the selection of the hypothesis with the greater probability. Equation (7.43) shows that this criterion would lead to the conclusion that a signal is present if $P(H_1 \mid \vec{V}) \geqslant 0.5$. However, in view of the fact that other considerations such as false alarm rate may suggest a change in the threshold, it seems desirable to decide that a signal is present whenever

$$P(H_1 \mid \vec{V}) \geqslant P_0 \tag{7.48}$$

where P_0 is a threshold to be determined later.

The ratio $P(H_0)/P(H_1)$ that occurs in Eq. (7.45) is the ratio of two probabilities and, therefore, is never negative. This means that $P(H_1 \mid \vec{V})$ is a monotonic function of the likelihood ratio $\ell(\vec{V})$, and as $\ell(\vec{V})$ varies from zero to infinity, $P(H_1 \mid \vec{V})$ varies from zero to unity. Consequently, the inequality Eq. (7.48) can be replaced by

$$\ell(\vec{V}) \geqslant \ell_0 \ , \tag{7.49}$$

where ℓ_0 is a new threshold value.

A similar argument shows that $P(H_0 \mid \vec{V})$ decreases monotonically from unity to zero as $\ell(\vec{V})$ varies from zero to infinity. The dependence of the two posterior probabilities on $\ell(\vec{V})$ is shown schematically in Fig. 7.1.

If it be assumed that a value for the threshold, ℓ_0, can be chosen in a logical manner, a detector based on posterior probabilities can be replaced

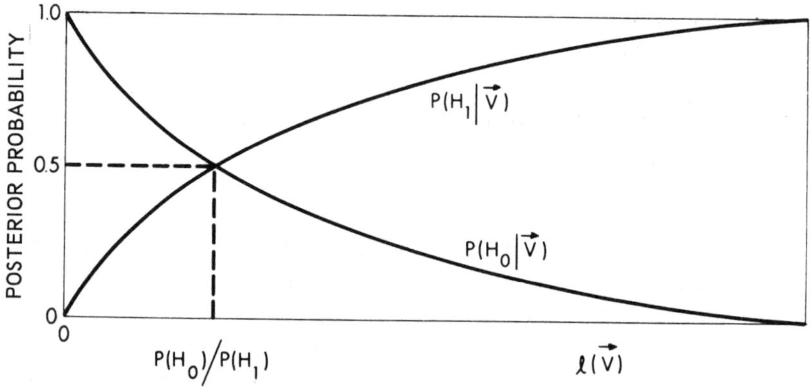

Figure 7.1–A schematic graph of the dependence of posterior probability on the likelihood ratio.

uniquely by a detector based on the likelihood ratio. Again, since $\ln \ell(\vec{V})$ is a monotonic function of $\ell(\vec{V})$, the inequality Eq. (7.49) can be replaced by

$$\ln \ell(\vec{V}) \geqslant L = \ln \ell_0 \ .$$

In many instances the use of the logarithm simplifies the receiver design.

7.9 A Simple Example

Before going further with the analysis of the likelihood ratio, it is well to consider an example so simple that the mathematical analysis will not obscure the concepts. Suppose that one wishes to measure the instantaneous value of a signal S which may have the value zero or S_0. The hypothesis H_0 is that $S = 0$ and the hypothesis H_1 is that $S = S_0$. The measurement is complicated by the presence of an additive random noise N whose value is governed by the Rayleigh probability density, Eq. (5.26)

$$p(N) = \frac{2N}{\sigma^2} e^{-N^2/\sigma^2} \tag{7.50}$$

where σ is the root-mean-square value of N.

In the present example the vector $\vec{V}$, the observation, has only one component, V, given by

$$V = N + S \ , \tag{7.51}$$

and one wishes to reach a decision of the value of S from a consideration of the likelihood ratio. If hypothesis H_0 is true, $S = 0$ and $V = N$. Hence, $P(V \mid H_0)$ is simply Eq. (7.50) with N replaced by V. On the other hand, if hypothesis H_1 is true, Eq. (7.51) shows that $N = V\text{-}S_0$. Consequently, one may use Eq. (7.50) for $P(V \mid H_1)$ provided N is replaced by $V\text{-}S_0$. It should be remembered that N is non-negative so that V can never be less than S_0. This means that

$$P(V \mid H_1) \left.\begin{aligned} &= 0 \ , \ 0 \leqslant V \leqslant S_0 \\ &= \frac{2(V\text{-}S_0)}{\sigma^2} \exp\left\{-(V\text{-}S_0)^2/\sigma^2\right\}, S_0 \leqslant V \ . \end{aligned}\right\} \tag{7.52}$$

The likelihood ratio, Eq. (7.46), becomes in this case,

$$\ell(V) = \left.\begin{aligned} &0 \ , \ 0 \leqslant \nu \leqslant 1 \\ &(1-\nu^{-1}) \exp\left\{+(2\nu\text{-}1)(S_0/\sigma)^2\right\}, \ 1 \leqslant \nu \ , \end{aligned}\right\} \tag{7.53}$$

where $\nu = V/S_0$. Some curves of $\ell(V)$ versus $\nu = V/S_0$ are plotted in Fig. 7.2 for various values of $(S_0/\sigma)^2$, the signal-to-noise ratio squared.

7.10 The Probability of Detection and the False Alarm Rate

In general the likelihood ratio defined in Eq. (7.46) is itself a random variable that is governed by the statistical parameters that control the noise and the signal. Hence, it is proper to introduce the concept of the probability density of $\ell(\vec{V})$. Let

$P[\ell(\vec{V}) \mid H_0]$ = probability density function governing $\ell(\vec{V})$ when no signal is present (7.54)

$P[\ell(\vec{V}) \mid H_1]$ = probability density function governing $\ell(\vec{V})$ when a signal is present. (7.55)

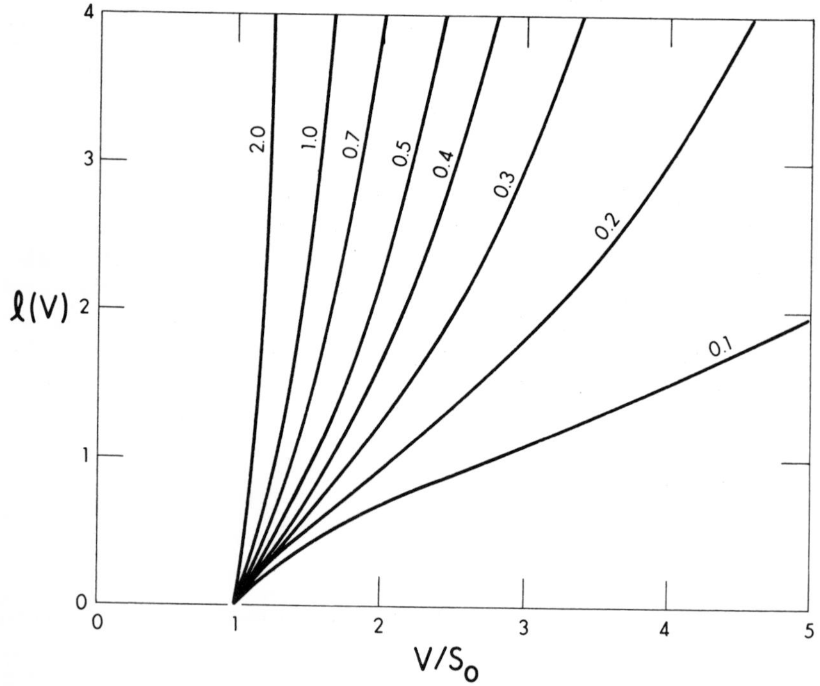

Figure 7.2–The likelihood ratio vs the message V for a dc signal obscured by Rayleigh noise.

Although it may be difficult to express these probability densities in a usable, analytical form, it is possible to prove some general results that will enable one to visualize their behavior.

The formula of conditional probability, Eq. (5.1), may be used to write

$$P[\ell(\vec{V}) \mid H_0]\; P(H_0) = P[\ell(\vec{V})]$$

$$P[\ell(\vec{V}) \mid H_1]\; P(H_1) = P[\ell(\vec{V})]$$

and

$$P[\vec{V} \mid H_0]\; P(H_0) = P(\vec{V})$$

$$P[\vec{V} \mid H_1]\; P(H_1) = P(\vec{V}) \; .$$

The ratio of the first pair of equations eliminates $P[\ell(\vec{V})]$, the ratio of the second pair eliminates $P(\vec{V})$, and the ratio of the resulting equations eliminates $P(H_0)/P(H_1)$. This yields the important result

$$\frac{P[\ell(\vec{V}) \mid H_1]}{P[\ell(\vec{V}) \mid H_0]} = \frac{P(\vec{V} \mid H_1)}{P(\vec{V} \mid H_0)} = \ell(\vec{V}) \; . \tag{7.56}$$

Thus the two graphs of the probability densities of the likelihood functions cross at $\ell(\vec{V}) = 1$, and $P[\ell(\vec{V}) \mid H_1]$ is greater than $P[\ell(\vec{V}) \mid H_0]$ when $\ell(\vec{V}) > 1$. In this sense one may say that large values of the likelihood ratio are associated with the presence of a signal.

It is customary in the literature to introduce two kinds of errors. A *Type I error,* or error of the first kind, occurs when one decides that a signal is present when, in fact, there is no signal. A *Type II error*, or error of the second kind, occurs when one decides that there is noise only when, in fact, a signal is present. When signal detection is based on a threshold value ℓ_0 for the likelihood ratio, the probability of these two errors are

$$\text{(Type I error)}\; \alpha = \int_{\ell_0}^{\infty} P[\ell(\vec{V}) \mid H_0]\; d\ell(\vec{V}) \tag{7.57}$$

$$\text{(Type II error)}\; \beta = \int_{0}^{\ell_0} P[\ell(\vec{V}) \mid H_1]\; d\ell(\vec{V}) \; . \tag{7.58}$$

The error of the first kind is often called the *false-alarm probability* and it sometimes plays a basic role in the decision making policy. For example, if a ship's captain took evasive action every time $\ell(\vec{V}) > \ell_0$, a high rate of false alarms could be prohibitively expensive in time and material. Frequently the concept of an error of the second kind is replaced by the detection probability $\beta_d = 1\text{-}\beta$. Thus one has

$$\beta_d = 1\text{-}\beta = \int_{\ell_0}^{\infty} P\,[\,\ell(\vec{V}\,|H_1)\,]\;d\ell(\vec{V})\,. \tag{7.59}$$

Equations (7.57) and (7.59) enable one to plot a graph of β_d versus a with ℓ_0 as a parameter as illustrated in Fig. 7.4. A curve of this kind is often called a receiver operating characteristic and the resulting diagram, Fig. 7.4, is referred to as ROC curves[4] or graphs. It is easily seen from the equations above that $a = \beta_d = 1$ when $\ell_0 = 0$ and $a = \beta_d = 0$ when $\ell_0 = \infty$. Further, the slope of a characteristic is given by

$$\frac{d\beta_d}{da} = \ell_0\;. \tag{7.60}$$

Different values of the signal-to-noise ratio yield different characteristic graphs. A second family of curves may be drawn on Fig. 7.4 by drawing the curves ℓ_0 = constant. With the aid of these curves one can plot β_d or a versus signal-to-noise ratio for each value of threshold level.

7.11 A Second Simple Example

The nature of the ROC graphs can be demonstrated most readily by working out a simple example. Suppose that one has a known signal $S(t)$ which may (hypothesis H_1) or may not (hypothesis H_0) be present, and that this signal is obscured by an additive, gaussian noise $N(t)$ with zero mean. The presence or absence of this signal is to be determined on the basis of M equally spaced samples $V_n = V(n\Delta t)$, $n = 1, 2, \ldots, M$, of the received message. Thus the observation $\vec{V}(=\vec{S}+\vec{N})$ is an M dimensional vector whose components are

$$V_n = S_n + N_n\quad,\quad n = 1, 2, \ldots, M\;. \tag{7.61}$$

The components S_n are known while the set of M values N_n are governed by the gaussian probability density, Eq. (3.29),

[4] A large number of interesting ROC curves, both theoretical and experimental, are given by Green and Swets (1966).

$$f(N_1,N_2,\ldots,N_M) = \frac{|a_{mn}|^{1/2}}{(2\pi)^{M/2}} \exp\left\{-\frac{1}{2}\sum_{m,n=1}^{M} a_{mn}N_mN_n\right\}. \quad (7.62)$$

The probability densities $P(\vec{V} \mid H_0)$ and $P(\vec{V} \mid H_1)$ are obtained from Eq. (7.62), as before, by substituting $N_m = V_m$ and $N_m = V_m\text{-}S_m$, respectively. Consequently, the likelihood ratio, $\ell(\vec{V})$, defined in Eq. (7.46) becomes

$$\ell(\vec{V}) = \exp\left\{\sum_{m,n=1}^{M} a_{mn}V_mS_n - \frac{1}{2}\sum_{m,n=1}^{M} a_{mn}S_mS_n\right\}. \quad (7.63)$$

Although Eq. (7.63) is valid only for the highly specialized case of a signal whose time of arrival and whose wave form are known exactly, it can be used to illustrate many of the features that characterize receivers designed to calculate likelihood ratio. It is evident from Eq. (7.63) that the statistics of the noise background in the form of the matrix (a_{mn}) plays a prominent role in the receiver design. This matrix yields a quadratic form in the signal components and a bilinear form $\sum_{m,n=1}^{M} a_{mn}V_mS_n$ in the message and signal components.

In order to simplify the following expression let

$$S_a = \sum_{m,n=1}^{M} a_{mn}S_mS_n \quad (7.64)$$

$$S'_m = \sum_{n=1}^{M} a_{mn}S_n \quad (7.65)$$

$$E_a = \sum_{m,n=1}^{M} a_{mn}V_mS_n = \sum_{m=1}^{M} V_mS'_m . \quad (7.66)$$

When this notation is introduced and the logarithm of $\ell(\vec{V})$ formed, one has the following simple form for the receiver:

$$\ell n\, \ell(\vec{V}) = E_a - \frac{1}{2} S_a . \quad (7.67)$$

Thus one evaluates the quantity E_a which is a linear combination of the M observations V_n and adopts the hypothesis H_1 if $E_a > \ell n\, \ell_0 + \frac{1}{2}S_a$. Since the quadratic form, Eq. (7.64) is positive definite, the quantity $\frac{1}{2}S_a$ is always positive and may be thought of as a bias on the threshold value $\ell_n \ell_0$.

The nature of the receiver can be understood better by considering the special case of white noise. In this case

$$a_{mn} = \delta_{mn}/\sigma^2 \tag{7.68}$$

and

$$E_a = \frac{1}{\sigma^2} \sum_{m=1}^{M} V_m S_m \ . \tag{7.69}$$

When this equation is compared with Eq. (7.11), it is seen that except for the factor σ^{-2}, this is the matched filter, expressed in terms of finite samples, which maximizes signal-to-noise ratio. Consequently, now one understands better the role of Eqs. (7.65) and (7.66). Equation (7.65) effectively distorts the signal shape (S_m) to a new shape (S'_m) such that the message (V_m) can be treated as though it were obscured by a white noise.

Actually, this explanation of Eq. (7.65) is helpful to the understanding of the nature of the receiver, but a comparison of Eqs. (7.29) and (7.65) is more illuminating. The structure of the receiver which maximizes the signal-to-noise ratio is identical with the structure of the receiver that provides a measure of the likelihood ratio. Thus one can dispense with the rather stringent assumption made earlier in this section that the time of arrival of the signal is a known quantity. The output of the receiver is observed continuously and whenever the output exceeds the threshold $\ell n\ \ell_0 + \frac{1}{2}S_a$, it is concluded that a signal is present. The basis for a choice of the value ℓ_0 will be considered now.

The probability of errors of the first and second kinds can be computed when one knows the probability density for the random variable E_a defined by Eq. (7.66). A straightforward method of calculating this probability density is to evaluate the characteristic function defined in Eq. (5.5) and take the Fourier transform as in Eq. (5.6). This calculation must be carried out for each of the hypotheses. If hypothesis H_1 applies, that is, if a signal is present, the characteristic function $\varphi_1(t)$ is by definition given by

$$\varphi_1(t) = E\left\{e^{itE_a}\right\} = \int_{-\infty}^{+\infty} e^{it \sum_{m=1}^{M} S'_m (N_m + S_m)} f(N_1, N_2, \ldots, N_m) d\vec{N} \ .$$

This M dimensional integral can be evaluated to give

$$\varphi_1(t) = e^{itS_a - \frac{1}{2}S_a t^2} \ .$$

The Fourier transform of $\varphi_1(t)$ yields the probability density

$$P(E_a \mid H_1) = \frac{1}{\sqrt{2\pi S_a}} e^{-\frac{1}{2}\frac{(E_a - S_a)^2}{S_a}} \quad , \tag{7.70}$$

$$P(E_a \mid H_0) = \frac{1}{\sqrt{2\pi S_a}} e^{-\frac{E_a^{\ 2}}{2S_a}} \quad . \tag{7.71}$$

Thus in each case the probability density function is a gaussian error function with standard deviation $\sqrt{S_a}$. When a signal is present, the mode is shifted in the positive direction by an amount S_a. The quantity S_a is a measure of the ratio of signal energy to noise energy. This can be seen most easily in the case of white noise by using Eq. (7.68). As S_a increases, the two probability densities, Eq. (7.70) and (7.71), broaden, but their modes separate more rapidly so a better resolution of the two hypotheses result.

Figure 7.3 is a plot of the two probability densities for $S_a = 1$. This illustration shows how the two errors arise since no matter where one selects the threshold for E_a, the curve $P(E_a \mid H_0)$ extends to the right and $P(E_a \mid H_1)$ extends to the left of this threshold.

If a threshold value E_0 is located on Fig. 7.3 and used as the criterion for a decision, the false alarm probability is

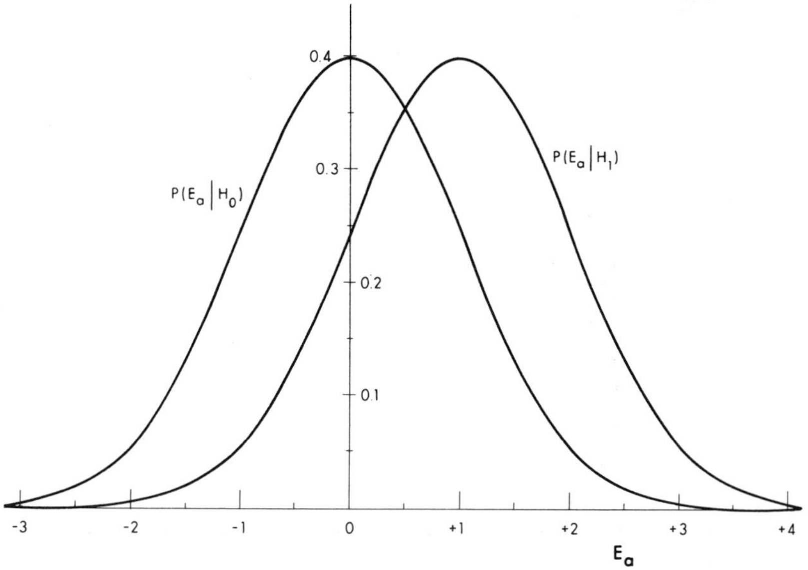

Figure 7.3–Probability densities for E_a when $S_a = 1$.

$$\alpha = \int_{E_0}^{\infty} P(E_a \mid H_0)\, dE_a = 1 - \Phi(E_0/\sqrt{S_a}) , \tag{7.72}$$

where[5]

$$\Phi(x) = \frac{1}{\sqrt{2\pi}} \int_{-\infty}^{x} \exp(-t^2/2)\, dt . \tag{7.73}$$

Similarly, the probability of detection is

$$\beta_d = \int_{E_0}^{\infty} P(E_a \mid H_1)\, dE_a = 1 - \Phi\{(E_0 - S_a)/\sqrt{S_a}\}. \tag{7.74}$$

As remarked before, when S_a is given a fixed value, Eqs. (7.72) and (7.74) provide a parametric form of a graph of β_d versus α. A set of such curves is given in Fig. 7.4 for several values of S_a, a measure of the ratio of signal power to noise power. These curves show how the false alarm diminishes as the signal power increases relative to the noise. Frequently, this figure is plotted using a logarithmic scale for the abscissa and a gaussian probability scale for the ordinate.

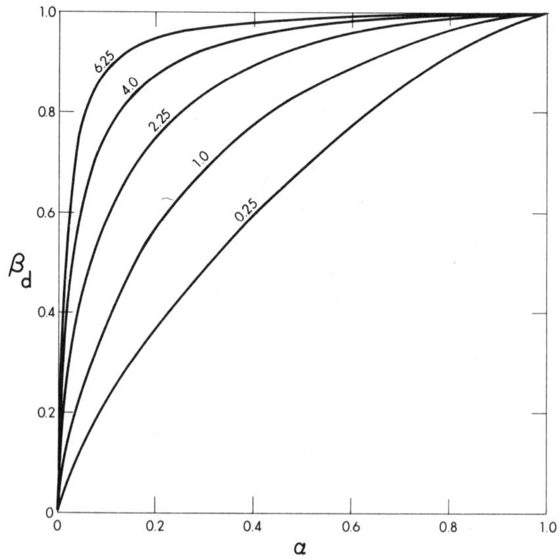

Figure 7.4–Receiver operating characteristics for the example of Sec. 7.11.

[5] There are many definitions of the function $\Phi(x)$. The present notation is the one used by Cramér (1946) who refers to $\Phi(x)$ as the normal distribution function.

PROBLEMS

7.1 Consider a filter whose response is given by Eq. (7.4). Show that if the input to this filter is a function $y(t)$ which has a Fourier transform $\hat{y}(f)$, the output, $z(t)$, may be expressed as a convolution,

$$z(t) = G(t) * y(t).$$

(a) Give an explicit definition of the function $G(t)$ in terms of the signal shape $E_i(t)$ and the formal Fourier transform of $[W(f)]^{-1}$.

(b) Show how the argument must be modified if $[W(f)]^{-1}$ does not have a Fourier transform.

7.2 It is permissible to process the signal $E(t)$ defined in Eq. (7.21) by extracting $A(t)$ and $B(t)$ directly from the signal. Show how this can be done. Since $\alpha(t)$ and $\beta(t)$ are known functions, one can proceed directly with the calculation of Eqs. (7.25) and (7.26). Discuss the relative merits of these two alternatives.

7.3 Show that the extreme value of the denominator of the right member of Eq. (7.35) is a minimum when the operator is given by Eq. (7.38).

7.4 Show that when the operator (b_j) is defined by Eq. (7.39), the value of $(S/N)^2$ given by Eq. (7.35) becomes

$$(S/N)^2_{\max} = \sum_{i,j=1}^{M} a_{ij}\, S_i S_j \;.$$

7.5 Calculate a set of ROC curves for the example of Sec. 7.9.

7.6 Modify the example described in Sec. 7.9 by assuming that the noise has a gaussian probability density of mean zero and standard deviation σ. Compare the likelihood ratio for this case with those of Fig. 7.2.

7.7 Calculate a few ROC curves for the combination of signal and noise described in Problem 7.6.

7.8 Should the sum, $\alpha + \beta$, of the probabilities defined in Eqs. (7.57) and (7.58) equal one? Give reasons for your answer.

7.9 Derive Eq. (7.60).

7.10 Derive Eqs. (7.70) and (7.71).

7.11 The discussion in Sec. 7.11 is deceptive in that both E_a and S_a depend on the noise level. Separate the noise level in the special case that $a_{mn} = \delta_{mn}/\sigma^2$, where δ_{mn} is the Kroneker delta and σ^2 is the mean-square value of the noise. Suppose, further, that $S_m = S_o s_m$ where S_o is the root-mean-square value of the signal. In this case the threshold can be expressed in a form that does not depend on the signal and noise levels as it did in Sec. 7.11. Plot a few ROC curves for this example and trace a curve of constant threshold on this figure.

7.12 Show that the inequality $P(H_1 \mid \vec{V}) \geqslant 0.5$, see Eq. (7.48), is equivalent to $L(\vec{V}) \geqslant 1$.

7.13 A set of ROC curves are constructed on the basis of a threshold value for some parameter E_a. Prove that the ROC curves are symmetric about the diagonal of slope -1 provided that $P(E_a \mid H_1)$ is identical with $P(E_a \mid H_0)$ except for a displacement along the E_a-axis and $P(E_a \mid H_0)$ is symmetric about some value, $E_a = M$, say.

CHAPTER VIII

Objective Criteria for Signal Detection

8.1 Introduction

The developments presented in the last chapter showed how one can detect a known signal in a noise background. It was found that signal detection could be expressed in terms of a threshold, but the choice of this threshold presented a serious problem since there was a conflict between the two kinds of errors that arose in the detection process. Fortunately, when the fundamental approach is stated more broadly, as in this chapter, the logical basis for a choice of the threshold becomes clearer. Further, this extended discussion provides automatically an answer to another problem that has not yet been raised. There are many circumstances in which the signal is not fully known but contains statistical parameters for whose variation allowance must be made. The correct way of averaging over these parameters is found in the form of a generalized likelihood ratio defined in Eq. (8.28).

During the last 20 years David Middleton has written a series of fundamental papers which have placed the problems of signal detection on a solid, theoretical footing. He has assembled his views in a monographic book (Middleton, 1960) which should be studied by everyone who aspires to a competence in this field. The following survey of his work leans heavily on Chapter XVIII of this book and on the paper by Middleton and Van Meter (1955).

It was pointed out in Chapter I that one may be concerned with a signal detection problem in which a simple "Yes" or "No" answer is all that one seeks. On the other hand, it may be that one wishes to extract one or more parameters of the signal. In the latter case one may still want to perform a detection operation. For example, if a system be designed to determine the time of arrival of a signal, and the system indicates an arrival time of, say, 20 seconds after transmission, it cannot be inferred that a signal caused the indication. An auxiliary circuit functioning purely as a signal detector can be used to provide a statement, "Yes, there is a signal," or "No, there is no signal so ignore the indicated time of arrival." In the case of marginal signals, and this is an important case, it is advisable to separate these two functions in order to improve the efficiency of each.

The following discussion will be facilitated by using the concept of signal space, observation space, and other spaces. These spaces may consist of a finite or denumerable set of discrete points or of a continuum in an Euclidean space of finite or denumerable number of dimensions or of even less simple spaces. Clearly, if one wishes to satisfy a mathematical reader, one would have to define explicitly what one means by a space by assigning properties to it. However, it seems sufficient for the present to give a few examples of these spaces and to rely on the reader's intuition to furnish general meanings to the statements. As a simple example suppose that the observer knows that at a certain time he can expect a message which will be a sinusoidal signal whose frequency will have one of five different, predetermined values $f_1, f_2, \ldots, f_5$, and the frequency that is present determines the signal (Honnest-Redlich, 1950; pp. 44-45). The signal space consists of five discrete points. More realistically, the signal space may consist of five intervals of widths Δf centered about the five frequencies f_i. Again, a sensor may be used to frequency modulate an oscillator so that the signal space may be a continuous interval (f_a, f_b) and the received frequency is a single valued function of the variable detected by the sensor. In each case one may speak of a signal space and usually one can assign a distribution function or a probability density which will give the probability that the signal will have any predetermined value or range of values.

It will be desirable to carry out integrations over the signal space and the other spaces. It is evident that one cannot give mathematical precision to statements unless the integrals are Lebesgue integrals, the probability is specified as a distribution function, and the spaces are restricted to those kinds for which Lebesgue integrals exist. However, those readers who are interested in simplicity of notation and are willing to rely on their intuition without seeking for counter examples that prove the equations are nonsensical may use the simple notation of Riemann integration without specifying the type of integration involved. It is understood, of course, that when the signal space contains discrete points as in some of the examples listed above, the integration yields sums and probability densities that must be interpreted as delta functions or simply as probabilities attached to each point. This gentlemen's agreement about notation is not uncommon in books on mathematical physics. For example, when the eigenvalues for a scattering problem assume both discrete and a continuum of values, Schiff (1949) uses a special symbol, a heavy block S, for this purpose to remind the reader that one sums over discrete values and integrates over the continuum. Dirac (1930) has popularized the use of delta functions in the integrand to yield discrete sums.

The situation that is most easily visualized arises when the receiver operates on N equally spaced samples. In this case the signal, the noise, and the message which is some combination of the signal and noise, may each be represented as a point in an N-dimensional space and designated by a vector. It is assumed that a frequency function is known for each of these variables. Let us follow Middleton and write

$\vec{S}$ = a signal
$\sigma(\vec{S})$ = frequency function of S
$\vec{N}$ = the noise sample
$W(\vec{N})$ = frequency function of the noise
$\vec{V}$ = message.

It will be assumed that the noise $\vec{N}$ is statistically independent of the signal $\vec{S}$ and that the received message $\vec{V}$ is the linear sum of the noise and the signal. Thus the message vector may be expressed as

$$\vec{V} = \vec{N} + \vec{S} \ . \tag{8.1}$$

The *message space,* or *observation space,* will be denoted Γ.

It will be convenient to express the frequency function $F(\vec{V})$ as a conditional probability depending on $\vec{S}$. Thus one will write $F(\vec{V} \mid \vec{S})$ for the frequency function of the message.[1]

Finally, one needs to introduce a *decision space* Δ which comprises the possible decisions $\vec{\gamma}$. Usually the structure of the decision space will be much simpler than that of the other spaces. In the case of signal detection the space Δ may consist of only two discrete points, while if one tries to recover as nearly as possible the original wave form of the signal, the space Δ may have the same dimensionality as the *signal space* Ω. The goal of the design is the determination of a *decision rule* $\delta(\vec{\gamma} \mid \vec{V})$ which determines $\vec{\gamma}$ when $\vec{V}$ is given. The decision rule need not be deterministic but may have random decision built into it. For example, if two decisions appear equally likely, it may be an advantage in some situations to have a randomness built into the decision.

These ideas may be expressed graphically as in Fig. 8.1. In considering this figure several points should be born in mind. First, the diagrammatic representation of the various spaces as circles does not imply anything about their structure or dimensionality. Secondly, the decision rule $\delta(\cdot)$ will be constructed using a knowledge of $\sigma(\vec{S})$ and $W(\vec{N})$, but the rule itself does not require any knowledge of the specific values of $\vec{S}$ nor of $\vec{N}$ that lead to the observation $\vec{V}$. Finally, it is helpful to visualize the decision rule δ as a mapping of the observation space Γ onto the decision space Δ. In general this is not a reversible 1-1 mapping since regions of Γ may map into points of Δ. In fact, it will turn out repeatedly that the problem of finding $\delta(\cdot)$ can be expressed as a problem of drawing boundaries in Γ. A recent book by Sebestyen (1962) has many illustrations of this process in which the boundaries are nonlinear and not necessarily connected.

Since one must face up to the possibility or erroneous decisions, it is necessary to assign a *loss function* to each combination of possible signal $\vec{S}$ and decision $\vec{\gamma}$. This function, which may be dependent on the decision rule, will

[1]The reader is referred to the footnote in Sec. 5.1 for this notation.

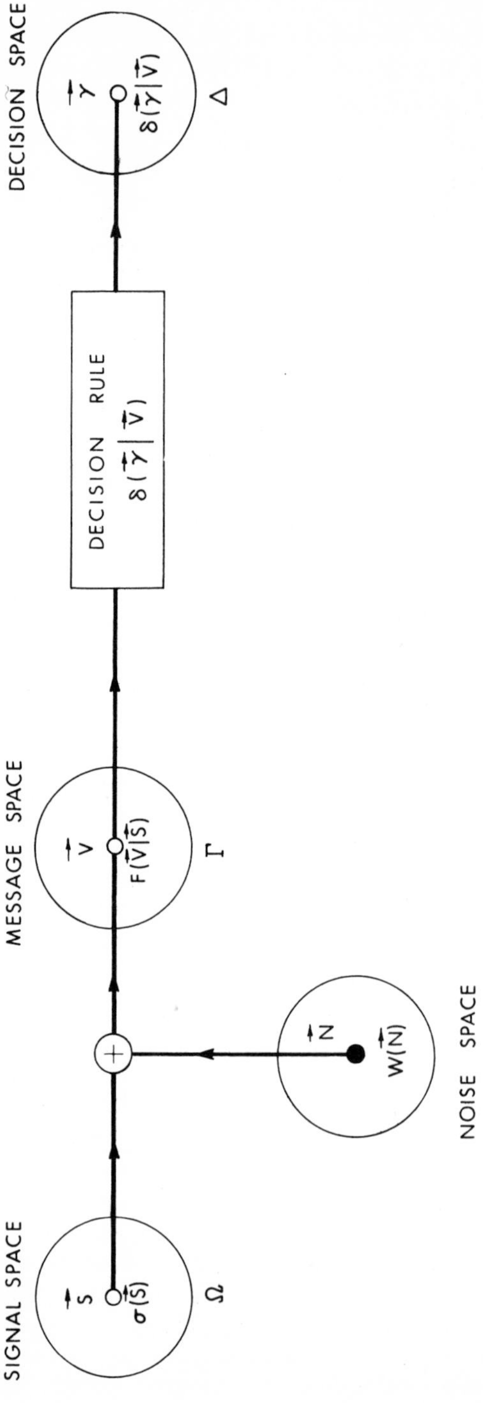

Figure 8.1—An illustration of the fundamental elements of statistical decision theory. After Van Meter (1955, Figure 2).

be denoted $L(\vec{S}, \vec{\gamma})$ and designated simply the loss function. The performance of the system can be evaluated, for example, by averaging the loss function over the range of possible messages $\vec{V}$ and decisions $\vec{\gamma}$ and perhaps over the range of signals $\vec{S}$. Thus, Middleton is led to a series of definitions, among which are the following:

If one thinks of $\delta(\vec{\gamma} \mid \vec{V})$ as a probability density over the space Δ of $\vec{\gamma}$, then[2]

$$\int_{\Delta} \delta(\vec{\gamma} \mid \vec{V})\, L(\vec{S}, \vec{\gamma})\, d\vec{\gamma} \tag{8.2}$$

is the expected value of the loss function L for a given signal $\vec{S}$ and a given message $\vec{V}$. If the space Δ is a set of discrete points, and this will often be the case, the integral is interpreted as a sum over these points and $\delta(\vec{\gamma} \mid \vec{V}) d\vec{\gamma}$ reduces to a unique probability δ_i at each point with

$$\Sigma \delta_i = 1 \tag{8.3}$$

where the sum extends over the set of discrete points. The message $\vec{V}$ will take a wide variety of forms and the expected value of the loss must be averaged over all possible messages. Hence, one must modify Eq. (8.2) by averaging over the range of possible messages, i.e., the observation space Γ. The result of this second average will be called the *conditional loss rating* and denoted $\mathfrak{L}(\vec{S}, \delta)$.

In the interest of simplicity the loss function L will be restricted substantially and new names will be introduced to reflect this simplification. As Middleton points out, one may introduce loss functions which depend on the decision function δ. The theory associated with such loss functions is substantially more elaborate than the theory found when one assumes that L depends only on the signal $\vec{S}$ and the decision $\vec{\gamma}$ but is independent of δ. When the loss function is subjected to this latter restriction, it will be called a *cost function* $C(\vec{S}, \vec{\gamma})$ and the associated averages will be called *risks*. In accordance with this convention one defines the *conditional risk* $r(\vec{S}, \delta)$ by

$$r(\vec{S}, \delta) = \int_{\Gamma} F(\vec{V} \mid \vec{S})\, d\vec{V} \int_{\Delta} C(\vec{S} \mid \vec{\gamma})\, \delta(\vec{\gamma} \mid \vec{V})\, d\vec{\gamma}\ . \tag{8.4}$$

The function $r(\cdot)$ is called a conditional risk because it is evaluated for a specific signal $\vec{S}$. The argument δ in the functional notation $r(\vec{S}, \delta)$ is a reminder that the risk depends on the specific decision rule that is used in making the decision, although the cost function $C(\cdot)$ does not depend on δ.

---

[2] In this and the following integrals $d\vec{\gamma}$ designates a volume element in the Δ space and, consequently, is a scalar quantity. This notation is common in statistical mechanics.

The next step in the generalization of the definition of risk depends on the experimenter's knowledge of the statistics of the signal $\vec{S}$. It was asserted above that the probability density $\sigma(\vec{S})$ is known but this may not be the case. If one can describe the kinds of signals $\vec{S}$ that may be received but cannot assess a probability density, one cannot calculate an expected value of $r(\vec{S}, \delta)$ averaged over all possible signals. In this case one must have recourse to the minimax concept introduced by von Neuman into the theory of games. On the other hand, if one can determine the statistics of the signal $\vec{S}$, one can calculate the expectation of $r(\cdot)$ for all possible signals. This leads to an *average, unconditional loss rating* $R(\sigma, \delta)$ defined by

$$\begin{aligned} R(\sigma, \delta) &= \int_{\Omega} \sigma(\vec{S})\, r(\vec{S}, \delta)\, d\vec{S} \\ &= \int_{\Omega} \sigma(\vec{S})\, d\vec{S} \int_{\Gamma} F(\vec{V} \mid \vec{S})\, d\vec{V} \int_{\Delta} C(\vec{S}, \vec{\gamma})\, \delta(\vec{\gamma} \mid \vec{V})\, d\vec{\gamma} \; . \end{aligned} \tag{8.5}$$

This expression is complete in one sense, but there is still a great deal of freedom left in the choice of the cost function $C(\cdot)$ so that a wide range of criteria is available to the designer.

Equation (8.4) may be expressed in an alternate form that makes it easier to visualize the concept of conditional risk. Let $p(\vec{\gamma} \mid \vec{S})$ be the probability density that a decision $\vec{\gamma}$ will be made when a signal $\vec{S}$ is present and the decision is based on the message $\vec{V}$ in accordance with the rule $\delta(\vec{\gamma} \mid \vec{V})$. Thus, by definition,

$$p(\vec{\gamma} \mid \vec{S}) = \int_{\Gamma} \delta(\vec{\gamma} \mid \vec{V})\, F(\vec{V} \mid \vec{S})\, d\vec{V} \; . \tag{8.6}$$

By using this definition one may rewrite Eq. (8.4) as

$$r(\vec{S}, \delta) = \int_{\Delta} C(\vec{S}, \vec{\gamma})\, p(\vec{\gamma} \mid \vec{S})\, d\vec{\gamma} \; . \tag{8.7}$$

One sees from this form that the conditional risk is the average value of the cost of the decision weighted according to the probability of this decision. The average is carried out over all possible decisions.

These general formulas will be given a more explicit formulation in Secs. 8.3 and 8.4. First, however, it is desirable to continue the theoretical discussion with a few more definitions.

8.2 Bayes Systems

Suppose for the present that the signal statistics $\sigma(\vec{S})$, the message statistics $F(\vec{V} \mid \vec{S})$, and the cost function $C(\vec{S}, \gamma)$ are known. Let us fix our attention on the decision function $\delta(\vec{\gamma} \mid \vec{V})$ which is at our disposal. For every decision function $\delta(\cdot)$ one has an average risk

$$R(\sigma,\delta) = \int_{\Omega} \sigma(\vec{S})\, d\vec{S} \int_{\Gamma} F(\vec{V} \mid \vec{S})\, d\vec{V} \int_{\Delta} C(\vec{S}, \vec{\gamma})\, \delta(\vec{\gamma} \mid \vec{V})\, d\vec{\gamma} \ . \tag{8.8}$$

One can order the decision functions $\delta(\cdot)$ according to the magnitude of the associated average risk $R(\cdot)$. This would appear to be a valid way to evaluate the decision functions since it seems satisfactory intuitively to assert that one decision function is better than another one if the average risk resulting from the first decision function is smaller.

Wald (1950) proves that there exists a decision function δ^* which yields the least average risk for any given set of signal and noise statistics and given cost function. This decision function, δ^*, will be called a *Bayes decision rule*, the system that utilizes this decision rule will be called a *Bayes system*, and the resulting value of the average risk will be called the *Bayes risk*. The preceding argument leads to a unique Bayes decision rule for given functions σ, F, and C. One can broaden the enquiry by considering a class of probability densities $\sigma(\vec{S})$ and finding the Bayes decision rule δ^* associated with each function σ. This leads to a *Bayes class of decision functions*.

In the preceding discussion it was assumed that $\sigma(\vec{S})$ is known so that risks could be averaged over all possible signals. This assumption leads to a unique value of the average risk and to the possibility of ordering decision rules according to the magnitude of the average risk. If the probability density $\sigma(\vec{S})$ is not known, one can still introduce a partial ordering of the decision rules. One can use Eq. (8.4) or the equivalent Eq. (8.7) to calculate the conditional risk for each possible signal $\vec{S}$ and decision rule $\delta(\cdot)$. It is conceivable that of two decision rules δ_1 and δ_2, δ_1 may yield a smaller conditional loss rating for a signal $\vec{S}_1$ but a larger conditional loss rating for another signal $\vec{S}_2$. In this case one cannot order the two decision rules according to their conditional loss rating. On the other hand, one may be able to show that the conditional loss rating yielded by a particular decision rule δ_3 never exceeds that of another decision rule δ_4 for any possible signal and $\delta_3 < \delta_4$ for some signal. In this case one says that the decision rule δ_3 is uniformly better than δ_4. This definition leads to a partial ordering of decision rules that is transitive. That is, if δ_3 is uniformly better than δ_4 and δ_4 is uniformly better than δ_5, δ_3 is uniformly better than δ_5.

It is well to stop the development at this point. It should be apparent that there are many interesting mathematical developments that lie ahead, but it would lead us too far from our present goal to follow any of them. The reader is referred to Middleton (1960) and to Wald (1950). The important aspect for our purpose is the generality of the concept of the Bayes decision rule that is provided through the functions σ, L, and C. Further, since the average risks can be ordered and the conditional risks partly ordered, one has the possibility of comparing decision rules with each other and with the Bayes decision rule.

The reader will have noted that the selection of a cost function is of critical importance. It may be difficult to select a satisfactory cost function but this is a problem of practical importance which should be faced by the practitioner. Likewise, the practical question of the statistical probability densities must be answered. As an example, it may be easy to assign statistical parameters to the signal if it is present, but how can one assess the probability that a signal is present? In a routine search with no previous alert, the probability that a signal is present is so small that one would normally approximate it by zero. This would certainly be unsatisfactory. This can be avoided either by considering conditional risks only or by assigning an excessively high cost to the decision of no signal when one is actually present. On the other hand, if the sonar operator has momentarily lost contact with a target, the probability of a signal being present is much higher than it would be in the case of a routine search.

The present account has been greatly simplified. Not only have the details of the proofs been omitted, but the possible subjects for consideration have been restricted. There exist classes of cost functions that are more general than those considered here. Further, as mentioned above, one can apply the theory of games both to the question of minimizing risk and to the terminology of the discussion. Finally, one can add restraints on the decision function $\delta(\cdot)$ to which the minimization procedures are subjected.

8.3 A Specific Example

The nature of the theory outlined in the first two sections can be more readily understood if explicit forms for the various functions are introduced. Let us consider the case of signal detection in which two possibilities occur: either a signal is not present or some member of the class of possible signals is present. Let

$$\begin{aligned} q &= \textit{a priori} \text{ probability that no signal is present} \\ p &= 1 - q = \textit{a priori} \text{ probability that some signal } \vec{S} \text{ is present.} \end{aligned}$$

Now the signal $\vec{S}$ is assumed not to be unique so there is a range of signals which may be denoted by a set Ω_1 in the signal space Ω. Let $\sigma_1(\vec{S})(\vec{S}\epsilon\Omega_1)$ be the probability density defined in Ω_1 so that

$$\sigma_1(\vec{S}) \equiv 0, \vec{S}\epsilon'\Omega_1 \quad ; \int_{\Omega_1} \sigma_1(\vec{S})\, d\vec{S} = 1 \,. \tag{8.9}$$

Here ϵ' means "is not an element of." Then one may write

$$\sigma(\vec{S}) = q\delta(\vec{S}) + p\sigma_1(\vec{S}) \tag{8.10}$$

where it is assumed that $\sigma_1(0) = 0$. The function $\delta(\vec{S})$ is the delta function defined in the Ω space. Equation (8.10) predicts $\sigma(0) = q$ as it should.[3]

The possible decisions that may be reached by the system are

γ_o : no signal is present

and

γ_1 : a signal is present.

Consequently, the average risk $R(\cdot)$ defined in Eq. (8.5) may be expressed as

$$R(\sigma,\delta) = \int_\Omega \sigma(\vec{S})\, d\vec{S} \int_\Gamma F(\vec{V} \mid \vec{S}) \left\{ C(\vec{S}, \gamma_o)\, \delta(\gamma_o \mid \vec{V}) + C(\vec{S}, \gamma_1)\, \delta(\gamma_1 \mid \vec{V}) \right\} d\vec{V} \quad \ldots . \tag{8.11}$$

One may think of the decision function $\delta(\cdot)$ as a probability density. Since a decision is always made in the present system, one must have

$$\delta(\gamma_o \mid \vec{V}) + \delta(\gamma_1 \mid \vec{V}) = 1 \text{ for all } \vec{V} . \tag{8.12}$$

There are four combinations of signals and decisions since for each decision a signal may or may not be present. Consequently, the cost function $C(\cdot)$ in Eq. (8.11) consists of four numbers and the integral over signal space Ω reduces to an integral over Ω_1 plus a term corresponding to $\vec{S} = 0$.

The four cost values will be designated as follows:

$$\left. \begin{aligned} C(\vec{S} = 0; \gamma_o) &= C_{1\text{-}a} \,, \quad C(\vec{S} \epsilon \Omega_1 \,; \gamma_o) = C_\beta \,, \\ C(\vec{S} = 0; \gamma_1) &= C_a \quad , \quad C(\vec{S} \epsilon \Omega_1 \,; \gamma_1) = C_{1\text{-}\beta} \,. \end{aligned} \right\} \tag{8.13}$$

Thus $C_{1\text{-}a}$ is the cost of making the correct decision that no signal is present while C_a is the cost of deciding that a signal is present when in fact there is none. Since the circumstances, i.e., the presence of a signal, are the same, one requires $C_{1\text{-}a} < C_a$. That is to say, in any system of costing one would require a wrong decision to cost more than a correct decision, other circumstances remaining unchanged. Likewise, $C_{1\text{-}\beta}$ is the cost of making the correct decision

---

[3] This is an inexact method of describing $\sigma(\vec{S})$. It is really the integral of $\sigma(\vec{S})$ over a small region containing $\vec{S} = 0$ that equals q.

when a signal is present while C_β is the cost of deciding that no signal is present when in fact a signal is present. It is necessary that $C_{1-\beta} < C_\beta$.

When Eq. (8.10) is introduced in Eq. (8.11) and the array of cost terms in (8.13) are utilized, one has, with a change in the order of integration,

$$R(\sigma,\delta) = q\int_\Gamma F(\vec{V} \mid 0)\left\{C_{1-a}\,\delta(\gamma_o \mid \vec{V}) + C_a\,\delta(\gamma_1 \mid \vec{V})\right\} d\vec{V}$$

$$+ p\int_\Gamma \left(\int_{\Omega_1} \sigma_1(\vec{S})\,F(\vec{V} \mid \vec{S})\,d\vec{S}\right) \times$$

$$\left\{C_\beta\,\delta(\gamma_o \mid \vec{V}) + C_{1-\beta}\,\delta(\gamma_1 \mid \vec{V})\right\} d\vec{V}\ . \qquad (8.14)$$

The integral over Ω_1, which gives the average value of $F(\vec{V} \mid \vec{S})$, may be designated by

$$\langle F(\vec{V} \mid \vec{S})\rangle_S = \int_{\Omega_1} \sigma_1(\vec{S})\,F(\vec{V} \mid \vec{S})\,d\vec{S}\ . \qquad (8.15)$$

The concept of two kinds of errors was introduced in Sec.7.10. A *Type I error*, or error of the first kind, occurs when one decides that a signal is present when, in fact, there is only noise. A *Type II error* or error of the second kind occurs when one decides that there is noise only when in fact a signal is present. The probabilities of the two errors for a given decision function are

$$\text{Type I error:}\quad a = \int_\Gamma F(\vec{V} \mid 0)\ \delta(\gamma_1 \mid \vec{V})\ d\vec{V} \qquad (8.16)$$

$$\text{Type II error:}\ \beta = \int_\Gamma \langle F(\vec{V} \mid \vec{S})\rangle_S\ \delta(\gamma_o \mid \vec{V})\ d\vec{V}\ . \qquad (8.17)$$

The following two integrals are recorded for reference.

$$\int_\Gamma F(V \mid 0)\ d\vec{V} = 1 \qquad (8.18)$$

and

$$\int_\Gamma \langle F(\vec{V} \mid \vec{S})\rangle_S\ d\vec{V} = \int_\Gamma\int_{\Omega_1} \sigma_1(\vec{S})\ F(\vec{V} \mid \vec{S})\ d\vec{V}d\vec{S} = 1\ . \qquad (8.19)$$

These equations simply state that one is certain to observe some value of $\vec{V}$.

By virtue of Eq. (8.12), one may derive the following equations from (8.16) and (8.17) with the aid of Eqs. (8.18) and (8.19).

$$1 - \alpha = \int_{\Gamma} F(\vec{V} \mid 0)\, \delta(\gamma_o \mid \vec{V})\, d\vec{V} \tag{8.20}$$

$$1 - \beta = \int_{\Gamma} \langle F(\vec{V} \mid \vec{S}) \rangle_S\, \delta(\gamma_1 \mid \vec{V})\, d\vec{V} \ . \tag{8.21}$$

With the aid of these simplified notations, Eq. (8.14) may be written

$$R = R_o + q\alpha(C_\alpha - C_{1-\alpha}) + p\beta(C_\beta - C_{1-\beta}) \tag{8.22}$$

where

$$R_o = qC_{1-\alpha} + pC_{1-\beta}. \tag{8.23}$$

The quantity R_o is, so to speak, an irreducible minimum of cost. It is the probability that no signal is present times the cost when a correct decision is made plus the probability that a signal is present times the cost when the correct decision is made. The terms in parentheses in Eq. (8.22) are positive so $R \geqslant R_o$ always.

The introduction of the parameters α and β has lead to the pleasingly simple form, Eq. (8.22), for the average risk R, but it has distracted us somewhat from the primary goal of the analysis. One recalls that the real problem is to find the decision function that minimizes the average risk. Equation (8.22) really includes two decision functions which are related by Eq. (8.12). Consequently, one must return to Eq. (8.14) and eliminate one of the decision functions, say $\delta(\gamma_1 \mid \vec{V})$. This gives

$$\begin{aligned} R(\sigma,\delta) = {} & qC_\alpha + pC_{1-\beta} \\ & + \int_{\Gamma} \delta(\gamma_o \mid \vec{V}) \, [p(C_\beta - C_{1-\beta}) \langle F(\vec{V} \mid \vec{S}) \rangle_S \\ & -q(C_\alpha - C_{1-\alpha})\, F(\vec{V} \mid 0) \,] \ \, d\vec{V} \ . \end{aligned} \tag{8.24}$$

In the derivation of this result it was necessary to use Eqs. (8.18) and (8.19).

The reader will have noticed in Eq. (8.24) that the constant term may be written

$$qC_\alpha + pC_{1-\beta} = R_o + q(C_\alpha - C_{1-\alpha}) \geqslant R_o \ ,$$

where R_o is the irreducible minimum of cost defined in Eq. (8.23). This inequality is not surprising, however, since the integral may be negative.

It will be noted that the first two terms in the right member of Eq. (8.24) do not depend on the decision function. The discussion following Eq. (8.13) showed that one always has $C_a > C_{1\text{-}a}$ and $C_\beta > C_{1\text{-}\beta}$. The other quantities which occur in the integrand of Eq. (8.24) are positive because they are probability densities. Hence

$$\delta(\gamma_o \mid \vec{V})\, p(C_\beta - C_{1\text{-}\beta}) \langle F(\vec{V} \mid \vec{S}) \rangle_S \geqslant 0$$

$$\delta(\gamma_o \mid \vec{V})\, q(C_a - C_{1\text{-}a})\, F(\vec{V} \mid 0) \geqslant 0 \,.$$

The decision function which minimizes $R(\sigma, \delta)$ can be determined by inspection. If

$$p(C_\beta - C_{1\text{-}\beta}) \langle F(\vec{V} \mid \vec{S}) \rangle_S > q(C_a - C_{1\text{-}a})\, F(\vec{V} \mid 0) \ , \tag{8.25a}$$

one can minimize R by choosing

$$\left.\begin{array}{l} \delta^*(\gamma_o \mid \vec{V}) = 0 \\ \text{and, hence,} \\ \delta^*(\gamma_1 \mid \vec{V}) = 1 \ . \end{array}\right\} \tag{8.26a}$$

On the other hand, if

$$p(C_\beta - C_{1\text{-}\beta}) \langle F(\vec{V} \mid \vec{S}) \rangle_S < q(C_a - C_{1\text{-}a})\, F(\vec{V} \mid 0) \ , \tag{8.25b}$$

one can minimize R by choosing

$$\left.\begin{array}{l} \delta^*(\gamma_o \mid \vec{V}) = 1 \\ \text{and} \\ \delta^*(\gamma_1 \mid \vec{V}) = 0 \ . \end{array}\right\} \tag{8.26b}$$

The decision rule described by Eqs. (8.25) and (8.26) is a Bayes decision rule. Further, it is a deterministic rule that contains no random choices.

The inequalities given by Eq. (8.25) divide the observation space Γ into two regions Γ_1 and Γ_2. The boundary separating these two regions is a surface whose equation may be written

$$\frac{p\langle F(\vec{V}\mid\vec{S})\rangle_S}{q\,F(\vec{V}\mid 0)} = \frac{C_\alpha - C_{1-\alpha}}{C_\beta - C_{1-\beta}} \quad (>0) \ . \tag{8.27}$$

The equation has been written in this form so that the costs are isolated on the right and the probability densities and the observations $\vec{V}$ are isolated on the left. The nature of the surface defined by Eq. (8.27) will depend on the statistics of the signal and the noise and must be derived in special cases.

If the reader recalls Sec. 5.1, he will recognize the close resemblance between the quantity on the left and the likelihood ratio defined in Eq. (7.36). The only difference is the presence of the extra factors p and q which are the *a priori* probabilities of the presence and absence of a signal and the average over the signal space Ω. Because of this close resemblance, Middleton defines the *generalized likelihood ratio,* Λ, by

$$\Lambda = \frac{p\langle F(\vec{V}\mid S)\rangle_S}{q\,F(\vec{V}\mid 0)} \quad . \tag{8.28}$$

If, now, one defines a symbol K by

$$K = \frac{C_\alpha - C_{1-\alpha}}{C_\beta - C_{1-\beta}} \quad (>0) \ , \tag{8.29}$$

one may summarize the decision rules, Eq. (8.25) and (8.26) as follows:

$$\left.\begin{array}{l}\text{Decide } \gamma_1 \text{ when } \Lambda \geqslant K \\ \text{Decide } \gamma_o \text{ when } \Lambda \leqslant K \ .\end{array}\right\} \tag{8.30}$$

The constant K, which is often called the *threshold,* is a positive constant that depends only on the costs C_i. The likelihood ratio depends on the *a priori* probability densities and on the length of the sample of data. The likelihood ratio Λ and the threshold K can each be replaced by any monotonic function of them. Middleton frequently uses the logarithm for this purpose: the reasons for and advantages of this choice are given in Middleton (1966).

Equation (8.28) forms an excellent starting point for the discussion of signal processing since many of the problems treated in the literature can be obtained as special cases of Eq. (8.28). For example, if one sets $p = q = 1/2$ and assumes that there is only one possible signal which may or may not be present, Eq. (8.28) reduces to the likelihood ratio defined in Sec. 5.1 and discussed in Sec. 7.7. The likelihood ratio, or generalizations of it such as Eq. (8.28), has been used as a starting point by many authors of whom one may mention Rudnick (1961), Bryn (1962), and Birdsall (1965).

8.4 The Case of a Signal with Unknown Parameters in Additive Gaussian Noise

The development of Eq. (8.28) enables us to continue the example that was considered in Sec. 7.11. The likelihood ratio, $\ell(\vec{V})$, given in Eq. (7.63) is the ratio $\langle F(\vec{V} \mid \vec{S}) \rangle_S / F(\vec{V} \mid 0)$ of Eq. (8.28) when there is a unique signal $\vec{S}$ present. In the present analysis, however, it will be assumed that the signal $\vec{S} = (S_1, S_2, \ldots, S_M)$ is a stochastic variable governed by a probability density $\sigma_1(\vec{S})$ defined in Eqs. (8.9) and (8.10). When the natural logarithm of Eq. (8.28) is introduced, the signal detection is governed by the following equation:

$$\ln \Lambda = \ln(p/q) + \ln \left\langle \exp \left\{ \sum_{m,n=1}^{M} a_{mn} V_m S_n - \frac{1}{2} \sum_{m,n=1}^{M} a_{mn} S_m S_n \right\} \right\rangle_S \qquad \ldots. \quad (8.31)$$

Since the case of small signals is of greatest interest, it is not unreasonable to expand the expression on the right in a power series in the signal components and retain only the linear and quadratic terms. It should be remembered that the matrix elements a_{mn} are inversely proportional to the square of the mean noise level so that the expansion is actually a power series in the signal-to-noise ratio.

When the expansion is carried out, one obtains

$$\ln \Lambda = \ln(p/q) + \langle \Sigma a_{mn} V_m S_n \rangle_S - \tfrac{1}{2} \langle \Sigma a_{mn} S_m S_n \rangle_S + \tfrac{1}{2} \langle (\Sigma a_{mn} V_m S_n)^2 \rangle_S - \tfrac{1}{2} \langle \Sigma a_{mn} V_m S_n \rangle_S^2 , \qquad \ldots. \quad (8.32)$$

where each summation is over $m,n = 1, 2, \ldots M$. The behavior of the first term, which is the only term that is linear in the components of $\vec{S}$, is of critical importance. If the phase of the signal is known so that $\langle S_n \rangle_S$ does not vanish, the first term of the expansion dominates the series when the signal-to-noise ratio is small. Middleton refers to this case as "coherent threshold detection." The nature of this assumption can be illustrated by a comparison of active sonar for targets of unknown range with communication over stable transmission paths. If echoes from a target of unknown range are detected, the phase of the returning signal will be distributed uniformly over 360° and $\langle S_m \rangle_S$ will vanish since the phase will be one of the statistical parameters included in

$\sigma_1(\vec{S})$. On the other hand, in communication over a stable transmission path the phase of the signal may be controlled with sufficient precision that the assumption $\langle S_m \rangle_S \neq 0$ is valid.

The problem of distinguishing between coherent and incoherent decisions is not always easy since there are intermediate cases. For example, in the case of a modulated carrier one may not know the range accurately enough to specify the phase of the carrier, but one can specify the phase of the modulation. Thus one is able to apply coherent detection techniques to the envelope although there is some loss in information when the carrier is removed. This point has already been discussed in Sec. 7.5 in connection with the matched (S/N) filter for narrow-band signals.

Middleton introduces the dichotomy of coherent and incoherent detection as described above. This is an unequal division, since the coherent case arises infrequently in sonar applications. Some workers in the field broaden the meaning of coherent detection to include those cases in which the phase characteristics of the envelope but not of the carrier are known. These workers then use "synchronous coherent" to indicate the more restricted case.

When the signal is incoherent and $\langle S_m \rangle_S = 0$, Eq. (8.32) simplifies to

$$\ell n\ \Lambda = \ell n\ (p/q) + \tfrac{1}{2} \langle (\Sigma a_{mn}\ V_m\ S_n)^2 \rangle_S - \tfrac{1}{2} \langle \Sigma a_{mn}\ S_m\ S_n \rangle_S \quad \ldots . \quad (8.33)$$

Specialized forms of this equation can be obtained by introducing specific probability density functions, $\sigma_1(\vec{S})$, and obtaining explicit values for these averages. A case of general interest that will be considered further in Chapter 10 arises when a signal which is a gaussian "white" noise is obscured by a gaussian "white" noise background. In this case $a_{mn} = \delta_{mn}/\sigma^2$, where σ is the root-mean-square noise, and $\langle S_m\ S_n \rangle_S = \delta_{mn}\ a_o^2$, where a_o is the root-mean-square value of the signal. Equation (8.33) becomes, for this special case,

$$\ell n\ \Lambda = \ell n\ (p/q) + (M\ a_o^2/2\sigma^2) \left\{ \frac{1}{M\sigma^2} \sum_{n=1}^{M} V_m^2 - 1 \right\} . \quad (8.34)$$

The structure of the receiver is especially simple in this case since it is only necessary to sum the squares of the message samples, V_m. If the received message, $\vec{V}$, is thought of as a point in an M-dimensional cartesian space, Γ, Eq. (8.34) can be interpreted as follows. The solution of the threshold is equivalent to the selection of a radius R of a hypersphere in Γ, and the hypothesis H_1 is chosen whenever the sample point $\vec{V}$ falls outside this sphere.

One can extend the discussion of the structure of the detector to include third order moments of the signal amplitudes but this does not seem justified in view of the complexity of the expressions and the lack of experimental data on third order moments of the noise. The problems of signal detection are significant only over a range of approximately 20 to 30 dB in the signal-to-noise ratio. If the signals are too weak, the problem is too difficult to solve, while if the signal is too strong, there is no problem.

8.5 Discussion of Likelihood Ratio Receivers

The generalized likelihood ratio receiver described by Eq. (8.28) or by the logarithm of both members of this equation provides a powerful tool for the design and evaluation of receivers. It can be shown (Peterson, Birdsall, and Fox, 1954, and Middleton, 1960, pp. 807-812) that many of the special detection criteria discussed in the literature are equivalent to the generalized likelihood ratio receivers with special assignments of the set of cost values, Eq. (8.13). Thus these systems are Bayes systems and are optimum in that they yield the least average risk.

The evaluation of the performance of a receiver or, equivalently, the construction of the receiver operating curves presents many analytical difficulties. As pointed out in Sec. 7.10, one must be able to evaluate the probability densities $P(\Lambda \mid H_i)$, $i = 0, 1$, for the statistics of the signal and the noise. The ease with which this can be done depends on the assumptions introduced for the statistical properties of the noise and the signal. It is frequently assumed that the noise samples $N_m (m = 1, 2, \ldots, M)$ are statistically independent and that each is governed by a gaussian probability density. The conditions under which these assumptions hold are outlined in Secs. 4.4 and 4.5. Relatively simple derivations of the probability densities $P(\Lambda \mid H_i)$ for various classes of signals and with less restrictive assumptions regarding the noise are given in Chapter IV of Helstrom (1960).

8.6 Suggestions for Further Reading

There is a wealth of fascinating material available for the reader who is interested in the ideas touched upon in this chapter. Undoubtedly, the best introduction to the subject is the paper by Middleton and Van Meter (1955), but if this is not available, the Harvard thesis of van Meter (1955) and Chapters 18 and 19 of Middleton's book (1960) are nearly as good. Chapter III of the book by Helstrom (1960) gives a clear but much briefer account of the subject. The foundations of the subject can be explored in the book by Wald (1950).

PROBLEMS

8.1 Show that

$$\left\langle \sum_{m,n=1}^{M} a_{mn} V_m S_n \right\rangle_S = 0$$

when $S_m = a_o \cos(2\pi f_o m\Delta t + \lambda)$ and λ is a random variable distributed over the interval $(0, 2\pi)$ with constant probability density. a_o, f_o, and Δt are constants.

8.2 Show that

$$\left\langle \sum_{m,n=1}^{M} a_{mn} V_m S_n \right\rangle_S = 0$$

when the components of the vector $\vec{S}$ are governed by a gaussian probability density similar in form to Eq. (7.52).

8.3 Reduce Eq. (8.32) to a simpler form when the signal $\vec{S}$ is governed by the same probability density as the noise vector $\vec{N}$ with the difference that each value of a_{mn} for the signal is p^2 times the value of a_{mn} for the noise. *Hint:* Remember that the matrix of the second order moments, $\langle S_m S_n \rangle$ is, in this case, proportional to the inverse of the matrix (a_{mn}).

8.4 Calculate a few ROC curves for the receiver described by Eq. (8.34). Use

$$\sum_{m=1}^{M} V_m^2$$

as the output of the receiver and the radius, R, of a sphere in M-dimensional space as the threshold.
Hint: The random variable ΣV_m^2 is governed by the chi-squared distribution. A trick for integrating volumes in the M-dimensional is described by Jeffreys (1961, pp. 103-104).

8.5 In Eq. (8.10) it is assumed that the null hypothesis γ_0 corresponded to $\vec{S} = 0$. In target classification one may wish to discriminate between unwanted signals $\vec{S}\ (\epsilon\Omega_0)$ and wanted signals $\vec{S}\ (\epsilon\Omega_1)$ where Ω_0 and Ω_1 are subsets of the signal space Ω which have no points in common $(\Omega_0 \times \Omega_1 = 0)$. In this case Eq. (8.10) can be generalized to

$$\sigma(\vec{S}) = q\,\sigma_0(\vec{S}) + p\,\sigma_1(\vec{S})$$

where

$$\int_{\Omega_0} \sigma_0(S)\,dS = \int_{\Omega_1} \sigma_1(S)\,dS = 1 \ .$$

Show that under these assumptions Eq. (8.27) becomes

$$\frac{p\,\langle F(\vec{V}\,|\,\vec{S})\,\rangle_{S_1}}{q\,\langle F(\vec{V}\,|\,\vec{S})\,\rangle_{S_0}} = \frac{C_a - C_{1-a}}{C_\beta - C_{1-\beta}}$$

where the definitions of the ensemble averages are patterned after Eq. (8.15).

CHAPTER IX

The Measurement of the Ambient Noise of the Ocean

9.1 The Vertical, Linear Array

In Chapters VII and VIII the reader has seen how one may design a detection system to detect a signal in the presence of a noise background. The analysis was carried out for a single channel only but in practice it is often desirable to use an array of detectors arranged in such a way that the signal, which is common to all hydrophones, is superimposed coherently while the noise detected by or generated in each channel tends to cancel. Closely connected with this noise reduction is the concept of directional beams. This subject is large and complex and will require several chapters for an adequate discussion. The present chapter has the modest goal of treating the response to noise of a linear array of nondirectional hydrophones. This limited program is not only useful as an introduction to more elaborate arrays, but also it is a hydrophone arrangement that has been used to measure the ambient noise in the ocean.

If the hydrophone array is located in the ocean far from the shore in a region of approximately constant depth, there is no reason to assume that the noise arriving from one azimuthal direction is different from that arriving from another direction. Since this assumption appears to be borne out by measurement, it is used as a starting point in the following discussion. Needless to say, this assumption of noise isotropy will not be valid when localized noise sources such as heavy ship traffic or storms are present.

Suppose that M nondirectional hydrophones are suspended in a vertical, linear array in the ocean. For the moment no assumption will be made about the spacing of these hydrophones. Although there are many ways in which the outputs of these hydrophones can be processed, a method frequently used consists of introducing an adjustable time delay in the output of each hydrophone, forming a weighted average of each instantaneous output, squaring this weighted average, and averaging over a finite time. This process is shown schematically in Fig. 9.1. In order to discuss this system in more detail, introduce the polar coordinate system of Fig. 9.2. It will be assumed that *all* noise sources are so far away that in the vicinity of the array the wave fronts are planes. This does not require that the ocean be homogeneous everywhere but only in the vicinity of the array.

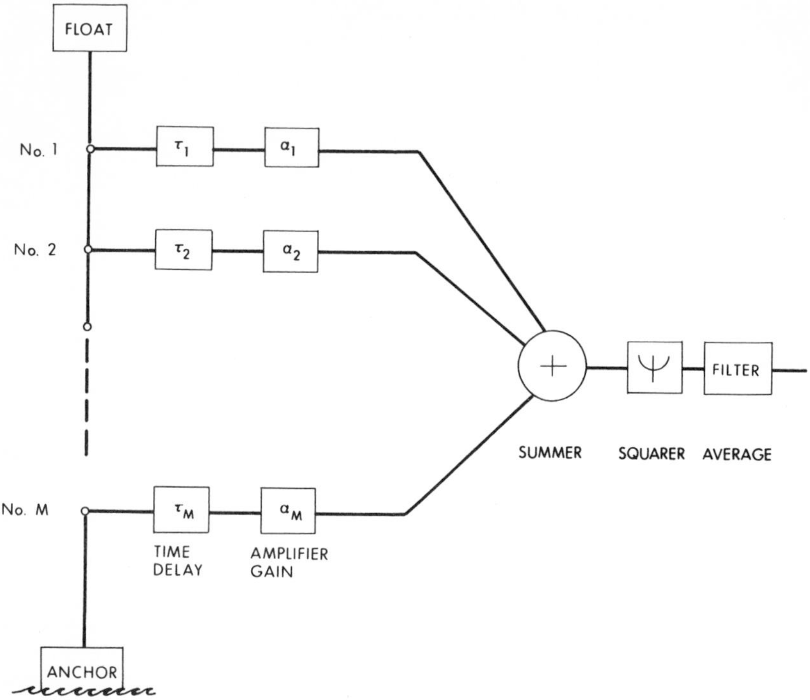

Figure 9.1–A linear array and one method of processing the output of the hydrophones.

Let

$y_n(t, \theta, \phi)d\Omega = y_n(t, \Omega)d\Omega$ = contribution to the output of the nth hydrophone due to sources in the solid angle $d\Omega$.

$$\ldots . \quad (9.1)$$

If one integrates $y_n(\cdot)$ over the entire solid angle, one has the output of a single hydrophone. The output of the array is

$$A(t) = \sum_{n=1}^{M} a_n \int_{4\pi} y_n(t, \Omega)\, d\Omega \; . \qquad (9.2)$$

If this output is squared and a time average is formed, one has

$$\overline{A^2{}_T(t)} = \frac{1}{T}\int_{-T/2}^{+T/2} A^2(t)\,dt$$

$$= \sum_{m,n=1}^{M} a_m a_n \int_{4\pi}\int_{4\pi} d\Omega d\Omega' \frac{1}{T}\int_{-T/2}^{+T/2} y_m(t,\Omega)y_n(t,\Omega')\,dt \quad \ldots. \quad (9.3)$$

where the order of integration has been changed.

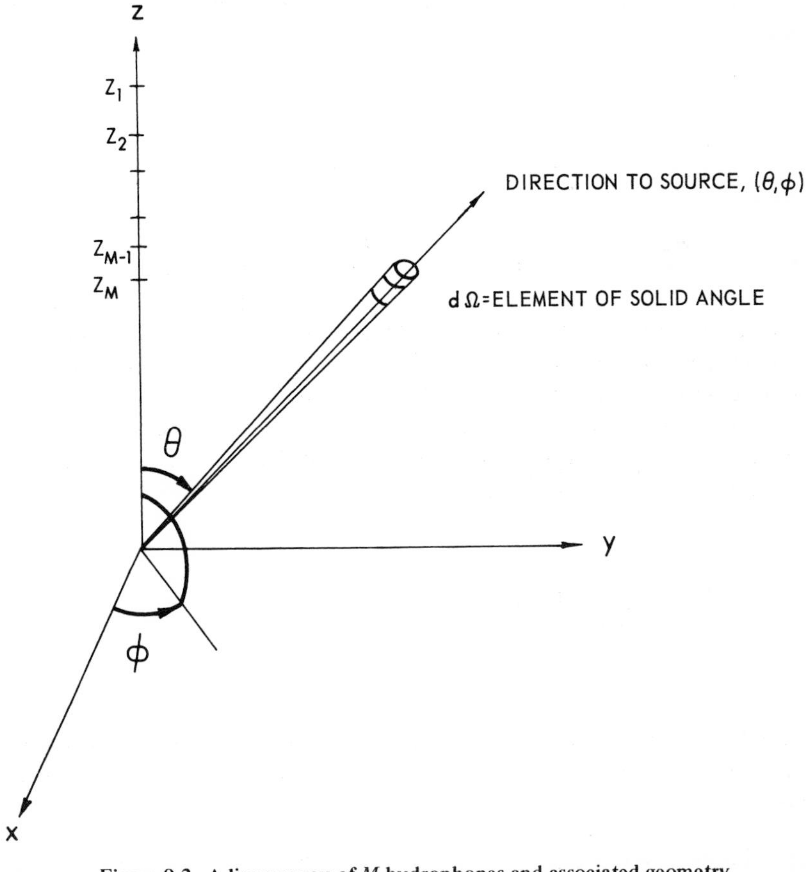

Figure 9.2–A linear array of M hydrophones and associated geometry.

It is evident from the discussion that $y_m(t,\Omega)$ and $y_n(t,\Omega)$ will be closely related because of the assumption of plane wave fronts. On the other hand, $y_m(t,\Omega)$ and $y_n(t,\Omega')$ may be quite different. If the sources of the ambient noise are highly localized and discrete, one would expect $y_m(t,\Omega)$ and $y_n(t,\Omega')$ to be independent random processes, $(m, n = 1, 2, \ldots M)$. This assumption is bolstered by the fact that deductions based on it agree with experimental observation. Noise sources such as breaking waves, collapsing bubbles, and biological organisms appear to be the likely origin of most of the noise. These sources are a form of the shot effect and since many events happen per second, one would expect the noise to have a gaussian first order distribution. On the other hand noises due to ships will have different properties. First, the ship is localized so that unless it is close to the array it will yield functions of the form $y_m(t,\Omega)\,\delta\,(\Omega\text{-}\Omega')$ where $\Omega' = (\theta',\phi')$ indicates the direction to the ship. Secondly, there are too few ships to give signals amenable to statistical averaging over (θ,ϕ).

It will be assumed that sources located in different directions are independent of one another, i.e., that

$$\lim_{T\to\infty} \frac{1}{T} \int_{-T/2}^{+T/2} y_m(t,\Omega) y_n(t,\Omega')\,dt = \rho_{mn}(\Omega)\,\delta\,(\Omega-\Omega')\,. \tag{9.4}$$

The reader will notice that this has the form of a cross-correlation function using direction in space (θ,ϕ) rather than time as the parameter. Further, the expression on the right is exactly analogous to Eq. (4.20) which is the autocorrelation function for white noise. The function $\rho_{mn}(\Omega)$ depends on the array design as well as on the distribution of sound sources.

The delta function $\delta(\Omega-\Omega')$ plays the same role in integrals over a solid angle that $\delta(t)$ does for integrals with respect to time. Hence, when Eq. (9.4) is applicable, Eq. (9.3) becomes

$$\overline{A^2(t)} = \sum_{m,n=1}^{M} a_m a_n \int_{4\pi} \rho_{mn}(\Omega)\,d\Omega\,. \tag{9.5}$$

In order to visualize more clearly the nature of the function $\rho_{mn}(\Omega)$ consider the responses of two hydrophones located at z_m and z_n to a plane, monochromatic wave arriving from the (θ,ϕ) direction. The received signals are

$$y_m(t,\Omega) = S(\theta,\phi)\cos[\omega(t-\tau_m) + kz_m \cos\theta + \beta]\ , \tag{9.6}$$

$$y_n(t,\Omega) = S(\theta,\phi)\cos[\omega(t-\tau_n) + kz_n \cos\theta + \beta] \ , \tag{9.7}$$

where $S(\theta,\phi)$ is a measure of the amplitude, τ_m is the time delay, β is a constant phase angle, ω is the angular frequency $2\pi f$, and $k = 2\pi/\lambda$. By Eq. (9.4)

$$\rho_{mn}(\Omega) = S^2(\theta,\phi)\,\overline{\cos[\omega(t-\tau_m) + kz_m \cos\theta + \beta] \times}$$

$$\overline{\cos[\omega(t-\tau_n) + kz_n \cos\theta + \beta]} \ . \tag{9.8}$$

Applying the formula $2\cos A \cos B = \cos(A+B) + \cos(A-B)$, one finds the time average easy to perform. This yields

$$\rho_{mn}(\Omega) = \tfrac{1}{2} S^2(\theta,\phi)\cos[\omega(\tau_n-\tau_m) + k(z_m-z_n)\cos\theta] \quad \ldots . \tag{9.9}$$

and

$$\overline{A^2(t)} = \frac{1}{2}\sum_{m,n=1}^{M} a_m a_n \int_{4\pi} \cos[\omega(\tau_n-\tau_m) + k(z_m-z_n)\cos\theta] \times$$

$$S^2(\theta,\phi)\, d\Omega. \quad \ldots . \tag{9.10}$$

This formula can be expressed in practical units as follows: Let $F(\theta,\theta_o)$ denote the normalized pattern response when the beam is steered to the angle θ_o. Thus

$$F(\theta,\theta_o) = \frac{\Sigma a_m a_n \cos[\omega(\tau_n-\tau_m) + k(z_m-z_n)\cos\theta]}{\Sigma a_m a_n \cos[\omega(\tau_n-\tau_m) + k(z_m-z_n)\cos\theta_o]} \ . \tag{9.11}$$

The function $S^2(\theta,\phi)$ is proportional to the noise power arriving from the direction (θ,ϕ). This quantity can be converted to practical units of (microbars)^2 per steradian and denoted $N(\theta,\phi)$. Finally, the constants generated by these changes can be combined with the factor 1/2 and the sensitivity of the system to write

$$V^2(\theta_o) = K^2 \int_0^{\pi}\int_0^{2\pi} F(\theta,\theta_o)\, N(\theta,\phi)\sin\theta\, d\theta\, d\phi \ , \tag{9.12}$$

where $V^2(\theta_o)$ is the mean square output of the system in volts squared when the conical beam is pointed in the direction θ_o. K is the on beam sensitivity in volts/microbar.

The derivation of Eq. (9.12) has been phrased explicitly in terms of the linear array, but it can be derived readily without recourse to a specific model for the receiver. This alternate method of development is given since it can be applied to a wide variety of situations.

Assume that a large number of independent point sources are distributed over a large sphere of radius r centered about a receiver whose direction response is $A(\theta,\phi)$. A typical source located at (θ_i,ϕ_i) produces a pressure of magnitude p_i/r at the receiver. The total pressure received is

$$p = \frac{1}{r}\sum_i A(\theta_i,\phi_i)\, p_i \tag{9.13}$$

where the sum is over all the sources. The mean square pressure is

$$\langle p^2 \rangle = \frac{1}{r^2}\sum_{i,j} A(\theta_i,\phi_i)\, A(\theta_j,\phi_j)\, \langle p_i p_j \rangle$$

$$= \frac{1}{r^2}\sum_i A^2(\theta_i,\phi_i)\, \langle p_i^2 \rangle, \tag{9.14}$$

since the sources are independent. Assume that each source has the same value $\langle p_i^2 \rangle = \langle p_o^2 \rangle$ but that the number of sources per unit area on the surface of the sphere is $\mathfrak{N}(\theta,\phi)$.

Under these assumptions it is convenient to divide the surface of the sphere into a network of small elements of solid angle $\Delta\Omega_j$. The sum over i is grouped into partial sums of those points falling into $\Delta\Omega_j$. The functions $A(\theta_i,\phi_i)$ and $\mathfrak{N}(\theta_i,\phi_i)$ may be treated as constants for all points (θ_i,ϕ_i) falling in the solid angle element $\Delta\Omega_j$. Under these assumptions Eq. (9.14) becomes

$$\langle p^2 \rangle = \frac{\langle p_o^2 \rangle}{r^2}\sum_j A^2(\theta_j,\phi_j)\, \mathfrak{N}(\theta_j,\phi_j)\, r^2 \Delta\Omega_j. \tag{9.15}$$

In the limit as $\Delta\Omega_j \to 0$ and the number of terms in the summation approaches infinity

$$\langle p^2 \rangle = \langle p_o^2 \rangle \int_{4\pi} A^2(\theta,\phi)\, \mathfrak{N}(\theta,\phi)\, \sin\theta d\theta d\phi. \tag{9.16}$$

Equation (9.16) has the same functional form as Eq. (9.12), and the equations can be made identical by suitable definitions.

Stone (1962) has studied the properties of Eq. (9.10) in order to answer questions about the resolution of noise distributions. He plots graphs that show the ability of the array to map regions of (θ,ϕ) that contain concentrations of noise power.

When the sources of noise have azimuthal symmetry, $N(\theta,\phi) = N(\theta)$ and the integral with respect to ϕ that occurs in Eq. (9.12) can be evaluated readily to give

$$V^2(\theta_o) = 2\pi K^2 \int_0^\pi F(\theta,\theta_o)\, N(\theta) \sin\theta d\theta. \tag{9.17}$$

Fox (1964) has applied Eq. (9.17) to measurements of ambient noise using an array of 40 elements. Various sets of weights $\{ a_m \}$ were used so that 28 beams could be formed, and measurements were made at four frequencies extending from 200 to 1,500 cps. The noise was filtered with a band-pass filter whose band width was 10% of the center frequency. Thus the theory developed here for monochromatic waves could be applied.

Since Eq. (9.17) is an integral equation in which $N(\theta)$ is the unknown function, one is tempted to approximate it by a finite set of linear equations and invert them. This procedure is not feasible because $F(\theta,\theta_o)$ is everywhere positive and this imposes impossible requirements on the accuracy of the experimental values $V^2(\theta_o)$ when one inverts the matrix. It may not be readily apparent from Eq. (9.11) that $F(\theta,\theta_o) \geqslant 0$, but Eq. (9.12) shows that $F(\theta,\theta_o)$ must be nonnegative since $V^2(\theta_o)$ must be positive for all nonnegative functions $N(\theta)$. Fox was able to obtain reliable values of $N(\theta)$ by approximating the integral equation (9.17) with a set of 28 linear equations and solving these by a method of successive approximations.

Fox plots a series of polar plots of $N(\theta)$ versus θ for three sea states (SS 1, 3, 5) and four frequencies. His results can be oversimplified by saying that at low frequencies (200 cps) $N(\theta)$ increases with θ and has its maximum value at $\theta = 90°$, while at the higher frequencies (1,500 cps) $N(\theta)$ decreases with increasing θ and has its largest value at $\theta = 0$. This result can be made plausible by considering the effects of refraction and attenuation. Because of the upward refraction of acoustic rays in the water, an element of solid angle at the array pointed in a near horizontal direction subtends an area on the ocean's surface that is much larger than predicted by the normal inverse square law. This phenomenon is least effective at angle θ near zero. The increase in area subtended for large θ is counteracted to some extent by the increased attenuation resulting from the longer paths. The observed behavior is consistent with the fact that the attenuation is least at the lowest frequency.

The factors listed in the last paragraph can be corrected for by ray diagrams and attenuation measurements, but there is another effect that complicates the picture. The sources at the surface that radiate the ambient noise field may themselves be directional. This directionality is an unknown which can be deduced from the measurements of $V^2(\theta)$ by a careful analysis of all the known effects including multiple bottom and surface bounces. Talham (1964) has carried out such an analysis and applied it to Fox's data (1964) for low sea state and low frequency. He obtained best agreement with the observations when he assumed that the near surface sources were nondirectional.

Axelrod *et al.* (1965) have reported a set of measurements similar to those of Fox (1964) but more extensive. It would appear that the two sets of measurements were made with the same hydrophone array and at the same location in the ocean although this is not stated in the paper.

9.2 An Array of Only Two Hydrophones

In the experiment described in the last section the noise was filtered with narrow-band filters and the directionality was achieved by using an array 300 feet in length. Alternately one can use a smaller array and achieve directionality by computing the autocorrelation function of a wide-band noise. The beam is steered as usual by introducing time delays.

Assume that one has two hydrophones, 1 and 2, as illustrated in Fig. 9.3 located at $z = +a$ and $z = -a$, respectively. Suppose further that a plane wave arrives from a direction (θ, ϕ) as illustrated, but that instead of a monochromatic wave as in Eqs. (9.6) and (9.7), the wave is a stochastic process $x(t, \lambda)$. Equations (9.6) and (9.7) can be modified for this case to be ($a_m = a_n = 1$)

$$y_1 = S(\theta,\phi)\, x[t-\tau_1+(a/c)(\cos\theta)+\beta,\lambda] \tag{9.18}$$

$$y_2 = S(\theta,\phi)\, x[t-\tau_2-(a/c)(\cos\theta)+\beta,\lambda] \ . \tag{9.19}$$

Instead of forming a sum and squaring, multiply y_1 and y_2 together and form a time average. The output becomes

$$\mathcal{E}_T(\theta,\phi) = \frac{S^2(\theta,\phi)}{T}\int_{-T/2}^{+T/2} x\left[t-\tau_1+\frac{a}{c}(\cos\theta)+\beta,\lambda\right] x\left[t-\tau_2-\frac{a}{c}(\cos\theta)+\beta,\lambda\right] dt \ . \tag{9.20}$$

The question of approximating an infinite time average by a finite time average has already been discussed in Sec. 6.1. If one assumes that T is made large enough, no serious error will be made by approximating the finite time average in Eq. (9.20) by the limit as $T \to \infty$. This yields

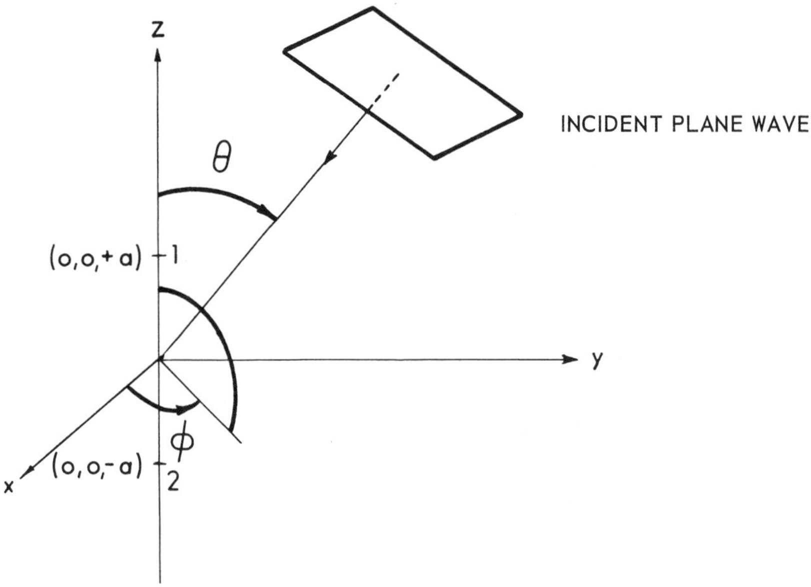

Figure 9.3–An array of two hydrophones and associated geometry.

$$\mathcal{E}(\theta,\phi) = S^2(\theta,\phi)\, C_x\left[\tau_1-\tau_2 - \left(2\frac{a}{c}\right)\cos\theta\right] \quad . \tag{9.21}$$

It is evident from this equation and the earlier discussions of the autocorrelation function of a wide-band noise that one can achieve a highly directional response. The major lobe will be pointed in the direction

$$\theta_{beam} = \cos^{-1}\frac{c(\tau_1-\tau_2)}{2a} \; . \tag{9.22}$$

In order to illustrate this example consider the response of a beam pointed at right angles to the line, $\tau_1 = \tau_2$, to plane waves of constant amplitude, $S(\theta,\phi) \equiv 1$, but variable direction θ. Assume that the noise source is a white noise of bandwidth W centered about f_o. One sees from Eq. (4.21) that the normalized output of the detector in this case is

$$\mathcal{E}(\theta) = \frac{\sin\left(\dfrac{2\pi W a}{c}\cos\theta\right)}{\dfrac{2\pi W a}{c}\cos\theta}\cos\left(\frac{4\pi f_o a}{c}\cos\theta\right). \tag{9.23}$$

It is instructive to compare this with the response of an unshaded line hydrophone of length $2a$ to a monochromatic wave of frequency f_o. It is easy to show that this normalized pattern is

$$\mathcal{E}_{line}(\theta) = \left\{ \frac{\sin \frac{2\pi f_o a}{c} \cos\theta}{\frac{2\pi f_o a}{c} \cos\theta} \right\}^2 \tag{9.24}$$

when the signal is detected with a square law detector.

The responses given by Eqs. (9.23) and (9.24) are plotted in Fig. 9.4 for the special case $W = f_o$. The product array has the advantage that the first minor lobe has a negative sign which enables one to reject it as pointed out by Welsby and Tucker (1959). For example, if $\mathcal{E}(\theta)$ is used as the intensity modulation on the oscilloscope, the negative, first minor lobe will not produce a brightening. In this case the product array has a definitely better major lobe. The large positive lobe at 4.7 on the abcissa scale can be removed by going to a wider bandwidth or by replacing the point, omnidirectional receivers by directional receivers having a rejection at this angle.

The preceding analysis of the directional response was based on the hypothesis of a single noise source located in a unique direction. Actually, the noise may arrive from all directions as in the examples discussed in Sec. 9.1. If these noise sources in the various directions are assumed to be independent, one can either integrate Eq. (9.21) over all angles (θ,ϕ) or multiply Eq. (9.12) (with $M = 2$ and $a_1 = a_2$) by a power spectrum $W(f)$ and integrate with respect to f. The mathematical analysis will not be carried out here, and the reader is referred to the papers by Faran and Hills (1952 *a,b*) and Dunham Laboratory (1963) for details.

Faran and Hills (1952 *a,b*) have made extensive theoretical and experimental determinations of the behavior of the product of the outputs of two hydrophones located in a noise field. They produced this noise field with an array of loudspeakers located on a semicircular arc and located the two receiving microphones near the center of this arc. The loudspeakers were driven with a noise source centered at 4 kcps, and the entire system was located in an anechoic chamber to avoid trouble with unwanted reflections. This arrangement was a practical compromise for the more general arrangement in which the loudspeakers would have been distributed over a spherical surface. A theoretical discussion of the noise field produced by these two distributions of sources and the response of the correlated outputs of the receivers may be found in a report by Usher and Schultheiss (1963).

Linnette and Thompson (1964) have published an account of ocean measurements in which they utilized an array of two omnidirectional hydrophones like that just analyzed. Their two hydrophones were separated vertically a distance of 13.2 feet and placed on a mud-sand bottom at a depth of 360 feet. By introducing band-pass filters they restricted the noise spectrum to one octave ranges centered at 700 cps in one set of measurements and at 1,000 cps in another set of measurements. They used time samples 15 seconds in length and introduced a maximum time delay, $\tau_1 - \tau_2 = 1{,}420$ microseconds, in the autocorrelation computation. This maximum delay corresponds

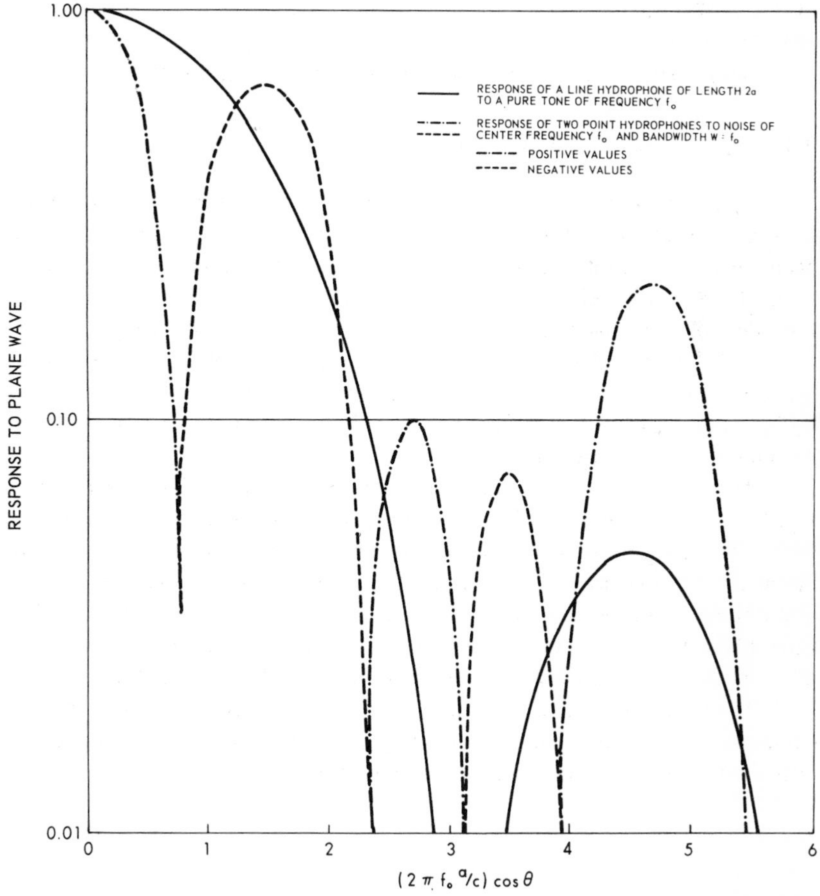

Figure 9.4–Comparison of the response of a line hydrophone to a monochromatic wave to that of two point hydrophones to noise.

to looking vertically upwards. Their article contains plots of autocovariance function versus time shift.

In order to have a theoretical model with which to compare the measurements, Linnette and Thompson assumed that the ambient noise was produced at the surface of the sea by independent noise sources distributed uniformly over the surface. It was assumed that the radiation was not isotropic but that it depended on the angle θ between the downward vertical at the source and the direction of the receiver. In particular it was assumed that the radiation pattern for the power depended on $\cos^n \theta$ and n was chosen to give the best fit with the observational data. The results indicated that $n = 3$ for wind speeds of 15 knots and decreased to near unity at wind speeds of 3-5 knots. This conclusion differs from that reached by Talham (1964), but one cannot be sure whether it is due to a difference in the sources or in the method of analysis. Linnette and Thompson did not make any allowance for energy reflected from the bottom.

Similar studies have been reported by Arase and Arase (1965).

9.3 An Example of Experimental Data

Figure 9.5 is a reproduction of the output of a system that utilizes a correlation receiver. Sixty-four separate channels are processed so that sixty-four beams can be viewed simultaneously. Each of these beams is portrayed on 1/64 of the paper width. A horizontal line across the paper at any instant of time gives the autocorrelation function of the source versus beam angle θ_{beam}, Eq. (9.22), as described by Eq. (9.21) for a fixed value of θ, the direction to the source. The target provides a central band of positive correlation bordered by bands of negative correlation as predicted by the dashed curves in Fig. 9.4. As time passes the target moves to the left.

The practical details of the circuit that provided the data portrayed in Fig. 9.5 can be understood better after the reader has read Sections 10.6 and 10.7. The outputs of the hydrophones were clipped and the polarity was sampled at a frequency approximately three times the highest frequency in the hydrophone outputs. The output of the correlator was filtered with an RC-filter whose time constant was approximately 100 seconds. The output signal of each channel was presented in a symmetrical, width-modulated trace.

The experimental data shown in Fig. 9.5 and the description of the equipment were furnished by Messrs. I. Engelsen and F. Bryn of the Norwegian Defence Research Establishment, Horten, Norway.

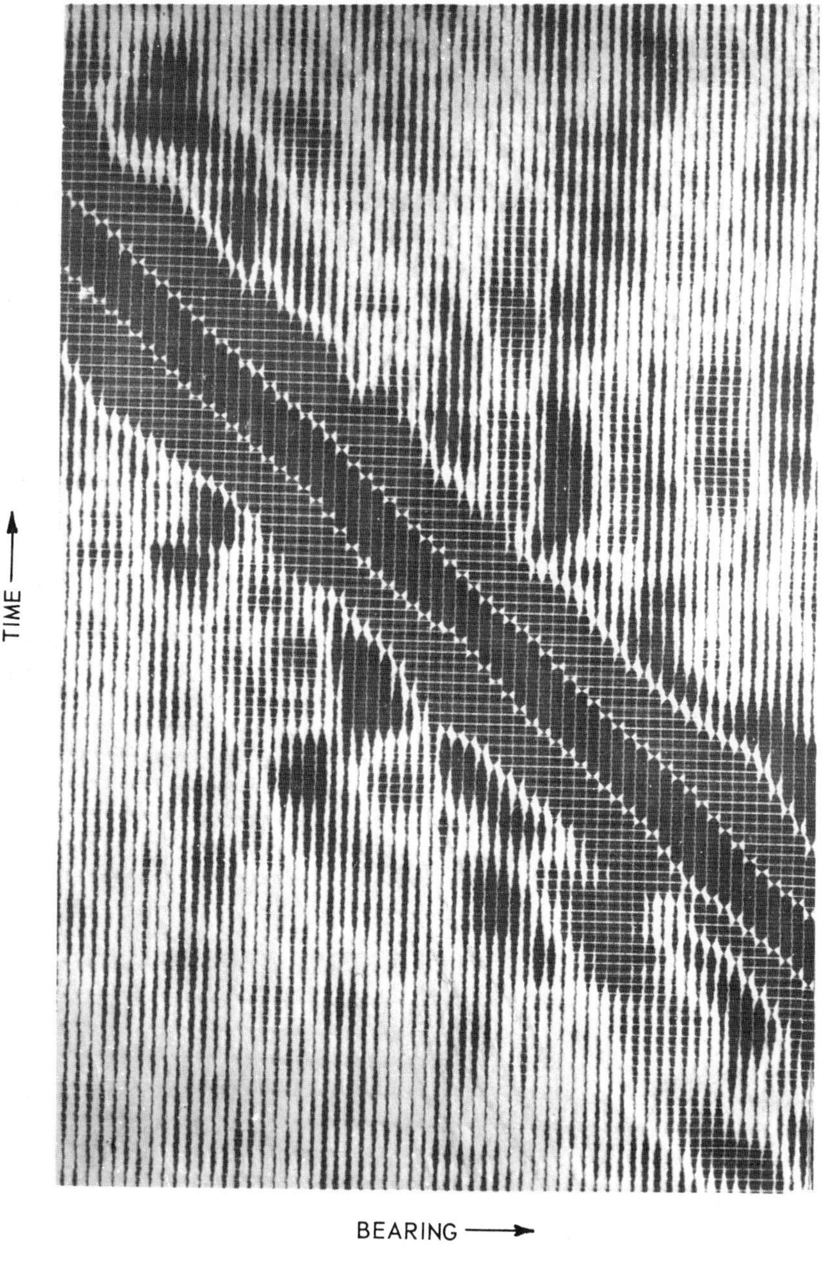

Figure 9.5–The output of a correlator with 64 channels. Dark areas have positive correlation, crosshatched areas have negative correlation.

PROBLEMS

9.1 Evaluate Eq. (9.10) for the special case $M = 2$, $a_1 = a_2 = 1$, $k(z_1 - z_2) = 6$, $S(\theta,\phi) \equiv 1, 0 < \theta < \pi/2$, and $S(\theta,\phi) \equiv 0$, $\pi/2 < \theta < \pi$. Plot $\overline{A^2(f)}$ versus the dimensionless parameter $\omega(\tau_1 - \tau_2)$.

9.2 A noise source whose power density is constant over the frequency band -5.0 to +5.0 kHz and zero for all other freqUencies is located in the direction $\theta = 90°$, $\phi = 0$. (See the coordinate system in Fig. 9.3).

(1) Plot a normalized response $\mathcal{E}(\theta,\phi)$ given by Eq. (9.21) versus $\tau_1 - \tau_2$. Extend the graph through the first "minor" lobes of $\mathcal{E}(\theta,\phi)$.

(2) Estimate the angular resolution for point sources on the assumption that dips of 3 dB in a response curve can be detected reliably.

9.3 Generalize Eq. (9.21) to the case of two similar but statistically independent noise sources located at $\theta = 90°$, $\phi = 0$ and $\theta = 90° - a$, $\phi = 0$. Assume that the time averaging is infinite. $2a/c = 0.1$ sec, and $C(\tau) = 1 - |\tau/T|$, $|\tau| \leqslant T$, $C(\tau) = 0$, $|\tau| > T$.

(1) Plot the response versus $\tau_1 - \tau_2$ for various values of a for $T = 0.01$ sec.

(2) Determine the minimum value of a for which the source can be resolved on the basis of the assumption that a dip of 3 dB in the response curve can be detected reliably.

CHAPTER X

Three Dimensional Arrays of Nondirectional Hydrophones

10.1 Introduction

In the last chapter the question of a linear array of M hydrophones was considered briefly, but only as a means of measuring directional properties of noise. The important question of the detection of a signal in a noise background was not considered. Certain aspects of this problem will be considered in the present chapter.

Suppose that a three-dimensional array of M hydrophones is available and that a variable time delay τ_i $(i = 1, 2, \ldots, M)$ can be inserted in the output of the ith hydrophone. These time delays will be chosen so that if a plane wave arrives from a given direction the outputs of the M delay lines will be in phase no matter what the wave shape is. The actual details of the directionality of the response will not be considered but each choice of the set of delays $\{\tau_i\}$ will yield a three dimensional beam pattern, and the beam can be steered in different directions by choosing different sets of delays $\{\tau_i\}$. This can be done sequentially by switching or simultaneously by using multiple delay lines.

The outputs of the M delay lines will be processed in some manner to provide new outputs on which signal detection and extraction are based. In each analysis it is necessary to select a specific method of processing the data and to make assumptions about the nature of the noise and the signal. The variability of the analysis is further increased by the fact that one needs to choose some definition of the signal-to-noise ratio in the output in order to define a processing gain. As one reads the published papers one is struck forcibly by the fact that the various assumptions listed above are conditioned by the requirements of the analysis as strongly as by the physical realities of the problem. Even so, the theoretical analyses are useful because they give one an insight into the problem and show which parameters are most important. However, one cannot hope to optimize the sonar system as long as the class of problems considered is limited by the requirement that the process be amenable to analysis. This is clearly a situation in which one should program the problem on a computer and use real data as the input. In this way one could model a wide variety of detection systems and use realistic criteria in assessing the gain of the system.

Figure 10.1 illustrates a few of the system configurations that have been subjected to analysis. The time delays τ_i have been omitted in each case in order to simplify the drawings. The system of Fig. 10.1(*a*) is the same as that of Fig. 9.1 except for the distribution of the hydrophones in three dimensions.[1] The system of Fig. 10.1(*b*) is the same as that of Fig. 10.1(*a*) except that the outputs of the delays have been quantized before they are summed. This quantization may be simply a perfect limiter or it may have several levels of quantization. When the quantization is limited to two levels, ±1, the system is known by the acronym DIMUS (DIgital MUltiple beam Steering). This system has been studied rather extensively both experimentally and theoretically at Navy Electronics Laboratory, San Diego. Professor Bonnet and his associates at Centre d'Étude Aléatoires de Grenoble (CEPHAG) have made extensive studies of the improvement that results when more levels of quantization are introduced.

The system of Fig. 10.1(*c*) is the natural extension of the two-hydrophone array of Fig. 9.3. Quantizers are included in Fig. 10.1(*c*) although the system will be analyzed with and without quantization. The system of Fig. 10.1(*c*) can be made to resemble strongly the systems of Fig. 10.1(*a*) and (*b*) by setting $M_1 = M_2 = M$ and $x_i^{(1)}(t) \equiv x_i^{(2)}(t)$. With these substitutions circuit (*c*) becomes identical with (*a*) when the quantizers are removed, and it differs from circuit (*b*) only in the location of the quantizers.

The multiplicative array has been studied extensively by Professor Tucker and Dr. Welsby at The University of Birmingham, England. Their work will be discussed separately in Chapter XIII since they utilize a planar array of detectors each of which has a directional pattern.

Figure 10.1(*d*) is an extension to M hydrophones of the system discussed in Chapter VII. This generalization introduces new and interesting features, but the system cannot be compared easily with the others discussed in this chapter. It was seen in Sec. 8.4 that this approach to signal detection is a special case of a Bayes system. The analysis of Fig. 10.1(*d*) and (*e*) will be given in Chapter XII. The circuit in Fig. 10.1(*e*) represents an embodiment of a likelihood ratio receiver.

In view of the complexity of the systems and the large number of hypotheses that can be made about the signal and noise statistics, each system will be analyzed first without a quantizer. The analyses will then be modified to incorporate the quantizers. Whenever it is relevant a subscript Q will be used to denote a quantity resulting from quantization and a subscript A will denote that the quantizer is absent.

[1] One other difference is that the weighting factors have been omitted in order to simplify the equations. The reader should repeat the analyses of this chapter with a weighting factor as an exercise.

10.2 Historical Note on the DIMUS System

The DIMUS system has an interesting background. In a sense it can be said that this system is a descendent of the work done at the Harvard Underwater Sound Laboratory (HUSL) during World War II. Professor F. V. Hunt, of Harvard University, who was the Director of HUSL, suggested (Hunt, 1951) that correlation techniques should be used in the detection of acoustic signals. These ideas were implemented by Faran and Hills (1952*a*, *b*) and by Anderson (1956) in important studies at Harvard University. Dr. Anderson's work was concerned with a method of computing autocorrelation functions rapidly, and it led to the development of a system known by the acronym DELTIC (DElay-Line-TIme-Compressor). The continuation of his studies on this and related systems at the Marine Physical Laboratory at San Diego resulted in the development by Dr. Anderson of the DIMUS system. Numerous important papers on the theory of the DELTIC and DIMUS systems have been published by members of the group at Navy Electronics Laboratory, San Diego, California, working under Dr. E. C. Westerfield.

10.3 Analysis of the "Standard Detector"

The present analysis of the circuit in Fig. 10.1(*a*) follows closely a paper by Usher (1964) with some references to the earlier paper by Rudnick (1960). Consider a system of M omnidirectional hydrophones placed in an array which may be three-dimensional. Beam-forming is achieved by inserting a delay line in the output of each hydrophone and by selecting this time delay so that when a plane wave arrives from the desired direction in space, the M outputs of the delay lines will be in phase. By combining the delay in the water path with the delay in the delay lines one does not have to specify the arrangement of the hydrophones. These statements are illustrated in Fig. 10.2. This assumption is especially convenient from a theoretical viewpoint when it is assumed that the noise signals received at each hydrophone are independent stationary time series. Under these assumptions the time delays in the noise signals can be ignored.

The outputs of the delay lines of Fig. 10.2 may be denoted[2] $s_i(t) + n_i(t)(i = 1, 2, \ldots, M)$ and these are the inputs of the processing system shown in Fig. 10.1(*a*). When the network delays are chosen for targets in a particular direction, the M output signals will be in phase only for sources in that direction. If the source is located in a different direction, the delays associated with the water paths change and so the T_i's change. Hence, the outputs associated with the signals may be written

[2]The parameter λ which has been used in the past to denote the ensemble variable will be omitted in this chapter to simplify the form of the equations. The reader should remember that the ensemble averages are over this parameter.

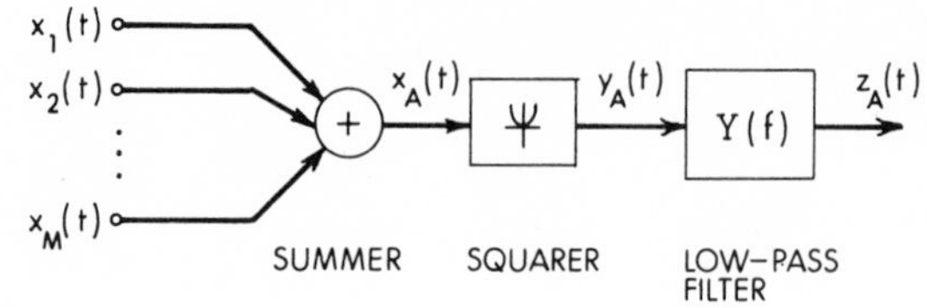

(a) THE "STANDARD DETECTOR"

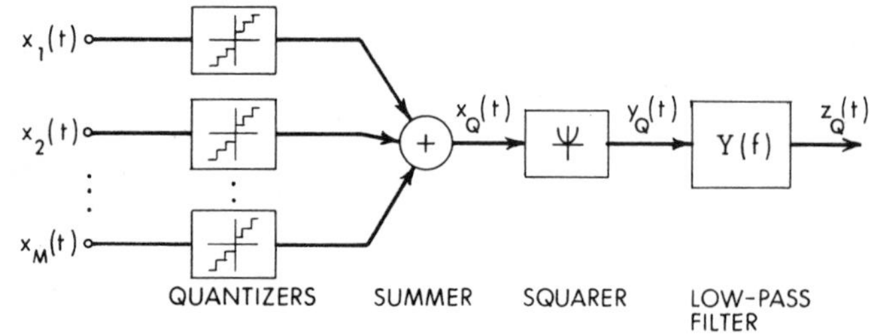

(b) CIRCUIT (a) MODIFIED BY QUANTIZING THE OUTPUTS OF THE HYDROPHONES

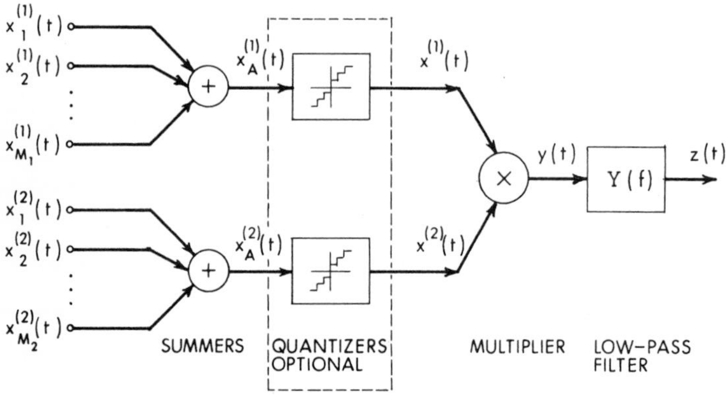

(c) A MULTIPLICATIVE ARRAY

(Figure 10.1–Continued on next page.)

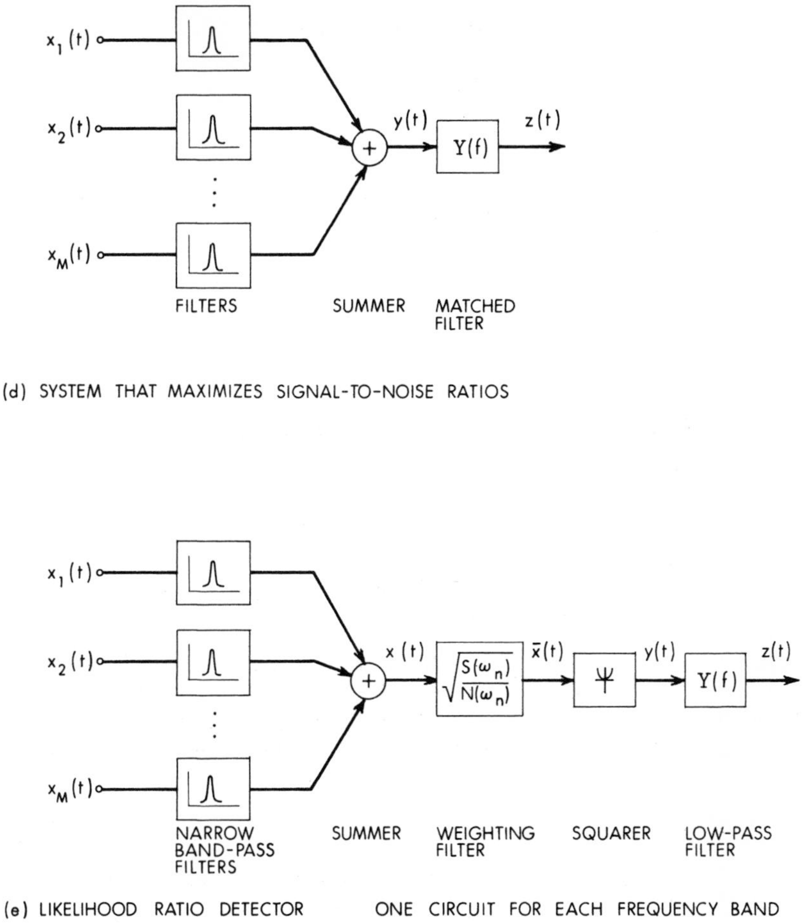

Figure 10.1–Block diagrams for some of the systems that are analyzed. Time delay boxes in the hydrophone lines are not shown.

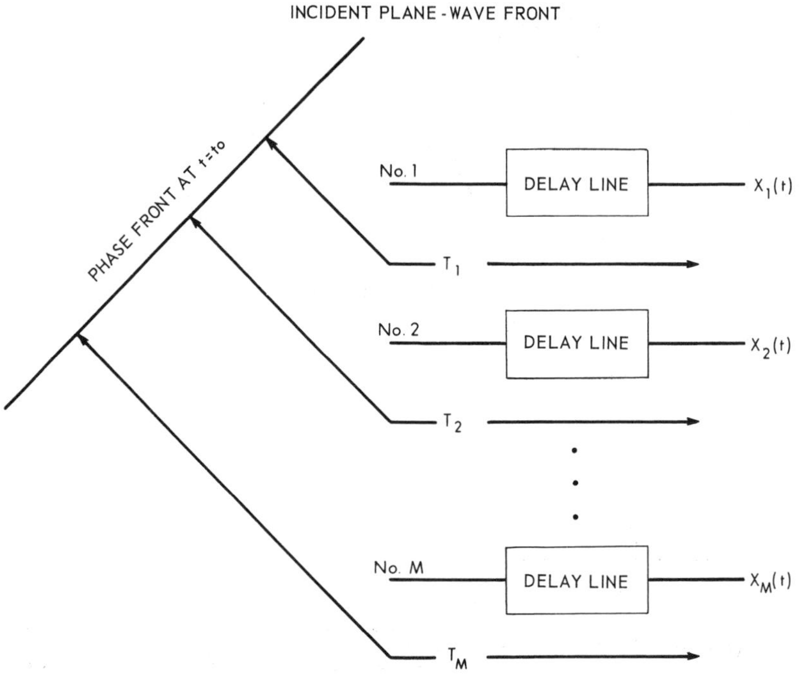

Figure 10.2–A plane-wave incident on an array of M hydrophones for a wave form a unique direction. (The time delay, T_i, includes water-path and the delay line.)

$$s_i(t) = s(t\text{-}t_o\text{-}T_i) \ , \tag{10.1}$$

where $s(\cdot)$ is a signal shape associated with the wave front and hence common to all of the hydrophones. Therefore, the outputs of the M delay lines may be written as

$$s(t\text{-}t_o\text{-}T) + n_i(t), i = 1, 2, \ldots, M. \tag{10.2}$$

Here t_o is an arbitrary constant determined by the choice of the time origin. In the analysis it will be assumed that the average values of $s(t)$ and $n_i(t)$ are zero. The output of the summer is

$$x_A(t) = \sum_{i=1}^{M} \{s_i(t) + n_i(t)\} \ , \tag{10.3}$$

where, as mentioned above, the subscript A means that the quantizer is absent. The output of the squarer is

$$y_A(t) = [x_A(t)]^2 = \sum_{i,j=1}^{M} \{s_i(t) + n_i(t)\}\{s_j(t) + n_j(t)\} \ . \qquad (10.4)$$

It was seen in Sec. 6.2 that the output of a low-pass filter will fluctuate about a mean value which is the ensemble average of $y_A(t)$. The ensemble average and the fluctuations thereabout can be computed only if one is prepared to introduce specific statistics for the signal $s(t)$ and the noise.

It is assumed that

(1) the functions $s(t)$ and $n_i(t)$ $(i = 1, 2, \ldots, M)$ are stationary, ergodic gaussian processes with zero time averages.

(2) $n_i(t)$ and $n_j(t)$ are independent of one another, $i \neq j$.

(3) $s(t)$ and $n_i(t)$ are independent of one another.

(4) the autocorrelation function of $n_i(t)$ is $N_i R(\tau)$. $R(\tau)$ is normalized so that N_i is the total power in the ith noise. It will be assumed that the N_i are not necessarily equal to each other.

(5) The signal $s(t)$ is a stochastic process with the same autocorrelation function as the $n_i(t)$. Thus the autocorrelation of the signal is $SR(\tau)$ where S is the total power in the signal.

There is no doubt that the reader may wish to question some or all of these assumptions. However, when the noise is dominated by reverberation, as in active sonar at near ranges, it is not unreasonable to assume that the noise and the signal have the same normalized autocorrelation functions. In the case of passive listening, if the noise and the signal are both broad band, the effect of the medium and the response of the transducers may result in the same autocorrelation functions.

When one takes the ensemble average of $y_A(t)$, the average of the cross product terms $s_i(t)n_j(t)$ vanishes because of assumptions (3) and (1). The average of the terms $n_i(t)n_j(t)$ $(i \neq j)$ vanishes because of assumptions (2) and (1). This leaves

$$\langle y_A \rangle = \sum_{i=1}^{M} \langle n_i^2(t) \rangle + \sum_{i,j=1}^{M} \langle s_i(t)\, s_j(t) \rangle \ . \qquad (10.5)$$

By virtue of assumption (4) $\langle n_i^2(t) \rangle = N_i$. This leaves only the evaluation of $\langle s_i(t)\, s_j(t) \rangle$. By virtue of Eq. (10.1) and assumption (5)

$$\langle s_i(t)\, s_j(t) \rangle = \langle s(t\text{-}t_o\text{-}T_i)\, s(t\text{-}t_o\text{-}T_j) \rangle = SR(T_i\text{-}T_j) \ . \qquad \ldots\ldots \quad (10.6)$$

The last step follows from the assumption of stationarity. It should be remembered that T_i-T_j contains the direction to the target since the time delays T_i

contain a part contributed by the water path which depends on the direction to the source. For convenience let us write

$$\tau_{ij} = T_i - T_j = \tau_{ji} \ . \tag{10.7}$$

One has from Eq. (3.14) that

$$R(\tau_{ij}) = R(\tau_{ji}) \ . \tag{10.8}$$

When the beam is steered on the target the τ_{ij} all vanish and $R(\tau_{ij}) = R(0) = 1$. It will be assumed that when the beam is steered well away from the target, all of the τ_{ij}'s are so large that every $R(\tau_{ij}) = 0, i \neq j$. This assumption depends on the array and the properties of the time series so, consequently, it must be checked for each special case.[3]

When Eq. (10.6) is substituted into Eq. (10.5) and use is made of Eq. (10.8), one finds readily that

$$\langle y_A \rangle = \sum_{i=1}^{M} N_i + MS + 2S \sum_{i=1}^{M} \sum_{j=i+1}^{M} R(\tau_{ij}) \ . \tag{10.9}$$

The diagonal terms have been separated out in the summation since $\tau_{ii} = 0$ and $R(\tau_{ii}) = 1$. As pointed out above, two cases are distinguished according as the beam is pointed at the target or away from the target. These two cases will be referred to as "on-target" and "off-target" and designated with subscripts O and L, respectively. Thus for the target case, since $R(\tau_{ij}) = 1$,

$$\langle y_{AO} \rangle = \sum_{i=1}^{M} N_i + M^2 S \ , \tag{10.10}$$

while for the off-target case $R(\tau_{ij}) = 0, i \neq j$, and

$$\langle y_{AL} \rangle = \Sigma N_i + MS \ . \tag{10.11}$$

The reader will notice that these two limiting values do not provide any measure of the directional response of the array. Nonetheless, it is helpful to draw a schematic picture of response $\langle y_A \rangle$ versus a generalized bearing angle as in Fig. 10.3.

---

[3] Rudnick (1960) does not introduce this assumption and obtains, as a result, the term $\overline{\sigma}''$ in his Eq. (28). However, this term constitutes a negligible correction for the special case considered by him.

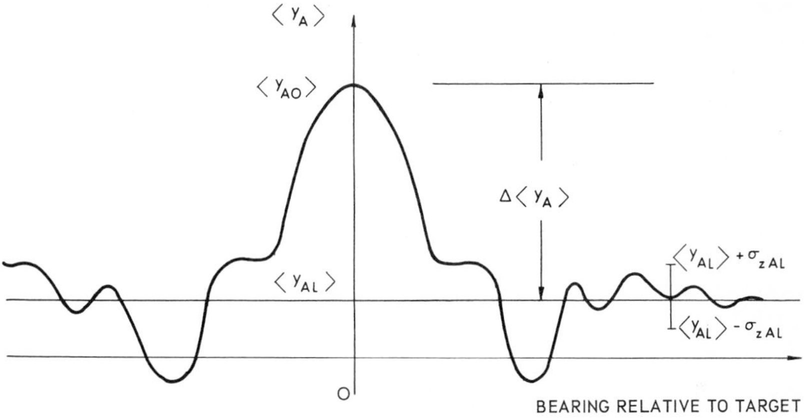

Figure 10.3–A schematic drawing showing the various quantities that measure signal response and output noise.

One may define the average signal output as

$$\Delta \langle y_A \rangle = \langle y_{AO} \rangle - \langle y_{AL} \rangle = M(M-1)\,S \ , \tag{10.12}$$

the difference between the on-target and the off-target responses. It seems desirable to normalize this by dividing by the off-target response. This yields as the normalized response in the absence of clipping

$$\frac{\Delta \langle y_A \rangle}{\langle y_{AL} \rangle} = \frac{(M-1)\dfrac{S}{\overline{N}}}{1 + \dfrac{S}{\overline{N}}} \ , \tag{10.13}$$

where

$$\overline{N} = \frac{1}{M} \sum_{i=1}^{M} N_i \ . \tag{10.14}$$

For weak signals such that $S \ll \overline{N}$, the normalized response increases proportionally to $S/\overline{N}$, but for large values of $S/\overline{N}$, the limiting value of $(M\text{-}1)$ is approached. In this upper limiting case the target energy dominates over the noise even when the beam is steered away from the target.

In the preceding analysis the averages have been expressed as ensemble averages. When the stochastic processes are ergodic, these ensemble averages can be replaced by the corresponding time averages provided the averaging time is infinite. In practice the time averages must be over a finite time so that the approximate values $\overline{y_{AL}}$ for $\langle y_{AL} \rangle$, etc.[4] will fluctuate about the true value. In fact, this behavior leads to a design compromise, since in order to increase the search rate one would like to make the averaging time as short as possible compatible with the other requirements. It is necessary to calculate the root-mean-square of the fluctuation of the value $\langle y_{AL} \rangle$ about the mean $\langle y_{AL} \rangle$ since these fluctuations will appear as false signals. Because of the non-linear nature of the squarer it is not possible to carry the assumption through to a specific answer without introducing specific forms for the low-pass filter and the normalized autocorrelation function $R(\tau)$.

If one is willing to assume that the low-pass filter in circuit 10.1(a) is the RC-filter of Fig. 6.2, one can write down the answer directly from Eq. (6.18). In this case the variance $\sigma_{zA}{}^2$ of the output is

$$\sigma_{zA}{}^2 = \frac{1}{RC} \int_{-\infty}^{+\infty} C_{xA}{}^2(\tau)\, d\tau \ , \tag{10.15}$$

where $C_{xA}(\tau)$ is the autocorrelation function of $x_A(t)$ defined in Eq. (10.3). If the reader is interested in a more general derivation of an expression for $\sigma_{zA}{}^2$ that does not depend on the assumption of an RC-filter, he can turn to the Appendix 10.1. Equation (10.15) has two parameters; the time constant of the filter which depends on RC and the integral of the square of the correlation function which depends on random function $x_A(t)$. Rudnick (1960) replaces these two parameters by times τ_1 and T as follows:

One can define a time τ_1 such that

$$C_{xA}{}^2(0)\, \tau_1 = \int_{-\infty}^{+\infty} C_{xA}{}^2(\tau)\, d\tau \ . \tag{10.16}$$

Rudnick refers to τ_1 as the correlation time of the process $x_A(t)$. One notices that this definition is equivalent geometrically to making the areas in Fig. 10.4(a) and (b) equal. An averaging time T, which in the case of the low-pass RC filter is 2 RC, is introduced to represent the post detection averaging time. With these definitions Rudnick obtains his Eq. (16) which is equivalent to

$$\sigma_{zA}{}^2 = C_{xA}{}^2(0)\, 2\tau_1/T \ . \tag{10.17}$$

---

[4]Each quantity u, say, for which the ensemble average was designated $\langle u \rangle$ will have a corresponding time average denoted $\overline{u}$.

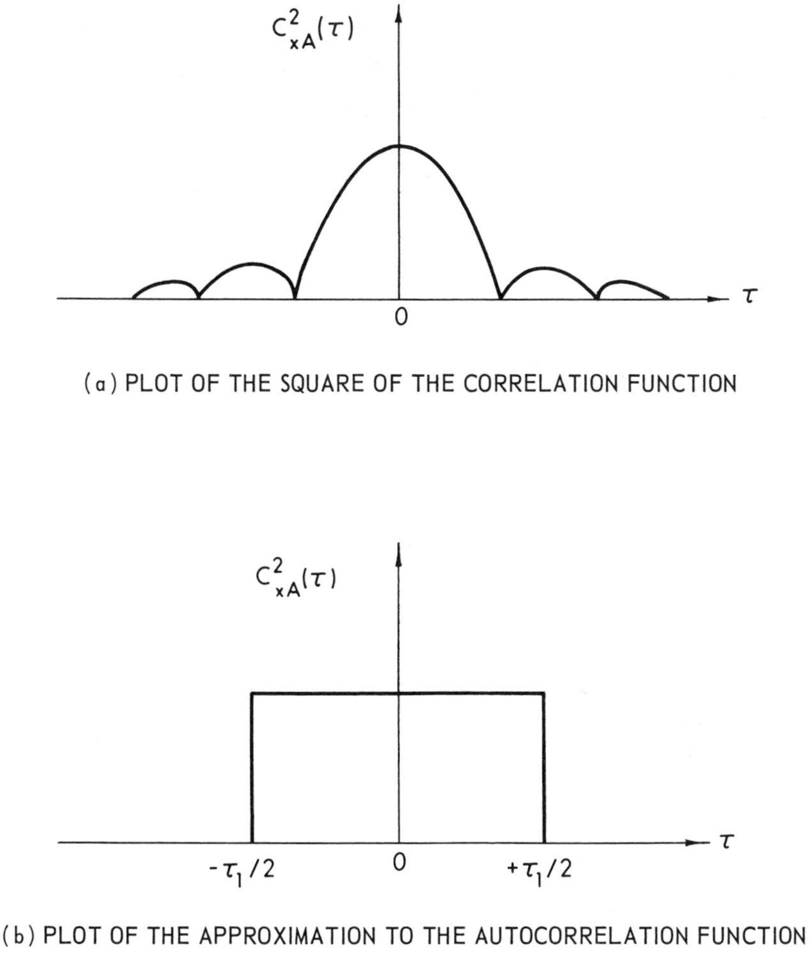
$C^2_{xA}(\tau)$
0
τ
(a) PLOT OF THE SQUARE OF THE CORRELATION FUNCTION
$C^2_{xA}(\tau)$
$-\tau_1/2$
0
$+\tau_1/2$
τ
(b) PLOT OF THE APPROXIMATION TO THE AUTOCORRELATION FUNCTION

Figure 10.4–Diagrams to illustrate the correlation time τ_1.

For the special case of the RC low-pass filter and the normalized autocorrelation function $R(\tau)$,

$$\frac{2\tau_1}{T} = \frac{1}{RC} \int_{-\infty}^{+\infty} R^2(\tau)\, d\tau \ . \tag{10.18}$$

The assumptions numbered (1) to (5) above make it easy to calculate $C_{xA}(\tau)$. One has

$$C_{xA}(\tau) = \left\langle \left\{ \sum_{i=1}^{M} [s_i(t) + n_i(t)] \right\} \left\{ \sum_{j=1}^{M} [s_j(t+\tau) + n_j(t+\tau)] \right\} \right\rangle$$

$$= \sum_{i,j=1}^{M} [\langle s_i(t)\, s_j(t+\tau) \rangle + \langle s_i(t)\, n_j(t+\tau) \rangle$$

$$+ \langle n_i(t)\, s_j(t+\tau) \rangle + \langle n_i(t)\, n_j(t+\tau) \rangle] \ . \tag{10.19}$$

By virtue of arguments similar to those following Eq. (10.5) one can show that

$$C_{xA}(\tau) = \left(\sum_{i=1}^{M} N_i \right) R(\tau) + S \sum_{i,j=1}^{M} R(\tau + \tau_{ij}) \ . \tag{10.20}$$

This equation can be simplified if we are willing to make special assumptions.

If the beam is on-target, all of the τ_{ij} vanish and

$$C_{xAO}(\tau) = \left[\sum_{i=1}^{M} N_i + M^2 S \right] R(\tau) \ . \tag{10.21}$$

If the beam is off-target, the τ_{ij} $(i \neq j)$ are presumably large enough to insure that the nondiagonal terms in the sum can be neglected. This gives

$$C_{xAL}(\tau) = \left[\sum_{i=1}^{M} N_i + MS \right] R(\tau) \ . \tag{10.22}$$

It is the latter case that is of more interest since one is concerned that the fluctuations in the output might be large enough to simulate a target when the beam is steered away from the target. Hence Eq. (10.15) becomes (adding the subscript L for off-target)

$$\sigma_{zAL}{}^2 = \left[\sum_{i=1}^{M} N_i + MS \right]^2 \frac{1}{RC} \int_{-\infty}^{+\infty} R^2(\tau)\, d\tau \ . \tag{10.23}$$

It could be that fluctuations in $\bar{z}_{AL}$ may be a more serious limitation on detection than the magnitude of $\Delta\bar{y}_A$. This suggests that perhaps the normalized response defined in Eq. (10.13) is not the best measure of the performance of the system and that instead one should define an output signal-to-noise ratio as[5]

$$\left(\frac{S}{N}\right)_{\text{out},A} = \frac{\Delta \langle y_A \rangle}{\sigma_{ZAL}} = \frac{(M-1)\frac{S}{\overline{N}}}{1+\frac{S}{\overline{N}}} \cdot \frac{1}{\left[\frac{1}{RC}\int_{-\infty}^{+\infty} R^2(\tau)\, d\tau\right]^{1/2}}, \quad (10.24)$$

where again $\overline{N} = \frac{1}{M}\sum_{i=1}^{M} N_i$.

The resemblance between Eqs. (10.13) and (10.24) is both pleasing and suggestive. First, one sees that the random fluctuations due to finite averaging times will exceed the target response unless

$$RC \geqslant \int_{-\infty}^{+\infty} R^2(\tau)\, d\tau \; .$$

This restriction is important both for determining circuit parameters and for calculating search rates. Secondly, one sees that the normalized response is an equally important measure of system performance. Since $(S/N)_{\text{out}}$ can be made infinite by letting $RC \to \infty$, it is clear that $(S/N)_{\text{out}}$ alone is not a sufficient measure of performance.

In view of the frequency with which Rudnick's paper is cited it is well to relate these equations to his work. He assumes that the input signal-to-noise ratio, S/N, is such that the root-mean-square fluctuation in the output, σ_{ZAL}, is just equal to the average signal output $\Delta\overline{y}_A$. When the output satisfies this condition, the processing gain is defined as the reciprocal of the input signal-to-noise ratio. Or, in terms of the present analysis, the processing gain G is defined as the value N/S that makes the term $(S/N)_{\text{out}}$ of Eq. (10.24) equal to unity. Thus, using Eq. (10.18) and the definition of G, one has for Eq. (10.24)

$$1 = \frac{(M\text{-}1)\frac{1}{G}}{1+\frac{1}{G}} \sqrt{\frac{T}{2\tau_1}} \; ,$$

[5] There is no uniformity of usage on this point. Thomas and Williams (1959) in their discussion of multiplicative arrays define $\frac{\text{signal}}{\text{noise}} = \frac{\text{square of the mean system output.}}{\text{variance of the system output.}}$ This sounds reasonable, but it yields a quantity of dimensions $(S/\overline{N})^2$ which appears undesirable.

or

$$G + 1 = (M-1)\sqrt{\frac{T}{2\tau_1}}$$

This is a slightly simplified version of Rudnick's Eq. (28). Rudnick refers to M-1 as the array gain and $\sqrt{T/2\tau_1}$ as the processing gain from post-rectification integration. This result which shows that the gain can be factored into a product of an array gain and a processing gain is a special case of a more general characteristic. This subject will be returned to in Sec. 19.3.

10.4 Analysis of the Multiplicative Detector

In the following analysis of the response of the multiplicative detector of Fig. 10.1(c) without quantizers the notation of Sec. 10.3 will be followed as closely as possible. Further, the five assumptions regarding the statistics and noise will still be assumed. Equation (10.3) for the sum of the outputs of the hydrophones will be modified with superscripts to indicate which set of hydrophones is being considered. Thus the outputs of the two summers are written as

$$x_A{}^{(1)}(t) = \sum_{i=1}^{M_1} \left\{ s_i{}^{(1)}(t) + n_i{}^{(1)}(t) \right\} \tag{10.25}$$

and

$$x_A{}^{(2)}(t) = \sum_{j=1}^{M_2} \left\{ s_j{}^{(2)}(t) + n_j{}^{(2)}(t) \right\} . \tag{10.26}$$

When the ensemble average for the product $\langle x_A{}^{(1)}(t) x_A{}^{(2)}(t) \rangle$ is written down, one sees that all products involving noise terms vanish. This leaves only terms like $\langle\, s_i{}^{(1)}(t)\; s_j{}^{(2)}(t)\,\rangle$. Following the procedure of Eq. (10.6) one has

$$\langle y_A \rangle = \left\langle x_A{}^{(1)}(t)\, x_A{}^{(2)}(t) \right\rangle$$

$$= \sum_{i=1}^{M_1} \sum_{j=1}^{M_2} \left\langle s(t-t_o-T_i{}^{(1)})\; s(t-t_o-T_j{}^{(2)}) \right\rangle . \tag{10.27}$$

Define

$$\tau_{ij} = T_i^{(1)} - T_j^{(2)} = -\tau_{ji} \ , \tag{10.28}$$

so that

$$\left\langle s(t-t_o-T_i^{(1)})\, s(t-t_o-T_j^{(2)})\right\rangle = SR(T_i^{(1)}-T_j^{(2)}) = SR(\tau_{ij}) \ . \tag{10.29}$$

This notation yields

$$\langle y_A \rangle = S \sum_{i=1}^{M_1} \sum_{j=1}^{M_2} R(\tau_{ij}) \ . \tag{10.30}$$

When the beam is on the target, all the $\tau_{ij} = 0$, and

$$\langle y_{AO} \rangle = M_1 M_2 S \ . \tag{10.31}$$

When the beam is off the target, assume as in the past that $R(\tau_{ij}) \sim 0$. This gives

$$\langle y_{AL} \rangle = 0 \ . \tag{10.32}$$

Defining the average signal level, $\Delta \langle y_A \rangle$ as in Eq. (10.12) one finds

$$\Delta \langle y_A \rangle = M_1 M_2 S \ . \tag{10.33}$$

When this is compared with Eq. (10.12) one sees that, for a given total number of hydrophones, $M_1 + M_2 = M$, the average signal level is much smaller when the hydrophones are divided into two groups and multiplied together.

One cannot normalize the average signal output as in Eq. (10.13) because $\langle y_{AL} \rangle = 0$. However, one can compute a root-mean-square fluctuation of $z_A(t)$ resulting from the finite time average and compute a signal-to-noise ratio as in Eq. (10.24). The output of the low-pass filter may be written, as in Eq. (6.9),

$$z_A(t) = \frac{1}{RC} \int_{-\infty}^{0+} e^{u/RC}\, x_A^{(1)}(u+t)\, x_A^{(2)}(u+t)\, du. \tag{10.34}$$

The product of two ergodic processes is not itself necessarily ergodic so one must work entirely with ensemble averages for the moment.

When one takes the ensemble average of Eq. (10.34) and interchanges the order of integration and averaging, all of the terms vanish except those of the form

$$\left\langle s(t+u-t_o-T_i^{(1)})\, s(t+u-t_o-T_j^{(2)}) \right\rangle .$$

Since $s(\cdot)$ is assumed to be an ergodic process, the average depends only on τ_{ij} and not u and may be factored out of the integrand. Consequently, by virtue of Eq. (10.27) one has

$$\langle z_A(t) \rangle = \langle y_A \rangle \tag{10.35}$$

as expected.

The ensemble average of the square of the departure of $z_A(t)$ from $\langle y_A \rangle$ is

$$\left\langle [z_A(t) - \langle y_A \rangle]^2 \right\rangle = \left\langle [z_A(t)]^2 \right\rangle - \langle y_A \rangle^2 . \tag{10.36}$$

As usual one writes

$$[z_A(t)]^2 = \frac{1}{(RC)^2} \int_{-\infty}^{0+} du_1 \int_{-\infty}^{0+} e^{(u_1+u_2)/RC}\, x_A^{(1)}(u_1+t)$$

$$x_A^{(2)}(u_1+t)\, x_A^{(1)}(u_2+t)\, x_A^{(2)}(u_2+t)\, du_2 \;. \qquad \ldots . \tag{10.37}$$

In order to evaluate the ensemble average of this expression one must expand the product of the four time series. The details are given in Appendix 10.2.

After Eq. (A 10.8) is substituted into Eq. (10.37), one may introduce the change variables

$$\sqrt{2}\, v_1 = u_2 + u_1 \;, \quad \sqrt{2}\, v_2 = u_2 - u_1 \;.$$

The integration with respect to v_1 can be evaluated immediately. This leaves

$$\langle z_A(t)^2 \rangle = \frac{1}{\sqrt{2}\, RC} \int_{-\infty}^{+\infty} \exp(-\sqrt{2}\, |v_2| / RC) \{\cdot\}\, dv_2$$

where

$$\{\cdot\} = M_1 M_2 \bar{N}^{(1)} \bar{N}^{(2)} [R(\sqrt{2}\nu_2)]^2$$

$$+ M_1 \bar{N}^{(1)} S \sum_{j,l=1}^{M_2} R(\sqrt{2}\nu_2 + \tau_{jl}^{(2)}) R(\sqrt{2}\nu_2)$$

$$+ M_2 \bar{N}^{(2)} S \sum_{i,k=1}^{M_1} R(\sqrt{2}\nu_2 + \tau_{ik}^{(1)}) R(\sqrt{2}\nu_2)$$

$$+ S^2 \sum_{i,k=1}^{M_1} \sum_{j,l=1}^{M_2} [R(\tau_{ij}) R(\tau_{kl}) +$$

$$R(\sqrt{2}\nu_2 - \tau_{ki}) R(\sqrt{2}\nu_2 + \tau_{il})$$

$$+ R(\sqrt{2}\nu_2 + \tau_{ik}^{(1)}) R(\sqrt{2}\nu_2 + \tau_{jl}^{(2)})] \; . \qquad \ldots . \qquad (10.38)$$

This equation can be simplified by the change of variable, $\sqrt{2}\,\nu_2 = s$.

It is not possible to say anything about this equation unless further assumptions are made. Perhaps the least restrictive assumption, from the point of view of the nature of the stochastic process, is the assumption usually made for the off-target case. As before, it will be assumed that when the array is directed away from the target, any τ which is not zero will be large enough to make $R(\tau)$ effectively zero. It was seen in Eq. (10.32) that $\langle y_{AL} \rangle = 0$ for the off-target case. Therefore,

$$\sigma_{zAL}{}^2 = \langle [z_A(t)]^2 \rangle = \frac{1}{2RC} \int_{-\infty}^{0+} \{\cdot\}\, ds = \frac{1}{4RC} \int_{-\infty}^{+\infty} \{\cdot\}\, ds \qquad (10.39)$$

where

$$\{\cdot\} = M_1 M_2 \; [\bar{N}^{(1)} \bar{N}^{(2)} + (\bar{N}^{(1)} + \bar{N}^{(2)}) S + S^2] \; R^2(s) \; . \qquad (10.40)$$

One is tempted to discuss the conditions under which σ_{zAL} is a minimum but this is not a relevant question since it is the ratio $\Delta \langle y_A \rangle / \sigma_{zAL}$ that is important. Before considering this ratio, it is desirable to specialize the assumption even further in order to obtain a comparison with the standard detector.

Assume that $M_1 = M_2 = M/2$ and $\overline{N}^{(1)} = \overline{N}^{(2)} = \overline{N}$. In this case one has for Eqs. (10.39) and (10.40)

$$\sigma_{zAL}{}^2 = M^2 \, [\overline{N} + S]^2 \, \frac{1}{16RC} \int_{-\infty}^{+\infty} [R(s)]^2 \, ds \, . \tag{10.41}$$

Consequently, when one follows the usage introduced in Eq. (10.24) for the definition of signal-to-noise ratio, one obtains

$$\left(\frac{S}{N}\right)_{\text{out}} = \frac{\Delta \langle y_A \rangle}{\sigma_{zAL}} = \frac{M\,S}{[\overline{N} + S] \left[\dfrac{1}{RC} \displaystyle\int_{-\infty}^{+\infty} [R(s)]^2 \, ds \right]^{1/2}} \tag{10.42}$$

for the multiplicative array. On the other hand, one may write Eq. (10.24) for the standard detector as

$$\left(\frac{S}{N}\right)_{\text{out}} = \frac{(M-1)\,S}{[\overline{N} + S] \left[\dfrac{1}{RC} \displaystyle\int_{-\infty}^{+\infty} [R(s)]^2 \, ds \right]^{1/2}} \, . \tag{10.43}$$

When the number of hydrophones, M, is large enough that $M\text{-}1 \cong M$, the two systems have the same signal-to-noise ratio. However, if there are only two hydrophones in the array, the multiplicative array is better by $\sqrt{2}$ or 3 dB.

Usher (1964) has considered the response of the multiplicative receiver when the noise level at each hydrophone is itself a random variable. This enables him to arrive at special expression for $\overline{N}^{(1)}$ and $\overline{N}^{(2)}$.

10.5 Digression on Ergodicity

The reader has undoubtedly noticed that the notation in the last two sections has fallen short of the ideal set forth in the earlier chapters. In particular $\langle x \rangle$ was used as before to designate an ensemble average, but $\overline{x}$ was used in this chapter to denote a *finite* time average. This latter is an abbreviated notation which is not ideal. In the earlier chapters $\overline{x}$ was used to denote the time average defined by

$$\lim_{T \to \infty} \frac{1}{T} \int_{-T/2}^{+T/2} x(t) \, dt \, , \tag{10.44}$$

while $\overline{x}_T$ was used to denote the finite time average

$$\frac{1}{T}\int_{-T/2}^{+T/2} x(t)\,dt\ . \tag{10.45}$$

This change of notation may tend to obscure a logical point that should be mentioned. In the discussion of the standard detector in Sec. 10.3 the sum $x_A(t)$ defined in Eq. (10.3) is an ergodic process since it is the sum of ergodic processes. Therefore, the time average defined in Eq. (10.44) is equal to and can be designated by $\langle x \rangle$ so that one may simplify the notation by using $\overline{x}$ for the finite time average of Eq. (10.45). Further, although the signal output defined in Eq. (10.12) and the mean-square fluctuation defined in Eq. (10.23) are ensemble averages, they represent equally well the time average and the fluctuation in time, respectively.

On the other hand, the output of the multiplicative detector involves the product of two ergodic processes. It is not necessary that the product of two ergodic processes be ergodic, so one cannot equate ensemble and time averages without further restrictions on the stochastic processes $x_i(t)$ and $n_i(t)$. Consequently, the ensemble average introduced in Eq. (10.36) is not necessarily equal to the corresponding time average. Nonetheless, this assumption, which seems reasonable, has been introduced tacitly and regularly in studies of the multiplicative detector.

This point may be stated another way by saying that the root-mean-square fluctuations σ_{ZAL} computed in Eqs. (10.39) and (10.41) are based on ensemble averages and may not necessarily represent the fluctuations in the output of the receiver considered as a function of time. However, it was pointed out in Sec. 3.1 that in the sonar application the source, receiver, target, and medium were normally in a state of motion so that perhaps the successive outputs of the receiver constituted samples from an ensemble rather than from a time series. If this be true, the ensemble averages are applicable in every case.

10.6 The Advantages and Disadvantages of Clipping and the Effect of Sampling on Signal Output

In the analyses of the last three sections the systems were ideal and the only non-linear processes introduced were those of multiplication which are linear in energy. The only loss of energy resulted from the low-pass filters. A change to digital techniques is most attractive from the viewpoint of equipment design, since the electronic circuits or magnetic memories can be made more compact and stable and problems arising from amplifier gain and stability are less severe. These and other considerations have caused the designers of equipment to consider clipped or, more generally, quantized signals as illustrated in Figs. 10.1(*b*) and (*c*). A factor that has led to the popularity of binary clipping is that one does not need to use an AGC circuit. Binary circuits can be built which will operate reliably with a dynamic range of 80 dB in the input. A further advantage of binary clipping is that when the system works improperly it usually fails completely so the operator is alerted. Linear circuits can function poorly without the operator being aware of it.

In the following analyses it will be seen that digital sampling becomes more advantageous when the noise level fluctuates widely from hydrophone to hydrophone. Although this question will be considered quantitatively, it is obvious qualitatively that in a linear system the output is dominated by those hydrophones which have the greatest power levels. On the other hand, it has been found that bearing accuracy and the ability of a system to resolve two targets of slightly different bearing suffers seriously when the signals are clipped.

When one replaces the analog messages by binary samples, there are two factors that act to change the system. In the first place the time intervals between the samples are integral multiples of some sampling time τ_0 so that the pattern formation is not likely to be optimum. In the second place there is the effect of the non-linear quantization. It is desirable to discuss these effects separately since they can be changed independently of one another. The effect of time sampling on the array gain will be considered now while the effect of quantization will be considered in Sec. 10.7.

Ideally, when the array is pointed at the target the time delays in the hydrophone circuits are adjusted so that all of the signals $s_i(t)$ of Eq. (10.1) add in phase. This assumption was utilized in Eq. (10.10) when it was assumed that $R(\tau_{ij}) = 1$ for all values of i and j when the beam was pointed at the target. Actually, if the delay times are quantized, one may assume $R(\tau_{ij}) = 1$ with strict accuracy only if $i = j$. In the case that $i \neq j$ there will be fluctuations so that τ_{ij} will assume one of the values $-\tau_o$, 0, $+\tau_o$. This may be assumed to be a random phenomenon when many directions for the pattern are considered. When this source of error is introduced, Eq. (10.10) must be replaced by

$$\langle y_{AO} \rangle = \sum_{i=1}^{N} N_i + M\,S + 2S \sum_{i=1}^{M} \sum_{j=i+1}^{M} R(\epsilon_{ij}) \tag{10.46}$$

where ϵ_{ij} takes one of the values $-\tau_o$, 0, $+\tau_o$.

If the time series are continuous, the autocorrelation function has a zero slope at the origin so the Maclaurin's expansion begins

$$R(\epsilon_{ij}) = R(0) + \tfrac{1}{2}R''(0)\,\epsilon_{ij}^2 + \ldots \tag{10.47}$$

The quantity $R''(0)$ is of interest in its own right. If both sides of Eq. (4.7) are differentiated with respect to τ and τ is set equal to zero in the resulting equation, one has

$$C(0)\,R''(0) = -\int_{-\infty}^{+\infty} (2\pi f)^2\, P(f)\, df\ .$$

But

$$C(0) = \int_{-\infty}^{+\infty} P(f)\, df\ ,$$

so

$$R''(0) = \frac{-\int_{-\infty}^{+\infty} (2\pi f)^2\, P(f)\, df}{\int_{-\infty}^{+\infty} P(f)\, df} = -\langle (2\pi f)^2 \rangle_P\ . \qquad (10.48)$$

In this notation $P(f)$ is treated as though it were proportional to a probability density for the frequency f.

Thus one may obtain a value for $R''(0)$ for the noise if the power spectrum $P(f)$ is known. Rice (1944, p. 193 of the 1954 Dover Ed.) has shown that the ratio on the right is related to the expected number of zeros per second for the process so $R''(0)$ can be determined rather easily from experimental data.

One finds from Eq. (10.47) that, since $R(0) = 1$,

$$2\sum_{i=1}^{M}\sum_{j=i+1}^{M} R(\epsilon_{ij}) \cong M(M-1) + R''(0)\sum_{i=1}^{M}\sum_{j=i+1}^{M} \epsilon_{ij}^{\,2}$$

$$= M(M-1)\left\{1 + \tfrac{1}{2}R''(0)\,\langle\, \epsilon_{ij}^{\,2}\,\rangle\right\}\ , \qquad (10.49)$$

where by definition,

$$\langle \epsilon_{ij}^2 \rangle = \frac{2}{M(M-1)} \sum_{i=1}^{M} \sum_{j=i+1}^{M} \epsilon_{ij}^2 \tag{10.50}$$

is an average value of the square of the error in the relative delays ϵ_{ij}. With the aid of this abbreviated notation one can replace Eq. (10.10) with the more accurate form

$$\langle y_A \rangle = \sum_{i=1}^{M} N_i + \left[M^2 - \frac{M(M-1)}{2} \langle (2\pi f)^2 \rangle_P \langle \epsilon_{ij}^2 \rangle \right] S . \tag{10.51}$$

In this case the average signal output of Eq. (10.12) becomes

$$\Delta \langle y_A \rangle = \langle y_{AO} \rangle - \langle y_{AL} \rangle = M(M-1)\, S \left\{ 1 - \frac{1}{2} \langle (2\pi f)^2 \rangle_P \langle \epsilon_{ij}^2 \rangle \right\} . \tag{10.52}$$

From this equation one can obtain an idea of how fine a sampling interval is needed for a given power spectrum.

10.7 The Standard Detector with Perfect Clipping

The effect of perfect clipping (without sampling) can be illustrated by analyzing the circuit of Fig. 10.1(*b*) and comparing the analysis with that given in Sec. 10.3 for the circuit of Fig. 10.1(*a*). The notation and the assumptions introduced in Sec. 10.3 will be retained. In particular the subscript Q will be used to remind the reader that clipping is present and each quantity with a subscript Q in this section can be compared with the corresponding quantity with a subscript A in Sec. 10.3. Thus the output of the summer is

$$x_Q(t) = \sum_{i=1}^{M} \{ s_i(t) + n_i(t) \}_Q , \tag{10.53}$$

and the autocorrelation function of the output of the summer is

$$\langle x_Q(t)\, x_Q(t+\tau) \rangle = \sum_{i=1}^{M} \sum_{j=1}^{M} \langle \{ s_i(t) + n_i(t) \}_Q$$

$$\{ s_j(t+\tau) + n_j(t+\tau) \}_Q \rangle \ . \tag{10.54}$$

One cannot expand the product in the right member of Eq. (10.53) into a sum of four products as in Eq. (10.19) because the clipping action is based on the sum $s_i(t) + n_i(t)$. However, when the inputs to each pair of clippers constitute a correlated, bivariate gaussian process, one can utilize the results of Sec. 3.7 to calculate the quantities in the angular brackets. It was shown in Eq. (3.39) that the correlation function $C_Q(\tau)$ of a clipped process is related to the normalized correlation function $R_A(\tau)$ of the unclipped process by

$$C_Q(\tau) = \frac{2}{\pi} \sin^{-1} R_A(\tau) \ . \tag{10.55}$$

If one denotes the normalized crosscorrelation function of a pair of unclipped signals by $\mu_{ij}(\tau)$, one has[6]

$$\mu_{ij}(\tau) = \frac{\langle \{ s_i(t) + N_i(t) \}_A \{ s_j(t+\tau) + n_j(t+\tau) \}_A \rangle}{[S + N_i]^{1/2} \ [S + N_j]^{1/2}} \ . \tag{10.56}$$

By repeating the arguments leading to Eq. (10.9) the reader can show that this equation simplifies to

$$\mu_{ij}(\tau) \begin{cases} = \dfrac{S\, R(\tau+\tau_{ij})}{[S+N_i]^{1/2} \ [S+N_j]^{1/2}} \ , & i \neq j \\ = R(\tau) \ , & i = j \ . \end{cases} \tag{10.57}$$

In deriving Eq. (10.57) one utilizes the assumption that the noise and the signal have the same normalized autocorrelation functions.

When Eq. (10.57) is substituted into Eq. (10.54), one has

$$\langle x_Q(t)\, x_Q(t+\tau) \rangle = M \rho(\tau) +$$

$$\frac{4}{\pi} \sum_{i=1}^{M} \sum_{j=i+1}^{M} \sin^{-1} \left\{ \frac{S\, R(\tau+\tau_{ij})}{[S+N_i]^{1/2} \ [S+N_j]^{1/2}} \right\} . \tag{10.58}$$

---

[6] Unfortunately, this assertion anticipates Eq. (11.9). The reader may prefer to read Chapter XI before completing this section.

The average output of the squarer, $\langle y_Q \rangle$, is obtained from this equation by setting $\tau = 0$. As usual, two cases will be distinguished; on-target denoted with a subscript 0 and off-target denoted with a subscript L. In the on-target case, $\tau_{ij} = 0$ and

$$\langle y_{QO} \rangle = M + \frac{4}{\pi} \sum_{i=1}^{M} \sum_{j=i+1}^{M} \sin^{-1} \left\{ \frac{S}{[S+N_i]^{1/2} \; [S+N_j]^{1/2}} \right\}. \tag{10.59}$$

In the off-target case it will be assumed as before that the τ_{ij} are so large that $R(\tau_{ij}) = 0$. This gives

$$\langle y_{QL} \rangle = M. \tag{10.60}$$

The average signal output analogous to Eq. (10.12) is

$$\Delta \langle y_Q \rangle = \langle y_{QO} \rangle - \langle y_{QL} \rangle$$

$$= \frac{4}{\pi} \sum_{i=1}^{M} \sum_{i=j+1}^{M} \sin^{-1} \left\{ \frac{S}{[S+N_i]^{1/2} \; [S+N_j]^{1/2}} \right\}. \tag{10.61}$$

One cannot pursue this development further without introducing some approximations and assumptions. For example, one can assume that the signal power is much less than the noise power and use the first one or two terms of the power series

$$\sin^{-1} x = x + \frac{1}{6} x^3 + \frac{3}{40} x^5 + \ldots \tag{10.62}$$

In addition, one must postulate some probability density for the noise levels N_i. The reader is referred to Usher (1964) who develops answers for two such probability densities.

In order to obtain a formula for comparison with the results of Sec. 10.3, assume that each of the N_i is equal to $\overline{N}$. This assumption is more stringent than that of Eq. (10.14). The use of this assumption and the first term of the power series in Eq. (10.62) enables one to write

$$\Delta \langle y_Q \rangle \cong \frac{2}{\pi} \frac{M(M-1)\, S}{\overline{N} + S}. \tag{10.63}$$

When this expression is normalized by dividing by the off-target signal response, Eq. (10.60), one has

$$\frac{\Delta \langle y_Q \rangle}{\langle y_{QL} \rangle} = \frac{2}{\pi} \cdot \frac{(M-1)\dfrac{S}{N}}{1+\dfrac{S}{N}} \tag{10.64}$$

which may be compared with the result in Eq. (10.13) for the unclipped case. One sees that the clipping introduces a deterioration in the normalized response corresponding to the factor $2/\pi$, i.e., about 2.0 dB. However, one usually judges systems on the basis of the deterioration in the signal-to-noise loss introduced by clipping. This is usually nearer 1.0 dB.

The analysis of Usher shows that the case in which all the N_i are equal is the one least favorable for the comparison, and that as the range of possible values for the N_i increases, the performances of the "clipped" detector becomes more favorable compared to and even surpasses that of the linear detector.

The question of the fluctuations in the output of the clipped detector has yet to be considered. In order to simplify the analysis assume that the signal $s_i(t)$ is so weak compared to the noise $n_i(t)$ $(i = 1, 2, \ldots, M)$ that the signal may be neglected in the calculation of the root-mean-square fluctuation, σ_{zQL}, when the beam is off-target. This assumption is not unrealistic, since these fluctuations in the absence of a signal could give rise to false target decisions.

When the signal $s_i(t)$ is neglected, the autocorrelation function, $C_{xQ}(\tau)$, of the input to the square law detector is given by Eq. (10.54) with $s_i(t) = 0$ $(i = 1, 2, \ldots, M)$; that is

$$C_{xQ}(\tau) = \sum_{i=1}^{M} \sum_{j=1}^{M} \langle n_{iQ}(t)\, n_{jQ}(t+\tau) \rangle$$

$$= \frac{2}{\pi} \sum_{i=1}^{M} \sin^{-1} R(\tau) = \frac{2M}{\pi} \sin^{-1} R(\tau) \; . \tag{10.65}$$

The individual noise levels N_i do not appear in this answer since the clipping process eliminates these differences.

One may use Eq. (10.15) again to calculate the variance of the output, $z_Q(t)$. When the beam is pointed off the target, this gives

$$\sigma_{zQL}{}^2 = \frac{4M^2}{\pi^2 RC} \int_{-\infty}^{+\infty} [\sin^{-1} R(\tau)]^2 \, d\tau \; . \tag{10.66}$$

This quantity cannot be compared directly with $\sigma_{zAL}{}^2$ of Eq. (10.23), but one can use the approximate Eq. (10.63) to calculate an output signal-to-noise ratio as defined in Eq. (10.24). This definition yields, in the present case,

$$\left(\frac{S}{N}\right)_{\text{out},Q} = \frac{\Delta\langle y_Q\rangle}{\sigma_{zQL}}$$

$$= \frac{(M-1)\dfrac{S}{\overline{N}}}{1+\dfrac{S}{\overline{N}}} \cdot \frac{1}{\left[\dfrac{1}{RC}\displaystyle\int_{-\infty}^{+\infty} [\sin^{-1} R(\tau)]^2 \, d\tau\right]^{1/2}}, \tag{10.67}$$

which should be compared with the result of Eq. (10.24). Now

$$[\sin^{-1} R(\tau)]^2 \geqslant [R(\tau)]^2$$

with equality only in the case $R(\tau) = 0$. Consequently, the denominator of Eq. (10.67) is larger than the denominator of Eq. (10.24). Hence,

$$\left(\frac{S}{N}\right)_{\text{out},A} > \left(\frac{S}{N}\right)_{\text{out},Q}$$

for the special case $N_i = \overline{N}$ $(i = 1, 2, \ldots, M)$. Better approximations for the integral in Eq. (10.66) are derived by Rudnick (1960) and Usher (1946).

10.8 Suggestions for Further Reading

The analysis of the circuits of Fig. 10.1 is continued in Chapter XII. The reader is referred to the paper by Thomas and Williams (1959) for an analysis of the circuit of Fig. 10.1(*c*) with ideal clippers.

The reader should realize that the ideal clipper whose output is ±1 is the most simple form of quantizer. It may well be that ultimately sonar systems will utilize more sophisticated quantizers. The relevant theoretical questions of multilevel quantization has been studied rather extensively by Professor Bonnet and his colleagues. (See Bonnet, 1964*a*.)

The reader will find interesting results on product arrays in Berman and Clay (1957) and Fakley (1959). There are several interesting papers on linear and clipped signal processors in an unpublished report from the Dunham Laboratory, Yale University (1963).

The DELTIC correlator mentioned in Sec. 10.2 is a useful device for which many applications in underwater acoustics have been found. A description of the DELTIC and other correlators is given by Allen and Westerfield (1964).

APPENDIX 10.1

Alternate Derivation of Eq. (10.15)

It has been assumed that $s_i(t)$ and $n_i(t)$ are gaussian processes. Hence, $x(t)$ is a gaussian process since it is a finite sum of the $s_i(t)$ and $n_i(t)$. Consequently, one can utilize Eq. (6.16) to write down the autocorrelation function of the output of the squarer, $C_{yA}(\tau)$ in terms of the autocorrelation function of the input, $C_{xA}(\tau)$. One has

$$C_{yA}(\tau) = C_{xA}{}^2(0) + 2C_{xA}{}^2(\tau) \ . \tag{A 10.1}$$

Since we are interested in the effect of a filter on $y_A(t)$, it is desirable to transform this autocorrelation function into a power spectrum. Using Eq. (4.8) and the formula, Eq. (2.21), for the delta function, one finds

$$W_{yA}(f) = C_{xA}{}^2(0)\,\delta(f) + 2\int_{-\infty}^{+\infty} C_{xA}{}^2(\tau)\, e^{-i2\pi f\tau}\, d\tau \ . \quad \ldots \tag{A 10.2}$$

The first term on the right is a dc spectral component which is the limiting value obtained for an infinite averaging time. The second term of the right member is the power in the fluctuation of the output which causes departures from the average value. The effect of this term can be reduced by filtering.

Let $S_{yA}(f)$ be the power spectrum of the fluctuations associated with the second integral on the right of Eq. (A 10.2). If $\hat{Y}(f)$ is the frequency response of the low-pass filter, the power spectrum of the fluctuations in the output is

$$S_{zA}(f) = |\hat{Y}(f)|^2\, S_{yA}(f) \ . \tag{A 10.3}$$

By virtue of Eq. (4.13) one can express the mean square value of the fluctuations resulting from $S_{zA}(f)$ as

$$\sigma_{zA}{}^2 = C_{zA}(0) = \int_{-\infty}^{+\infty} |\hat{Y}(f)|^2\, S_{yA}(f)\, df \ . \tag{A 10.4}$$

This is as far as one can carry the analysis without introducing specific circuits. Suppose the low-pass filter is the simple RC-circuit of Fig. 6.2. Then

$$|\hat{Y}(f)|^2 = [1 + (f/f_o)^2]^{-1} \qquad \text{(A 10.5)}$$

where $f_o = (2\pi RC)^{-1}$. This still does not enable one to evaluate the integral in Eq. (A 10.3), but if f_o is large enough, one can approximate this integral by assuming that $S_{yA}(f)$ is a constant, $S_{yA}(0)$ over the range of frequencies in which $|\hat{Y}(f)|^2$ is significantly different from zero. Hence

$$\sigma_{zA}{}^2 \cong S_{yA}(0) \int_{-\infty}^{+\infty} \frac{df}{1+(f/f_o)^2} = \pi f_o S_{yA}(0) \ .$$

But $S_{yA}(f)$ is the Fourier transform of the fluctuating part of $C_{yA}(\tau)$ and $\pi f_o = 1/2RC$. So

$$\sigma_{zA}{}^2 \cong \frac{1}{RC} \int_{-\infty}^{+\infty} C_{xA}{}^2(\tau)\, d\tau \ . \qquad \text{(A 10.6)}$$

APPENDIX 10.2

Details Relevant to Eq. (10.37)

Introducing an impromptu abbreviated notation, one may write (by virtue of Eqs. (10.25) and (10.26))

$$\langle \cdot \rangle = \langle x_A^{(1)}(u_1+t)\, x_A^{(2)}(u_1+t)\, x_A^{(1)}(u_2+t)\, x_A^{(2)}(u_2+t) \rangle$$

$$= \left\langle \sum_{i=1}^{M_1} \sum_{j=1}^{M_2} \sum_{k=1}^{M_1} \sum_{l=1}^{M_2} \{\cdot\} \right\rangle \qquad \text{(A 10.7)}$$

where

$$\{\cdot\} = [s_i^{(1)}(u_1+t) + n_i^{(1)}(u_1+t)] \cdot [s_j^{(2)}(u_1+t) + n_j^{(2)}(u_1+t)] \times$$

$$[s_k^{(1)}(u_2+t) + n_k^{(2)}(u_2+t)] \cdot [s_l^{(2)}(u_2+t) + n_l^{(2)}(u_2+t)] \ .$$

If, for the moment, one omits the arguments of the functions, one can write

$$\begin{aligned}
\{\cdot\} = {} & s_i^{(1)}s_j^{(2)}s_k^{(1)}s_l^{(2)} + s_i^{(1)}s_j^{(2)}n_k^{(1)}n_l^{(2)} \\
& + \underline{s_i^{(1)}s_j^{(2)}s_k^{(1)}n_l^{(2)}} + \underline{s_i^{(1)}s_j^{(2)}s_l^{(2)}n_k^{(1)}} \\
& + n_i^{(1)}n_j^{(2)}s_k^{(1)}s_l^{(2)} + n_i^{(1)}n_j^{(2)}n_k^{(1)}n_l^{(2)} \\
& + \underline{n_i^{(1)}n_j^{(2)}s_k^{(1)}n_l^{(2)}} + \underline{n_i^{(1)}n_j^{(2)}s_l^{(2)}n_k^{(1)}} \\
& + \underline{s_i^{(1)}n_j^{(2)}s_k^{(1)}s_l^{(2)}} + \underline{s_i^{(1)}n_j^{(2)}n_k^{(1)}n_i^{(2)}} \\
& + s_i^{(1)}n_j^{(2)}s_k^{(1)}n_l^{(2)} + s_i^{(1)}n_j^{(2)}s_l^{(2)}n_k^{(1)} \\
& + \underline{s_j^{(2)}n_i^{(1)}s_k^{(1)}s_l^{(2)}} + \underline{s_j^{(2)}n_i^{(1)}n_k^{(1)}n_l^{(2)}} \\
& + s_j^{(2)}n_i^{(1)}s_k^{(1)}n_l^{(2)} + s_j^{(2)}n_i^{(1)}s_l^{(2)}n_k^{(1)} \ .
\end{aligned}$$

The noise and the signals are independent of each other and each has an average of zero. So when one takes the ensemble average one can be certain that the terms underlined vanish. This eliminates one-half of the terms. Since the noises at the different hydrophones are assumed to be independent, one can eliminate immediately the terms of the form $s\, s\, n^{(1)}\, n^{(2)}$.

Hence, one has

$$\langle \cdot \rangle = \sum_{i,k=1}^{M_1} \sum_{j,l=1}^{M_2} \langle \{:\} \rangle ,$$

where

$$\{:\} = s_i^{(1)} s_j^{(2)} s_k^{(1)} s_l^{(2)} + n_i^{(1)} n_k^{(1)} n_j^{(2)} n_l^{(2)}$$

$$+ s_i^{(1)} s_k^{(1)} n_j^{(2)} n_l^{(2)} + s_j^{(2)} s_l^{(2)} n_i^{(1)} n_k^{(1)} .$$

The noise terms $n^{(1)}$ and $n^{(2)}$ are independent of each other so

$$\langle n_i^{(1)} n_k^{(1)} n_j^{(2)} n_l^{(2)} \rangle = \langle n_i^{(1)} n_k^{(1)} \rangle \langle n_j^{(2)} n_l^{(2)} \rangle .$$

Similarly for the product of two noises and two signals. Finally, the signals $s_\lambda^{(\mu)}(\cdot)$ ($\lambda = i, j, k, l; \mu = 1, 2$) are all obtained from the same function $s(\cdot)$ through a time shift. Therefore, although we started with a multiple product of stochastic processes to which the ergodic hypothesis did not apply, the independence assumed for the individual terms was so great that we have been able to reduce the ensemble averages to elemental terms to which one can apply the ergodic hypothesis.

Thus, one has

$$\langle n_i^{(1)}(u_1 + t)\, n_k^{(1)}(u_2 + t) \rangle = N_i^{(1)} R(u_2 - u_1)\, \delta_{ik}$$

$$\langle n_j^{(2)}(u_1 + t)\, n_l^{(2)}(u_2 + t) \rangle = N_j^{(2)} R(u_2 - u_1)\, \delta_{jl} .$$

In order to discuss the ensemble average of the signals it is necessary to define more time delays. In addition to Eq. (10.28),

$$\tau_{ij} = T_i^{(1)} - T_j^{(2)} , \tag{10.28}$$

let us define

$$\tau_{ik}^{(1)} = T_i^{(1)} - T_k^{(1)} ,$$

and

$$\tau_{jl}^{(2)} = T_j^{(2)} - T_l^{(2)} .$$

With these definitions one can write

$$\langle s_i^{(1)}(u_1 + t)\, s_k^{(1)}(u_2 + t) \rangle$$

$$= \langle s(t + u_1 - t_o - T_i^{(1)})\, s(t + u_2 - t_o - T_k^{(1)}) \rangle$$

$$= S\, R(u_2 - u_1 + \tau_{ik}^{(1)}) \ ,$$

and

$$\langle s_j^{(2)}(u_1 + t)\, s_l^{(2)}(u_2 + t) \rangle$$

$$= \langle s(t + u_1 - t_o - T_j^{(2)})\, s(t + u_2 - t_o - T_1^{(2)}) \rangle$$

$$= S\, R(u_2 - u_1 + \tau_{jl}^{(2)}) \ .$$

Finally, one needs the fourth order average

$$\langle s_i^{(1)}(u_1 + t)\, s_j^{(2)}(u_1 + t)\, s_k^{(1)}(u_2 + t)\, s_l^{(2)}(u_2 + t) \rangle =$$

$$\langle s(t + u_1 - t_o - T_i^{(1)})\, s(t + u_1 - t_o - T_j^{(2)})\, s(t + u_2 - t_o - T_k^{(1)}) \ .$$

$$s(t + u_2 - t_o - T_l^{(2)}) \rangle$$

Since $s(\cdot)$ is a gaussian process, one can use the equation given by Freeman (1958, p. 246, Eq. (8.5-4) or by Middleton (1960, p. 343, Eq. (7.29*a*)). This equation reads, omitting once again the arguments,

$$\langle s_i^{(1)} s_j^{(2)} s_k^{(1)} s_l^{(2)} \rangle = \langle s_i^{(1)} s_j^{(2)} \rangle \langle s_k^{(1)} s_l^{(2)} \rangle$$

$$+ \langle s_j^{(2)} s_k^{(1)} \rangle \ \langle s_i^{(1)} s_l^{(2)} \rangle \ + \ \langle s_i^{(1)} s_k^{(1)} \rangle \langle s_j^{(2)} s_l^{(2)} \rangle$$

$$= S^2\, [R(\tau_{ij}) R(\tau_{kl}) + R(u_2 - u_1 - \tau_{kj}) R(u_2 - u_1 + \tau_{il})$$

$$+ \ R(u_2 - u_1 + \tau_{ik}^{(1)}) R(u_2 - u_1 + \tau_{jl}^{(2)})\ ] \ .$$

Upon collecting terms one finds for Eq. (A. 10.7)

$$\langle \cdot \rangle = M_1 M_2 \overline{N}^{(1)} \overline{N}^{(2)}\, R(u_2 - u_1)^2$$

$$+ M_1 \overline{N}^{(1)}\, S \sum_{j,l=1}^{M_2} R(u_2 - u_1 + \tau_{jl}^{(2)})\, R(u_2 - u_1)$$

$$+ M_2 \overline{N}^{(2)} \; S \sum_{i,k=1}^{M_1} R(u_2 - u_1 + \tau_{ik}{}^{(1)}) \, R(u_2 - u_1)$$

$$+ S^2 \sum_{i,k=1}^{M_1} \sum_{j,l=1}^{M_2} [\, R(\tau_{ij}) \, R(\tau_{kl})$$

$$+ R(u_2 - u_1 - \tau_{ki}) \, R(u_2 - u_1 + \tau_{il})$$

$$+ R(u_2 - u_1 + \tau_{ik}{}^{(1)}) \, R(u_2 - u_1 + \tau_{jl}{}^{(2)}) \,] \qquad \text{(A 10.8)}$$

where, as before,

$$\overline{N}^{(1)} = \frac{1}{M_1} = \sum_{i=1}^{M_1} N_i{}^{(1)} \; , \; \overline{N}^{(2)} = \frac{1}{M_2} \sum_{j=1}^{M_2} N_j{}^{(2)} \quad .$$

CHAPTER XI

Multidimensional Stochastic Processes

11.1 General Considerations

The theory presented in Chapter X suffered from a serious restriction in that the noise at each hydrophone was assumed to be independent of the noises at the other hydrophones. This assumption simplified the analysis considerably but it is not realistic, since the noise wave field may have a significant correlation between different hydrophones. However, before the effect of this correlation is introduced into the discussion of the circuits of Fig. 10.1, it is well to consider in general the theory of multidimensional stochastic processes.

The discussion of a stochastic process can be generalized readily by considering a multicomponent process for which a sample is not one but M functions $x^{(i)}(t, \lambda)$, $i = 1, 2, \ldots, M$. If $M = 2$, one may associate the two components to form a complex number (or vector)

$$z(t, \lambda) = x^{(1)}(t, \lambda) + ix^{(2)}(t, \lambda) \ . \tag{11.1}$$

For general values of M one may consider the sample functions $[x^{(1)}, x^{(2)}, \ldots, x^{(M)}]$ for any value of the time t as a vector in an M-dimensional space. Naturally, the M-dimensional process can be generalized by letting each component of the M-dimensional process be a complex number.

For the moment let us restrict the discussion to $M = 2$ and think of the process as generating a single component having a complex value as in Eq. (11.1). In this case one must introduce complex conjugates for many of the factors in the formulas of the first ten chapters, but if this be done, valid results will be obtained. This modification is motivated from the mathematical point of view because the product of a complex number with its complex conjugate yields a real number which is the square of the magnitude of the complex number. The introduction of the complex conjugate is also desirable from the physical point of view. If, for example, an alternating current is represented by a complex number, the power dissipated in a one-ohm resistor is one-half the product of the current and its complex conjugate.

In keeping with this suggestion one changes the definition of second order joint moments in Eqs. (3.14) and (3.15) and in the definition of the covariance function in Eq. (3.13) by replacing the second factor with its complex conjugate. In the case of ergodic processes $C(\tau)$ is in general complex but $C(0)$ is real. The Schwartz inequality, Eq. (3.17), becomes

$$\left| \int_a^b f(x)\, g^*(x)\, dx \right|^2 \leqslant \int_a^b f(x)\, f^*(x)\, dx \int_a^b g(x)\, g^*(x)\, dx \quad \ldots . \tag{11.2}$$

for complex functions. Finally, the definition of a gaussian process that is given in Sec. 3.6 is still valid but the matrix elements a_{mn} and the second order moments μ_{ij} will be complex quantities.

11.2 Covariance and Correlation Functions

In the case of underwater sonar systems one usually has several transducers, say M transducers, as in Fig. 10.1(a), whose outputs constitute an M-dimensional random process. The set of M time functions $\{x^{(i)}(t, \lambda)\}$, $i = 1, 2, \ldots, M$, constitutes a single sample of the ensemble so it is characterized by a single value λ of the ensemble variable. The parameter λ is a member of the set of points Λ that characterizes the ensemble. Thus one is led to consider a vector stochastic process[1]

$$[x_1(t, \lambda), x_2(t, \lambda), \ \ldots, x_M(t, \lambda)] \tag{11.3}$$

with M real components.

When one has an M-dimensional, real stochastic process whose components are given by Eq. (11.3), one can form M^2 real covariance functions defined by

$$\langle x_j(t, \lambda)\, x_k(t + \tau, \lambda) \rangle \ . \tag{11.4}$$

It is convenient to think of these M^2 quantities as the elements of an $M \times M$ matrix which we shall denote the covariance matrix. If the process is stationary, the covariance functions depend only on τ so one can define the correlation matrix as the matrix whose elements are the correlation functions defined by

$$C_{jk}(\tau) = \langle x_j(t, \lambda)\, x_k(t + \tau, \lambda) \rangle \ . \tag{11.5}$$

[1] The index superscript (i) has been replaced for convenience by the index subscript i. This should cause no confusion with the earlier use of subscript i for a time sample.

One sees readily that

$$C_{jk}(-\tau) = C_{kj}(+\tau) \quad . \tag{11.6}$$

If, in addition the process is ergodic, one has

$$C_{jk}(\tau) = \lim_{T \to \infty} \frac{1}{T} \int_{-T/2}^{+T/2} x_j(t, \lambda)\, x_k(t + \tau,\lambda)\, dt \quad . \tag{11.7}$$

The limit on the right of this equation will be called the time correlation function.

Since the components $x_i(t, \lambda)$ are real, the following inequality is true for all real a,

$$[x_j(t, \lambda) + a x_k(t + \tau,\lambda)]^2 \geqslant 0 \quad .$$

Upon expanding the square and taking ensemble averages one finds

$$a^2 \langle x_k^2(t + \tau,\lambda) \rangle + 2a \langle x_j(t, \lambda)\, x_k(t + \tau,\lambda) \rangle + \langle x_j^2(t, \lambda) \rangle \geqslant 0 \quad .$$

This inequality must be valid for all real a so the discriminant must never be greater than zero. Hence, one has

$$\langle x_j(t, \lambda)\, x_k(t + \tau,\lambda) \rangle^2 \leqslant \langle x_j^2(t, \lambda) \rangle \langle x_k^2(t + \tau,\lambda) \rangle \quad . \tag{11.8}$$

If the process is stationary, the ensemble averages can be replaced with the correlation functions as defined by Eq. (11.5). Hence, one has

$$C_{jk}^2(\tau) \leqslant C_{jj}(0)\, C_{kk}(0)$$

or

$$\frac{|C_{jk}(\tau)|}{\sqrt{C_{jj}(0)\, C_{kk}(0)}} \leqslant 1 \tag{11.9}$$

as a fundamental inequality for the elements of the matrix (C_{jk}). Equation (11.8) is an equation for ensemble averages that is the analog of Schwartz's inequality. Equation (11.9) contains Eq. (3.20) as a special case for $j = k$.

11.3 Power Spectra

One would like to assume that the M^2 correlation functions $C_{jk}(\tau)$ have Fourier transforms in the same sense that the correlation function $C(\tau)$ of a single component process has a Fourier transform as in Eqs. (4.7) and (4.8). The existence and the properties of these Fourier transforms are demonstrated in an important paper by Cramér (1940). Cramér establishes the necessary and sufficient conditions for the existence of distribution functions which can be interpreted as integrated power densities and which constitute the Fourier-Stieltjes transform.

If these distribution functions are absolutely continuous, there exist functions $\hat{C}_{jk}(f)$ which are the conventional Fourier transforms of the $C_{jk}(\tau)$. It is not unduly restrictive to assume that for the class of noises and signals considered in this book there exist Fourier transforms of the correlation functions so that one may always write

$$C_{jk}(t) = \int_{-\infty}^{+\infty} \hat{C}_{jk}(f)\, e^{+i2\pi ft}\, df \tag{11.10}$$

$$\hat{C}_{jk}(f) = \int_{-\infty}^{+\infty} C_{jk}(t)\, e^{-i2\pi ft}\, dt \ . \tag{11.11}$$

As long as one restricts the discussion to real functions $x_i(t, \lambda)$, the functions $C_{jk}(\tau)$ are real, and one must have

$$\hat{C}_{jk}(-f) = \hat{C}_{jk}{}^*(f) \ . \tag{11.12}$$

Since the functions $C_{jk}(\tau)$ are real, it is easy to show with the aid of Eqs. (11.6) and (11.11) that

$$\hat{C}_{jk}(f) = \hat{C}_{kj}{}^*(f) \tag{11.13}$$

and, consequently, that

$$\hat{C}_{jk}(-f) = \hat{C}_{kj}(f) \ . \tag{11.14}$$

The Fourier transform $\hat{C}_{jj}(f)$ of the autocovariance function $C_{jj}(\tau)$ for one component is identical with the function $W(f)$ defined in Eq. (4.8) and denoted the "power spectrum" of the stochastic process $x_j(t, \lambda)$. This notation will be generalized and the functions $\hat{C}_{jk}(f)$ will be called the "cross power spectra." The convenient notation $W(f)$ used for processes with only one component will be given up for the sake of uniform notation. The physical meaning of the functions $\hat{C}_{jk}(f)$ sometimes puzzles the student. It is a measure of the power that is common between the two stochastic series. Two physical interpretations will be given.

As the first example suppose that three independent, stationary noise sources are connected with summing resistors as indicated in Fig. 11.1. Suppose that each noise function $n_i(t)$ has a mean of zero and a root-mean-square value of σ. Suppose further, as indicated in Fig. 11.1, that these outputs are combined in a linear manner to give two signals $e_1(t)$ and $e_2(t)$ defined by

$$e_1(t) = an_1(t) + bn_2(t) \ , \ a^2 + b^2 = 1 \ ,$$

$$e_2(t) = cn_2(t) + dn_3(t) \ , \ c^2 + d^2 = 1 \ .$$

If we assume that the three sources are independent, and stationary, a moment's calculation shows that

$$\langle e_1{}^2(t) \rangle = a^2 \langle n_1{}^2(t) + 2ab \langle n_1(t)\, n_2(t) \rangle$$

$$+ \ b^2 \langle n_2{}^2(t) \rangle$$

$$= a^2\sigma^2 + b^2\sigma^2 = \sigma^2 \ .$$

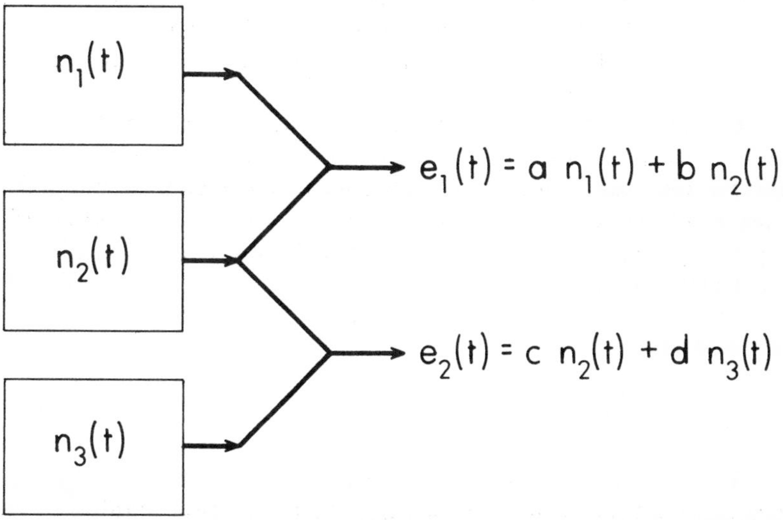

Figure 11.1–The formation of two noise signals, $e_1(t)$ and $e_2(t)$ from three independent noise sources.

This sequence of steps follows since $n_1(t)$ and $n_2(t)$ are independent and each has a mean value of zero. Similarly one can show that $\langle e_2{}^2(t) \rangle = \sigma^2$.

The crosscovariance function can be computed from the following ensemble averages:

$$\begin{aligned}\langle e_1(t)\, e_2(t+\tau) \rangle &= ac \langle n_1(t)\, n_2(t+\tau) \rangle \\ &\quad + ad \langle n_1(t)\, n_3(t+\tau) \rangle \\ &\quad + bc \langle n_2(t)\, n_2(t+\tau) \rangle \\ &\quad + bd \langle n_2(t)\, n_3(t+\tau) \rangle \\ &= bc \langle n_2(t)\, n_2(t+\tau) \rangle \ .\end{aligned}$$

The last equation follows from the independence of the three noise sources $n_i(t)$. The last member on the right is a function of τ only since $n_2(t)$ is stationary. Therefore, the function on the left is also a function of τ only. Hence, one obtains the crosscorrelation function

$$c_{12}(\tau) = \langle e_1(t)\, e_2(t+\tau) \rangle = bc\ C_{22}(\tau) \ .$$

Thus the crosscorrelation function depends only on the nature of the noise source $n_2(t)$ that is common to $e_1(t)$ and $e_2(t)$.

Since $|b| \leqslant 1$ and $|c| \leqslant 1$, one has $|C_{12}(\tau)| \leqslant |C_{22}(\tau)| \leqslant |C_{22}(0)| = \sigma^2$. The second step follows from Eq. (11.9) for a single noise.

The second illustration of the interpretation of cross-power density will be given at the end of Sec. 11.4

Two important properties of the power spectral functions $\hat{C}_{jk}(f)$ are proved by Cramér (1940). These results will be stated for future reference for the special case of absolutely continuous power spectra. Although the components $x_k(t, \lambda)$ of the M-dimensional process have been assumed real, the power spectral functions $\hat{C}_{jk}(f)$ will be complex when $j \neq k$. Nonetheless, Eq. (11.13) insures that the quadratic form

$$\sum_{j,k=1}^{M} \hat{C}_{jk}(f)\, z_j z_k{}^* \tag{11.15}$$

is real for all sets of complex numbers $\{z_j\}$. Cramér proves that this is a nonnegative Hermite form for all values f. In the case that $M = 2$, this result requires that

$$|\hat{C}_{12}(f)|^2 \leqslant \hat{C}_{11}(f)\,\hat{C}_{22}(f) \tag{11.16}$$

for all f.

11.4 The Effect of Filters on Multidimensional Processes

Suppose that each of the M time series of Eq. (11.3) is passed through a filter whose impulse response is $Y_i(t)$, $i = 1, 2, \ldots, M$. As mentioned in Sec. 2.2, $Y_i(t) \equiv 0$, $t < 0$, but it may contain a term involving $\delta(t)$. The output of each filter is a new time series $y_i(t, \lambda)$ related to $x_i(t, \lambda)$ by, see Eq. (2.15)

$$y_i(t, \lambda) = \int_{0-}^{\infty} x_i(t-\tau,\lambda)\, Y_i(\tau)\, d\tau \ . \tag{11.17}$$

The evaluation of the correlation function

$$D_{jk}(\tau) = \langle y_j(t, \lambda)\, y_k(t+\tau, \lambda) \rangle \tag{11.18}$$

is given in Appendix 11.1 for the special case that the set of functions $\{x_i(t, \lambda)\}$ are stationary in the wide sense. There it is shown that

$$D_{jk}(\tau) = \int_{-\infty}^{+\infty} \hat{C}_{jk}(f)\, \hat{Y}_j^*(f)\, \hat{Y}_k(f)\, e^{+i2\pi f\tau}\, df \tag{11.19}$$

and

$$\hat{D}_{jk}(f) = \hat{C}_{jk}(f)\, \hat{Y}_j^*(f)\, \hat{Y}_k(f) \ . \tag{11.20}$$

One might note for future reference that $\hat{D}_{jj}(f)$ is real and that

$$\hat{D}_{jk}(-f) = \hat{D}_{jk}^*(f) \ . \tag{11.21}$$

We can now return to the illustration of the physical interpretation of $C_{jk}(\tau)$ by supposing that each of the filter responses is zero everywhere except in two small bands of width W centered about $+f_o$ and $-f_o$. The filter response is assumed to be unity in these small bands. This ideal filter cannot be realized exactly, but it can be approximated arbitrarily closely. It is supposed further that W is so small that $\hat{C}_{jk}(f)$ is essentially constant and equal to $\hat{C}_{jk}(\pm f_o)$ over the pass-bands of the filters. For this ideal filter Eq. (11.19) becomes

$$D_{jk}(\tau) = W\left\{\hat{C}_{jk}(-f_o)\, e^{-i2\pi f_o\tau} + \hat{C}_{jk}(f_o)\, e^{+i2\pi f_o\tau}\right\} \tag{11.22}$$

By virtue of Eq. (11.12) one may write

$$D_{jk}(\tau) = 2W \mid \hat{C}_{jk}(f_o) \mid \cos\left\{2\pi f_o \tau + \arg \hat{C}_{jk}(f_o)\right\} . \tag{11.23}$$

Alternately, one may take the Fourier transform of Eq. (11.22) to get

$$\hat{D}_{jk}(f) = W \hat{C}_{jk}(-f_o)\, \delta\,(f + f_o) + W \hat{C}_{jk}(f_o)\, \delta\,(f - f_o) . \tag{11.24}$$

One is now in a position to interpret the covariance function. If two noise signals are passed through identical, ideal narrow band-pass filters, the outputs will have a covariance function which is an undamped cosinusoid of amplitude $2\ W \mid \hat{C}_{jk}(f_o) \mid$ and phase-arg $\hat{C}_{jk}(f_o)$. Alternately, this covariance function will have an associated power spectrum which consists of two line spectra located at $\pm f_o$ and having complex amplitude equal to $W\ \hat{C}_{jk}(\pm f_o)$. These physical interpretations of the covariance function are given by Mermoz (1964).

It is understood, of course, that if the situation described in the last few paragraphs were carried out experimentally, the observed value for one trial may deviate from the ensemble average $2\ W \mid \hat{C}_{jk}(f_o) \mid$. This behavior is closely related to the conceptual experiment of passing a noise through an extremely narrow band-pass filter. The output will resemble a sinusoidal wave whose frequency is equal to that of the center of the pass-band. However, neither the amplitude nor the phase of the output are deterministic.

11.5 The Danger in Omitting the Ensemble Average

The reader will have noticed that in each of the examples utilized to discuss the concept of the covariance function the ensemble average was carried out. This is an essential feature the omission of which can lead to errors. The danger arises because one often has only a single sample of the process and cannot perform an ensemble average. The following argument illustrates the nature of this error.

Suppose that one has a sample of finite length of each of two members of the multidimensional process of Eq. (11.3). One calculates the time cross-correlation function

$${}_TC_{jk}(\tau) = \frac{1}{T} \int_{-\infty}^{+\infty} x_{jT}(t)\, x_{kT}(t + \tau)\, dt \tag{11.25}$$

where the subscript T reminds the reader that only a finite sample of the data is available. One can apply Parseval's formula, Eq. (2.6) to the right member to give

$$_TC_{jk}(\tau) = \frac{1}{T} \int_{-\infty}^{+\infty} \hat{x}_{jT}^*(f)\, \hat{y}_{kT}(f)\, e^{-i2\pi f\tau}\, df \ . \tag{11.26}$$

At this point one is tempted to move the factor $1/T$ inside the integral and to define

$$\frac{1}{T} \hat{x}_{jT}^*(f)\, \hat{y}_{kT}(f) \tag{11.27}$$

as the cross-power density associated with the cross-correlation function $_TC_{jk}(\tau)$. This procedure would give a formula analogous to Eq. (4.7) for a single component when one takes the limit as $T \to \infty$. This argument is in error since it does not introduce the ensemble average. In order to obtain correct results one must take the ensemble average of Eq. (11.26) and, by the same token, define the cross-power density as the ensemble average of the expression (11.27). The reader is referred to Middleton (1960, pp. 139-141) for further details.

11.6 Suggestions for Further Reading

The reader is referred to pp. 184-193 of Middleton (1960) for further discussions of the crosscorrelation power spectra and the effect of filters.

The problem of practical computation of cross-power spectra and the accuracy of these calculations is considered by Goodman (1957). The necessary numerical tables are presented by Alexander and Vok (1963). Numerous papers on multidimensional time series were presented at a Symposium edited by Rosenblatt (1963).

APPENDIX 11.1

Evaluation of Equation (11.8)

By virtue of the definition, Eq. (11.18) and Eq. (11.17), one has

$$D_{jk}(\tau) = \left\langle \int_{0-}^{+\infty} x_j(t-\tau_1, \lambda)\, Y_j(\tau_1)\, d\tau_1 \int_{0-}^{+\infty} x_k(t+\tau-\tau_2, \lambda) \cdot Y_k(\tau_2)\, d\tau_2 \right\rangle$$

$$= \int_{0-}^{\infty} Y_j(\tau_1)\, d\tau_1 \int_{0-}^{\infty} \langle x_j(t-\tau_1, \lambda)\, x_k(t+\tau-\tau_2, \lambda) \rangle \cdot Y_k(\tau_2)\, d\tau_2 \,. \qquad \text{(A11.1)}$$

Now, if the set of functions $\{x_j(t, \lambda)\}$ are stationary in the wide sense, one has

$$\langle x_j(t-\tau_1, \lambda)\, x_k(t+\tau-\tau_2, \lambda) \rangle = C_{jk}(\tau+\tau_1-\tau_2) \;,$$

so that Eq. (A11.1) becomes

$$D_{jk}(\tau) = \int_{0-}^{\infty}\int_{0-}^{\infty} Y_j(\tau_1)\, Y_k(\tau_2)\, C_{jk}(\tau+\tau_1-\tau_2)\, d\tau_1\, d\tau_2 \;.$$

Now

$$C_{jk}(\tau+\tau_1-\tau_2) = \int_{-\infty}^{+\infty} \hat{C}_{jk}(f)\, e^{+i2\pi f(\tau+\tau_1-\tau_2)}\, df \;,$$

so that

$$D_{jk}(\tau) = \int_{-\infty}^{+\infty} \hat{C}_{jk}(f)\, e^{+i2\pi f\tau}\, df \int_{0-}^{\infty} Y_j(\tau_1)\, e^{+i2\pi f\tau_1}\, d\tau_1 \;\cdot$$

$$\int_{0-}^{\infty} Y_k(\tau_2)\, e^{-i2\pi f\tau_2}\, d\tau_2 \ .$$

It was pointed out earlier that if the networks are physically realizable, the functions $Y_j(\tau)$ and $Y_j(\tau)$ vanish identically for $\tau < 0$ so the integrals may be extended to $-\infty$ without changing their values. In this case they become Fourier transforms of $\hat{Y}_j{}^*(f)$ and $\hat{Y}_k(f)$, respectively. Hence

$$D_{jk}(\tau) = \int_{-\infty}^{+\infty} \hat{C}_{jk}(f)\, \hat{Y}_j{}^*(f)\, \hat{Y}_k(f)\, e^{+i2\pi f\tau}\, df \ .$$

Finally one can take the transforms of both sides to give

$$\hat{D}_{jk}(f) = \hat{Y}_j{}^*(f)\, \hat{C}_{jk}(f)\, \hat{Y}_k(f) \ . \tag{A11.2}$$

It is left as an exercise for the reader to express this equation as a matrix equation.

CHAPTER XII

Further Analyses of Three-Dimensional Arrays

12.1 Introduction

In the analyses presented in Chapter X it was assumed for simplicity that the noise at each hydrophone is independent of the noise at the other hydrophones. This assumption was made in order to simplify the analysis. The discussion in Chapter XI prepares the reader for an extension to the important case of noise fields which produce a correlation between the outputs of the various hydrophones.

An analysis for the standard detector discussed in Sec. 10.3 has been given by Rudnick (1960) for slightly different assumptions from those introduced in Sec. 10.3. The major difference is that Rudnick considers the noise signals at the hydrophones to be correlated so that he must introduce the correlation matrix whose elements are given by Eq. (11.4). On the other hand, he assumes that the total noise power at each hydrophone is the same. Although the analysis in Rudnick's paper is highly condensed, it is worth the effort required to read it. He carried out a detailed analysis of a three-dimensional array of 32 hydrophones and shows the deterioration caused by sampling the time series and by clipping.

It seems more desirable to go on to the analysis of the circuits shown in Figs. 10.1(*d*) and 10.1(*e*) rather than to reproduce the analysis of Rudnick.

12.2 Maximizing the Signal-to-Noise Ratio for an Array of Hydrophones

Mermoz (1964) has carried out the analysis of the filters that maximize the signal-to-noise ratio for an additive array of M hydrophones as illustrated in Fig. 10.1(*d*) or Fig. 12.1. He shows that significant improvements may be obtained under some conditions when allowance is made for the correlation between the noises at different elements. The following discussion follows Mermoz rather closely.

It is not necessary to assume as before that the signals arrive as a plane wave so that the signals received at the different hydrophones are the same except for a displacement in time as stated in Eqs. (10.1) and (10.2). Instead it will be assumed in the general analysis that a different known signal arrives at each hydrophone. Later the analysis will be specialized to signals of identical shapes. The output of each hydrophone is subjected to a filter whose frequency response is $\hat{Y}_i(f)$ as illustrated in Fig. 12.1.

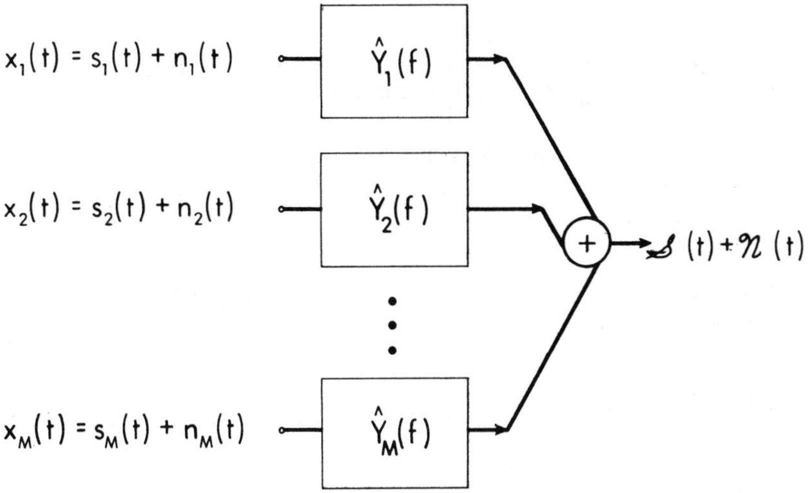

Figure 12.1–A set of matched filters for a three-dimensional array of M hydrophones.

It is assumed that in the absence of noise the output of the summer is

$$\mathcal{S}(t) = \sum_{i=1}^{M} \int_{0-}^{\infty} Y_i(\tau)\, s_i(t-\tau)\, d\tau \tag{12.1}$$

while in the absence of the signal the output is

$$\mathcal{N}(t) = \sum_{i=1}^{M} \int_{0-}^{\infty} Y_i(\tau)\, n_i(t-\tau)\, d\tau \ . \tag{12.2}$$

Since the system is linear, the output in general is $\mathcal{S}(t) + \mathcal{N}(t)$ which is the function $y(t)$ of Fig. 10.1(d). One is in a position now to formulate explicitly the problem that will be solved. As in Sec. 7.2, let S be the maximum value of $|\mathcal{S}(t)|$ considered as a function of time and let N^2 be the mean square value of $\mathcal{N}(t)$. What are the properties of the M filters $\hat{Y}_i(f)$ that will yield the maximum value of S/N?

The quantity N^2 can be computed readily by processes which are by now thoroughly familiar to the reader. One has

$$N^2 = \langle \mathcal{N}^2(t) \rangle = \left\langle \sum_{j=1}^{M} \sum_{k=1}^{M} \int_{0-}^{\infty} \int_{0-}^{\infty} n_j(t-\tau_1)\, n_k(t-\tau_2) \right.$$

$$Y_j(\tau_1)\, Y_k(\tau_2)\, d\tau_1\, d\tau_2 \Big\rangle \ .$$

It is assumed that the order of the ensemble average and of the summation and integration can be interchanged to give

$$N^2 = \sum_{j=1}^{M} \sum_{k=1}^{M} \int_{0-}^{\infty} \int_{0-}^{\infty} \langle n_j(t-\tau_1)\, n_k(t-\tau_2) \rangle\, Y_j(\tau_1)\, Y_k(\tau_2)\, d\tau_1\, d\tau_2 .$$

If the noise process detected by the M hydrophones is stationary, one can utilize Eq. (11.5) to write

$$N^2 = \sum_{j=1}^{M} \sum_{k=1}^{M} \int_{0-}^{\infty} \int_{0-}^{\infty} C_{jk}(\tau_1 - \tau_2)\, Y_j(\tau_1)\, Y_k(\tau_2)\, d\tau_1\, d\tau_2 \ . \quad (12.3)$$

12.3 A Digression on the Properties of the Noise Output

Equation (12.3) is of sufficient interest to justify a few comments before continuing the analysis. The quantity on the left is positive by definition so the quantity on the right must be positive for a large class of functions $Y_j(\tau)$. This imposes a serious restriction on the set of functions $\{ C_{jk}(\tau) \}$ that form the correlation matrix. It will be remembered that two conditions were imposed on the functions $\hat{Y}_j(f)$ in order that the filters be physically realizable. The first of these was that Real $\hat{Y}_j(f)$ be an even function of f while $Im\ \hat{Y}_j(f)$ be an odd function of f. This condition is fundamental, because if it were not satisfied, the output of the filter would not necessarily be real when the output is real.

The second condition that was placed on the functions $\hat{Y}_j(f)$ in order that the filters be physically realizable is less restrictive in that it can be weakened for the present purpose. This condition is that the Fourier transform, $Y_j(\tau)$, of $\hat{Y}_j(f)$ ($j = 1, 2, \ldots, M$) must be identically zero for $\tau < 0$. This condition is necessary for filters operating in "real" time in order to have a logical sequence of cause and effect. If $Y_i(\tau)$ were nonzero for a negative value of τ, an output signal would result before the input is applied. However, there are many situations in which one does not filter in real time. For example, if the data have been recorded completely before the filtering operation is carried out, there is no reason why $Y_j(\tau)$ should vanish for negative τ. In this case one may extend the lower limits of the integrals to $-\infty$.

Hence, one has the following important conclusion. A set of M^2 real functions $\left\{C_{jk}(\tau)\right\}$, j, $k = 1, 2, \ldots, M$, can serve as a correlation matrix only if the quantities

$$\sum_{j=1}^{M} \sum_{k=1}^{M} \int_{-\infty}^{+\infty} \int_{-\infty}^{+\infty} C_{jk}(\tau_1 - \tau_2)\, Y_j(\tau_1)\, Y_k(\tau_2)\, d\tau_1\, d\tau_2$$

are nonnegative for all functions $Y_j(\tau)$ which have Fourier transforms and for which

$$Y_j(-\tau) = Y_j^*(\tau) \; . \tag{12.4}$$

The symmetry of this result would have been more striking if one had considered complex noises so that $C_{jk}(\tau_1 - \tau_2)$ were a complex function.

It is possible to rearrange Eq. (12.3) so as to determine the power spectrum associated with the noise $\mathfrak{N}(t)$. The order of the integrations in Eq. (12.3) may be changed to give

$$N^2 = \sum_{j=1}^{M} \sum_{k=1}^{M} \int_{0-}^{\infty} Y_j(\tau_1) \left[\int_{0-}^{\infty} Y_k(\tau_2)\, C_{jk}(\tau_1 - \tau_2)\, d\tau_2 \right] d\tau_1 \; . \quad \ldots \tag{12.5}$$

The quantity in square brackets is the convolution of $C_{jk}(\cdot)$ and $Y_k(\cdot)$. The integral can be extended formally to $-\infty$ if one wishes, since for the class of realizable filters being considered, $Y_k(\tau_2)$ vanishes for negative τ_2. By virtue of formula number (3) of Appendix 2.1, one has

$$\int_{0-}^{\infty} Y_k(\tau_2)\, C_{jk}(\tau_1 - \tau_2)\, d\tau_2 = \int_{-\infty}^{+\infty} \hat{C}_{jk}(f)\, \hat{Y}_k(f)\, e^{+i2\pi f \tau_1} df \; . \quad \ldots \tag{12.6}$$

Hence, after the order of integration is again changed, one has

$$N^2 = \sum_{j=1}^{M} \sum_{k=1}^{M} \int_{-\infty}^{+\infty} \hat{C}_{jk}(f)\, \hat{Y}_k(f) \left[\int_{0-}^{\infty} Y_j(\tau_1)\, e^{+i2\pi f \tau_1} d\tau_1 \right] df \; .$$

The term in the square brackets is the complex conjugate of $\hat{Y}_j(f)$, so one has

$$N^2 = \int_{-\infty}^{+\infty} \left[\sum_{j=1}^{M} \sum_{k=1}^{M} \hat{C}_{jk}(f)\, \hat{Y}_j^*(f)\, \hat{Y}_k(f) \right] df \; . \tag{12.7}$$

Equation (11.13) shows that when the terms of the double sum are grouped in pairs

$$\hat{C}_{jk}(f)\, Y_j^*(f)\, Y_k(f) + \hat{C}_{kj}(f)\, Y_k^*(f)\, Y_j(f) \ ,$$

the sum is real. There remains only the proof that the double summation in Eq. (12.7) is nonnegative before one can conclude that

$$\hat{P}_\Sigma(f) = \sum_{j=1}^{M} \sum_{k=1}^{M} \hat{C}_{jk}(f)\, \hat{Y}_j^*(f)\, \hat{Y}_k(f) \tag{12.8}$$

is the power density of the noise $\mathfrak{N}(t)$. It was remarked immediately after Eq. (11.15) that the proof of this assertion is given by Cramér (1940). Alternately, one may use Eqs. (11.15)–(11.18) to make a direct calculation of the power spectrum of the output of the summer. This calculation leads directly to the result that $\hat{P}_\Sigma(f)$ is the power density of $\mathfrak{N}(t)$ and, hence, to the conclusion that $\hat{P}_\Sigma(f)$ is nonnegative.

It should be remembered that the results of this section are valid for any set of filters whether or not the filter responses maximize the output signal-to-noise ratio.

12.4 The Filters that Maximize the Signal-to-Noise Ratio

The analysis developed in the following section is based on a paper by Mermoz, and it represents a generalization to M dimensions of the procedure followed in Section 7.6. In the solution to the one dimensional problem, the optimum filter described by Eq. (7.4) contained a factor exp($-2\pi fT$) which corresponds to a time delay in the input signal of amount T. Since T may be negative, one is at liberty to select an arbitrary time t_o and ask what filter yields a maximum value for $|S(t_o)|/N$. One may rest assured that this is not a restriction, since if the output were larger at another time t', the arbitrary time delay T contained in the signal would have shifted the larger output from t' to t_o. Further, if the response of each filter in Fig. 12.1 were changed by a common real factor, there would be no change in the ratio $|S(t_o)|/N$. Hence, one may formulate the optimization problem by seeking those filters which minimize N subject to the condition that $S(t_o)$ remain constant. This latter condition is essential for otherwise $Y_i \equiv 0$ would be the solution of the minimization problem.

Consequently, one seeks a set of functions $\{Y_j(\tau)\}$, $0- \leqslant \tau < \infty$, $j = 1, 2, \ldots, M$, such that

$$N^2 = \sum_{j=1}^{M} \sum_{k=1}^{M} \int_{0-}^{\infty} \int_{0-}^{\infty} C_{jk}(\tau_1 - \tau_2)\, Y_j(\tau_1)\, Y_k(\tau_2)\, d\tau_1\, d\tau_2 \tag{12.9}$$

is a minimum subject to the condition that

$$\mathcal{S}(t_o) = \sum_{j=1}^{M} \int_{0-}^{\infty} Y_j(\tau)\, s_j(t_o-\tau)\, d\tau \tag{12.10}$$

is constant.

It is evident that the notation and, hence, the manipulations can be simplified by introducing matrices. Let $\mathfrak{s}$, $\mathcal{Y}$ and $\mathcal{Z}$ denote one column matrices defined by

$$\mathfrak{s} = \begin{pmatrix} s_1 \\ s_2 \\ \cdot \\ \cdot \\ \cdot \\ s_M \end{pmatrix}, \quad \mathcal{Y} = \begin{pmatrix} Y_1 \\ Y_2 \\ \cdot \\ \cdot \\ \cdot \\ Y_M \end{pmatrix}, \quad \mathcal{Z} = \begin{pmatrix} Z_1 \\ Z_2 \\ \cdot \\ \cdot \\ \cdot \\ Z_M \end{pmatrix}, \tag{12.11}$$

and let $\tilde{\mathfrak{s}}$, $\tilde{\mathcal{Y}}$ and $\tilde{\mathcal{Z}}$ be the one rowed, transposed matrices, respectively. Also let

$$\mathcal{C} = \begin{pmatrix} C_{11} & C_{12} & \dots & C_{1M} \\ C_{21} & C_{22} & \dots & C_{2M} \\ \cdot & \cdot & \cdot & \cdot \\ C_{M1} & C_{M2} & \dots & C_{MM} \end{pmatrix} \tag{12.12}$$

be the matrix of the correlation functions. The problem will be rephrased in this simpler notation. One seeks a matrix $\mathcal{Y}$ such that

$$N^2 = \int_{0-}^{\infty} \int_{0-}^{\infty} \tilde{\mathcal{Y}}(\tau_1)\mathcal{C}(\tau_1-\tau_2)\mathcal{Y}(\tau_2)\, d\tau_1\, d\tau_2 \tag{12.13}$$

is a minimum subject to the condition that

$$\mathcal{S}(t_o) = \int_{0-}^{\infty} \tilde{\mathcal{Y}}(\tau)\mathfrak{s}(t_o-\tau)\, d\tau \tag{12.14}$$

is constant.

If one has a solution $\mathcal{Y}(\tau)$ of this problem, it is evident that a small perturbation of the solution of the form

$$\mathcal{Y}(\tau) \rightarrow \mathcal{Y}(\tau) + a\mathcal{Z}(\tau), \tag{12.15}$$

where a is a scalar quantity, must not change the value of N^2. Of course, the new matrix $\mathcal{Z}(\cdot)$ is subject to the restriction that

$$\int_{0-}^{\infty} \tilde{\mathcal{Z}}(\tau)\mathfrak{s}(t_0-\tau)\, d\tau = 0 \ . \tag{12.16}$$

This equation asserts, in a manner of speaking, that the matrix functions $\mathfrak{s}(t_0\text{-}\tau)$ and $\mathcal{Z}(\tau)$ are orthogonal.

If one substitutes Eq. (12.15) into Eq. (12.13) and evaluates the condition

$$\left.\frac{\partial N^2}{\partial a}\right|_{a=0} = 0 \ ,$$

which is a necessary condition if N^2 has a minimum, one finds that the equation

$$\int_{0-}^{\infty}\int_{0-}^{\infty} [\tilde{\mathcal{Y}}(\tau_1)\mathcal{C}(\tau_1-\tau_2)\mathcal{Z}(\tau_2) + \tilde{\mathcal{Z}}(\tau_1)\mathcal{C}(\tau_1-\tau_2)\mathcal{Y}(\tau_2)]\ d\tau_1\ d\tau_2 = 0 \quad \ldots \tag{12.17}$$

must be satisfied.

The second term in the integrand of Eq. (12.17) is a 1X1 matrix and is, therefore, equal to its own transpose. Further, the transpose of a matrix product is the product of the transposes written in reverse order. Hence one has

$$\tilde{\mathcal{Z}}(\tau_1)\mathcal{C}(\tau_1-\tau_2)\mathcal{Y}(\tau_2) = \widetilde{\tilde{\mathcal{Z}}(\tau_1)\mathcal{C}(\tau_1-\tau_2)\mathcal{Y}(\tau_2)} = \tilde{\mathcal{Y}}(\tau_2)\tilde{\mathcal{C}}(\tau_1-\tau_2)\mathcal{Z}(\tau_1) \ .$$

One can make the interchange of the integration variables τ_1 and τ_2 without changing the value of the integral. This change leads to $\tilde{\mathcal{C}}(\tau_2-\tau_1)$ for the central factor, but by virtue of Eq. (11.6) one has

$$\tilde{\mathcal{C}}(\tau_2-\tau_1) = \mathcal{C}(\tau_1-\tau_2) \ . \tag{12.18}$$

One sees that the integral of the second term in Eq. (12.17) is the same as the integral of the first term.

Hence, the necessary condition on $\mathcal{Y}$ and $\mathcal{Z}$ is

$$\int_{0-}^{\infty}\int_{0-}^{\infty} \tilde{\mathcal{Y}}(\tau_1)\mathcal{C}(\tau_1-\tau_2)\mathcal{Z}(\tau_2)\, d\tau_1\, d\tau_2 = 0 \ . \tag{12.19}$$

This equation can be made formally more simple by introducing a new matrix function $\mathcal{X}(\tau_2)$ defined by

$$\tilde{\mathcal{X}}(\tau_2) = \int_{0-}^{\infty} \tilde{\mathcal{Y}}(\tau_1)\mathcal{C}(\tau_1-\tau_2)\,d\tau_1 \ , \tag{12.20}$$

so that Eq. (12.19) becomes

$$\int_{0-}^{\infty} \tilde{\mathcal{X}}(\tau_2)\mathcal{Z}(\tau_2)\,d\tau_2 = 0 \ . \tag{12.21}$$

At the same time one has the condition, Eq. (12.16)

$$\int_{0-}^{\infty} \tilde{\mathcal{Z}}(\tau)\,\mathscr{s}(t_o-\tau)\,d\tau = 0 \ . \tag{12.16}$$

These two equations are consistent when one assumes

$$\mathcal{X}(\tau) = K\mathscr{s}(t_o-\tau) \ . \tag{12.22}$$

The reader should notice the similarity between Eqs. (12.14) and (12.12) on the one hand, and Eq. (7.11) on the other. The presence of a noise matrix has led one to replace the matrix of filter responses $\mathcal{Y}(\cdot)$ by a new matrix $\mathcal{X}(\cdot)$ but the elements of the new matrix are proportional to $s_i(\cdot)$ with the *time scale reversed*. This same behavior was found in the one dimensional case.

A solution of Eq. (12.16) can be obtained as follows. Since it has been assumed that the wave forms $s_i(\cdot)$ are known, one can select two times τ_a and τ_b such that $\tau_a \neq \tau_b$, $s_i(t_o-\tau_a) \neq 0$, and $s_i(t_o-\tau_b) \neq 0$, $i = 1, 2, \ldots, M$ but which are otherwise arbitrary. The functions $Z_i(\tau)$ which are the elements of $\mathcal{Z}$ will be defined as

$$Z_i(\tau) = \frac{\delta(\tau-\tau_a)}{s_i(t_o-\tau_a)} - \frac{\delta(\tau-\tau_b)}{s_i(t_o-\tau_b)} \ . \tag{12.23}$$

It is readily seen that these functions satisfy Eq. (12.16). When they are substituted into Eq. (12.21), one finds that this equation is satisfied too when $\mathcal{X}(\tau)$ is defined by Eq. (12.22). Unfortunately, the goal of the analysis is not the matrix $\mathcal{X}(\tau)$ but the matrix $\mathcal{Y}(\tau)$

When the matrix $\mathcal{X}(\tau)$ is eliminated from Eqs. (12.20) and (12.22), one obtains the following integral equation for the unknown $\mathcal{Y}(\tau)$,

$$\int_{0-}^{\infty} \tilde{\mathcal{Y}}(\tau_1)\mathcal{C}(\tau_1-\tau_2)\,d\tau_1 = K\tilde{\mathfrak{s}}(t_0-\tau_2) \ . \tag{12.24}$$

Now, the elements of $\mathcal{Y}(\tau_1)$ are the impulsive responses of realizable filters so the lower limit of the integration can be extended to $-\infty$ without changing the value of the integral. Since the resulting integral is a convolution, one realizes that the integral equation can be changed to an algebraic equation by taking the Fourier transform of the equation. First, however, it is convenient to take the transpose of the equation and make use of Eq. (12.18). This gives

$$\int_{0-}^{\infty} \mathcal{C}(\tau_2-\tau_1)\mathcal{Y}(\tau_1)\,d\tau_1 = K\,\mathfrak{s}(t_0-\tau_2) \ , \tag{12.25}$$

the resulting Fourier transform of which is

$$\hat{\mathcal{C}}(f)\hat{\mathcal{Y}}(f) = K\,e^{-i2\pi f t_o}\,\hat{\mathfrak{s}}(-f)$$

$$= K\,e^{-i2\pi f t_o}\,\hat{\mathfrak{s}}^*(f) \ . \tag{12.26}$$

These new matrices are defined by setting their elements equal to the Fourier transforms of the elements of the corresponding matrices with time arguments. An obvious check on this analysis is to note that in the case $M = 1$, Eq. (12.26) reduces to Eq. (7.4) as it should.

As in the one-dimensional case, one is led to an arbitrary constant K in the filter responses. This means of course that one can increase the gain without limit and thereby increase the output signal to any desired value. Needless to say, however, the noise is amplified equally so there is no change in the signal-to-noise ratio. This point can be illustrated more formally as follows.

Let k be the maximum value of the signal, i.e., from Eq. (12.14)

$$k = \mathcal{S}(t_0) = \int_{0-}^{\infty} \tilde{\mathcal{Y}}(\tau_2)\,\mathfrak{s}(t_0-\tau_2)\,d\tau_2 . \tag{12.27}$$

Multiply this equation by K and utilize Eq. (12.25) to give

$$kK = \int_{0-}^{\infty}\int_{0-}^{\infty} \tilde{\mathcal{Y}}(\tau_2)\,\mathcal{C}(\tau_2-\tau_1)\,\mathcal{Y}(\tau_1)\,d\tau_1\,d\tau_2 \ .$$

When the simple change of variables $(\tau_1, \tau_2) \rightarrow (\tau_2, \tau_1)$ is introduced, the right member becomes N^2 by virtue of Eq. (12.13). By definition k is the maximum value of the signal so

$$\left(\frac{S}{N}\right)^2_{\text{Max}} = \frac{k^2}{N^2} = \frac{k}{K} \tag{12.28}$$

as stated above.

Although the complete solution of our problem is implicit in Eq. (12.26), it is desirable to solve this set of equations explicitly for $\hat{\mathcal{Y}}(f)$. If the matrix $\hat{\mathcal{C}}(f)$ has a nonvanishing determinant $\Delta(f)$, there exists an inverse matrix whose transpose is

$$\widetilde{\hat{\mathcal{C}}(f)^{-1}} = \left(\frac{M_{jk}(f)}{\Delta(f)}\right) \tag{12.29}$$

where $M_{jk}(f)$ is the cofactor of the element (j,k) in the determinant $\Delta(f)$.

If one foregoes the matrix notation, the solution of Eq. (12.26) may be written

$$\hat{Y}_k(f) = \frac{Ke^{-i2\pi f t_o}}{\Delta(f)} \sum_{j=1}^{M} M_{jk}(f)\ \hat{s}_j^*(f)\ . \tag{12.30}$$

This completes the formal solution for the design of the M filters when the shape of the signal and the noise matrix are known. It is left as an exercise for the reader to show that these filters satisfy the important conditions $\hat{Y}_k(-f) = \hat{Y}_k^*(f)$, $k = 1, 2, \ldots, M$.

It has already been assumed that $\Delta(f)$ does not vanish for real f. Since $\Delta(-f) = \Delta(f)$, one concludes from Eq. (12.30) that $\Delta(f)$ must not vanish for any complex value of f because otherwise the filter would yield an output before the input is applied.

12.5 Special Properties of the Output of the Optimum Filters

If one prefers to express Eq. (12.30) in matrix form, then as seen from Eq. (12.27), it is better to express the transpose of $\mathcal{Y}(f)$. Hence, using Eq. (12.29), one finds

$$\tilde{\hat{\mathcal{Y}}}(f) = Ke^{-i2\pi f t_o}\ \tilde{\hat{s}}^*(f)\ \widetilde{\hat{\mathcal{C}}\ (f)^{-1}}\ . \tag{12.31}$$

Suppose now that this equation is multiplied on the right by the matrix

$$\hat{\mathfrak{s}}(f)\, e^{+i2\pi f t_o}$$

and the resulting equation is integrated with respect to f from $-\infty$ to $+\infty$. The integral on the left is the matrix form of Eq. (12.10) so one has

$$\mathcal{S}(t_o) = K \int_{-\infty}^{+\infty} \tilde{\hat{\mathfrak{s}}}^*(f)\, \widetilde{\hat{\mathcal{C}}(f)^{-1}}\, \hat{\mathfrak{s}}(f)\, df \; . \tag{12.32}$$

The left member of this equation has already been defined in Eq. (12.27) as k and Eq. (12.28) shows that k/K is equal to $(S/N)^2$. Hence, one has the following compact form for the signal-to-noise ratio for the optimum detector.

$$\left(\frac{S}{N}\right)^2_{\text{Max}} = \int_{-\infty}^{+\infty} \hat{D}(f)\, df \; , \tag{12.33}$$

where

$$\hat{D}(f) = \tilde{\hat{\mathfrak{s}}}^*(f)\, \widetilde{\hat{\mathcal{C}}(f)^{-1}}\, \hat{\mathfrak{s}}(f) \; . \tag{12.34}$$

The function $\hat{D}(f)$ has an interesting and suggestive relationship to the spectrum of the output $\mathcal{S}(t)$ when the inputs to the optimum filters are the signals alone. Since $\mathcal{S}(t)$ is the sum of the outputs of the individual filters, the Fourier transform of the output is the sum of the Fourier transforms of the outputs of the individual filters. Hence,

$$\hat{\mathcal{S}}(f) = \tilde{\hat{\mathcal{Y}}}(f)\, \hat{\mathfrak{s}}(f) \; ,$$

but, by Eq. (12.31), one has

$$\hat{\mathcal{S}}(f) = K e^{-i2\pi f t_o}\, \tilde{\hat{\mathfrak{s}}}^*(f)\, \widetilde{\hat{\mathcal{C}}(f)^{-1}\, \hat{\mathfrak{s}}(f)} \; .$$

Introducing Eq. (12.34), one finds

$$\hat{\mathcal{S}}(f) = K e^{-i2\pi f t_o}\, \hat{D}(f) \; . \tag{12.35}$$

One notices that in the special case $K = 1$, $t_o = 0$, the spectrum of the output is $\hat{D}(f)$.

It has just been shown that when the set of M filter responses $\mathcal{Y}(\tau)$ has been designed to yield a maximum signal-to-noise ratio, the spectrum of the output when signals alone are present is related to the function $\hat{D}(f)$ by Eq. (12.35). It will now be shown that when noise only is present at the inputs, the spectrum of the output is proportional to $\hat{D}(f)$. Further if $K = 1$ and $t_o = 0$, the spectrum of the output when signals alone are present is *identical* to the spectrum of the output when noise only is present at the output. The result was encountered in the case of one channel, Sec. 7.4, and the explanation offered there is still applicable.

It was shown in Eq. (12.8) and the following discussion that when correlated noise inputs are applied to a set of M filters the sum of the M outputs has a power $\hat{P}_\Sigma(f)$ which may be expressed in matrix notation as

$$\hat{P}_\Sigma(f) = \tilde{\hat{\mathcal{Y}}}^*(f)\hat{\mathcal{C}}(f)\hat{\mathcal{Y}}(f) \ . \qquad (12.36)$$

Although this result is valid for any filter responses, the immediate interest is in the set of filter responses given by Eq. (12.31). When Eq. (12.31) is substituted into Eq. (12.36), one finds

$$\hat{P}_\Sigma(f) = K^2\,\tilde{s}(f)\,\widetilde{\hat{\mathcal{C}}^*(f)^{-1}}\,\hat{\mathcal{C}}(f)\hat{\mathcal{C}}(f)^{-1}\,\hat{s}^*(f) \ .$$

Now $\hat{\mathcal{C}}\hat{\mathcal{C}}^{-1}$ is the identity matrix and may be omitted. Further, $\hat{P}_\Sigma$ is real so one may take the complex conjugate without changing the value. Thus

$$\hat{P}_\Sigma(f) = K^2\,\tilde{s}^*(f)\,\widetilde{\hat{\mathcal{C}}(f)^{-1}}\,\tilde{\hat{s}}(f) \ ,$$

or, using Eq. (12.34),

$$\hat{P}_\Sigma(f) = K^2\,\hat{D}(f) \qquad (12.37)$$

as stated above.

One is now in a position to discuss the magnitude and sign of the output $\mathcal{S}(t_o)$ when the input is signal alone. From Eq. (12.35) one can show readily that

$$\mathcal{S}(t) = \int_{-\infty}^{+\infty} \hat{\mathcal{S}}(f)\,e^{+i2\pi ft}\,df = K\int_{-\infty}^{+\infty} \hat{D}(f)\,e^{i2\pi f(t-t_o)}\,df, \qquad (12.38)$$

and

$$\mathcal{S}(t_o) = K\int_{-\infty}^{+\infty} \hat{D}(f)\,df \ . \qquad (12.39)$$

Now $\hat{D}(f)$ is a nonnegative function so the sign of $\mathcal{S}(t_o)$ is the same as that of K which may be considered positive without loss of generality. If one takes the absolute value of Eq. (12.38), one has

$$|\mathcal{S}(t)| \leq K \int_{-\infty}^{+\infty} |\hat{D}(f)|\, df = K \int_{-\infty}^{+\infty} \hat{D}(f)\, df = \mathcal{S}(t_o) \; . \tag{12.40}$$

The second step is valid since $\hat{D}(f)$ is nonnegative as shown by Eq. (12.37). One sees that there is no value of the time for which $\mathcal{S}(t)$ is larger in magnitude than $\mathcal{S}(t_o)$. Further $\mathcal{S}(t)$ is symmetric about the point $t = t_o$ since $\hat{D}(f)$ is an even function of f. This symmetry property is also true in the case of a single channel.

Equation (12.29) and many that follow it have a factor $\Delta(f)$ in the denominator. This was justified by the assumption that $\Delta(f)$ does not vanish, but it would be wise to inquire more closely into the validity of this assumption. There are two situations of interest which lead to the vanishing of the determinant $\Delta(f)$. First, if the noise at the output of any single hydrophone, say the jth hydrophone, vanishes, then $\hat{C}_{jk}(f) = 0$ for all values of k and $\Delta(f) = 0$. In this case one would use the jth hydrophone alone in the detection process. Secondly, if the noise at two different hydrophones, say the jth and the kth hydrophones, differ only in amplitude and a constant time displacement, then $\hat{C}_{jl}(f) = \text{constant } x\ \hat{C}_{kl}(f)$ for all values of l and the determinant vanishes. These conditions are rather artificial and it seems better to consider the singular case $\Delta(f) = 0$ as an approximation to exceptionally quiet conditions. This point will be returned to later.

12.6 Special Cases for the Input Signals and Noise

In the preceding sections the general problem of designing a set of matched filters for M hydrophones was considered. The solution to the problem of designing these filters to maximize signal-to-noise ratio was given in Eqs. (12.30) or (12.31) in the form of a complex frequency response for each filter. Further insight into the properties of this solution can be obtained by restricting the generality of the problem.

For the first illustration suppose that the M input noises $n_i(t)$ (sees Fig. 12.1) are independent of each other so that the correlation functions $C_{jk}(\cdot)$ vanish unless $j = k$. In this case the set of Eqs. (12.36) becomes a simple set of M equations each of which contains only one unknown, and the desired filter responses can be written down immediately. They are

$$\hat{Y}_k(f) = \frac{K\, e^{-i2\pi f t_o}\, \hat{s}_k{}^*(f)}{\hat{C}_{kk}(f)} \; . \tag{12.41}$$

Of course this result could have been obtained equally well from Eq. (12.30). If the determinant $\Delta(f)$ has nonvanishing elements only on the main diagonal, the cofactors $M_{jk}(f)$ vanish unless $j = k$. If $j = k$, $M_{kk}(f)$ is simply $\Delta(f)/\hat{C}_{kk}(f)$. Thus in the case of independent noise inputs each filter is designed as though there was only one channel present.

When the input noises are uncorrelated and the filters are designed by Eq. (12.41), the signal-to-noise ratio given by Eq. (12.33) becomes

$$\left(\frac{S}{N}\right)^2 = \sum_{k=1}^{M} \int_{-\infty}^{+\infty} \frac{|\hat{S}_k(f)|^2 \, df}{\hat{C}_{kk}(f)} . \tag{12.42}$$

If it be further assumed that the noise spectra are constant and each equal to W_o over the frequency band of the signal, one has the simpler formula

$$\left(\frac{S}{N}\right)^2 = \frac{1}{W_o} \sum_{k=1}^{M} \int_{-\infty}^{+\infty} |\hat{S}_k(f)|^2 \; df . \tag{12.43}$$

The sum over k yields the total energy in all the signals, while the factor W_o is a constant that does not change with M. The improvement that is obtained while the number of hydrophones is increased is apparent.

Suppose that the generality of the noise processes is restored but that restrictions on the M signals $s_k(t)$ are introduced. In the case that is of most interest the M hydrophones will detect the arrival of a plane wave. If each hydrophone is omnidirectional, one can say that, to a first approximation, each signal $s_k(t)$ is identical to all other signals except for a translation in time. Actually, the signal received at any hydrophone will be distorted by the waves diffracted from nearby objects including the M-1 other hydrophones. One may argue either that such distortion is negligible or that it can be removed by suitable inverse filters. In any case it will be assumed that the signals $s_k(\cdot)$ received by the hydrophones have identical wave shapes but are translated in time because of the differences in the travel paths from the source. In accordance with the techniques of beam forming, an all-pass time delay network is added to each input so that all of the wave forms are brought into coincidence.

These beam-forming techniques enable one to assume

$$s_j(t) \equiv s(t) \quad , \; j = 1, 2, \ldots, M. \tag{12.44}$$

In this case one may express the filter responses given by Eq. (12.30) as the product of the two factors

$$K\, e^{-i2\pi f t_o}\, \hat{s}^*(f) \tag{12.45}$$

and

$$\hat{p}_k(f) = \frac{1}{\Delta(f)} \sum_{j=1}^{M} M_{jk}(f) \; . \tag{12.46}$$

The first factor is independent of the noise and depends only on the signal $s(t)$ whose detection is sought and the two arbitrary constants K, t_o. This is the response of an optimum filter for a single channel when the background noise has uniform density.

The second factor $\hat{p}_k(f)$ depends on the noise and not on the signal $\hat{s}(f)$. However, it should be remembered that the correlation coefficients $C_{jk}(\cdot)$ which are the elements of the determinant $\Delta(f)$ and the cofactors $M_{jk}(f)$ must be calculated from the outputs of the all-pass delay lines rather than from the outputs of the hydrophones. It might be noted that if the M noise components are mutually uncorrelated before they enter the delay networks, the noise components will still be uncorrelated at the outputs. The introduction of the all-pass delay lines will not introduce a correlation.

The summation over j in Eq. (12.46) is equal to the value of the $M \times M$ determinant which can be obtained from $\Delta(f)$ by replacing all the elements in the jth column by one. The effect of the filters $\hat{p}_k(f)$ is to whiten and balance the noise components so that one can process the output of the summer with the single filter, Eq. (12.45), which is suitable for white noise.

The separation of the filter given by Eqs. (12.45) and (12.46) may be used to rearrange the circuit of Fig. 12.1 to that shown in Fig. 12.2. Mermoz (1964) designates that part of the circuit enclosed by dashed lines as *the proper filter of the array.* He also defines the gain of this proper filter and demonstrates that it has many interesting properties.

It has been suggested occasionally in the literature that the following design procedure is adequate when the M signals $s_k(t)$ are identical in shape. After the beam shape is formed by introducing suitable time delays in each channel, one can form a linear sum of the M channels and pass this sum through a matched filter designed for the signal's wave shape. One can now specify the circumstances under which this procedure is acceptable. It is evident that the identity of the signal wave shapes is not sufficient since Eq. (12.46) requires a different filter for each channel. The further assumption of uncorrelated noise components is not sufficient since in this case although the functions $\hat{p}_k(f)$ defined in Eq. (12.46) reduce to $[\hat{C}_{kk}(f)]^{-1}$ as in Eq. (12.41), they still may differ from channel to channel. It is only when the M noise components are mutually independent and have identical power spectra, i.e., $\hat{C}_{kk}(f) = W_o(f)$, $k = 1, 2, 3, \ldots M$, that one can justifiably sum the outputs of the M delay lines and introduce a single matched filter. It is evident that this procedure will give optimum performance only under highly specialized conditions.

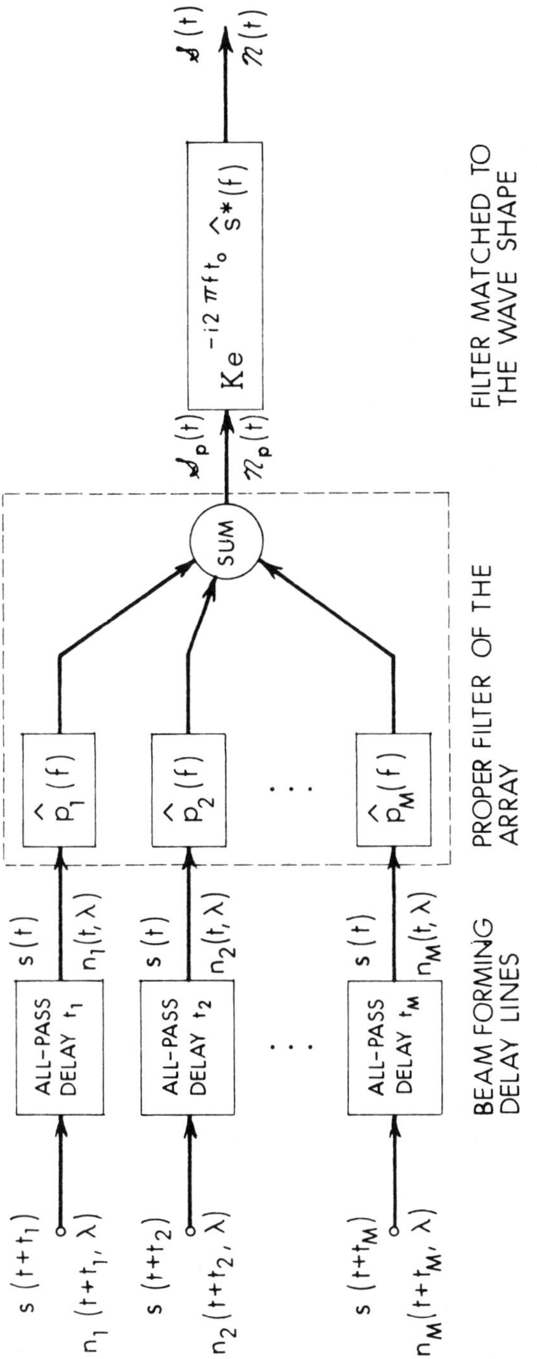

Figure 12.2—The design of the receiver when the M signals $s_j(t)$, have identical wave shapes.

12.7 The Likelihood-Ratio Receiver

The receiver shown in block diagram in Fig. 10.1(*e*) is commonly referred to as a likelihood-ratio receiver, but so far as the writer is aware, no one has attempted to construct an operational receiver of this kind. An extensive analysis of the theory of this detector has been presented by Bryn (1962) to which the reader is referred. The analytic approach followed by Bryn illustrates many of the concepts developed in the present work. First, he selects a finite time sample of the data and represents it as a Fourier series as in Eq. (4.27). Next, he utilizes the assumption set forth just before Eq. (4.35), namely, that the Fourier coefficients of each series are independent gaussian random variables. Finally, Bryn assumes that the noise spectra have a finite bandwidth so that the number of Fourier coefficients required is finite. In this manner it is argued that the sample of data can be characterized by a finite number of gaussian variables and that the probability density of each sample may be written in the form of Eq. (3.29). Actually, as Bryn points out, a correlated gaussian probability density is applicable to the Fourier coefficients at any one frequency component, and the joint probability density for all components is the product of the probability densities for each frequency.

Bryn writes the likelihood ratio as in Eq. (8.28) with $p = q = 1/2$, and the probability densities of the message with and without noise are obtained as in Eqs. (8.31) and (8.32). The expression for the likelihood ratio is expanded in a power series in terms of the signal components to terms of the second order as required for incoherent detection. This extremely brief outline indicates the general approach used by Bryn to determine the structure of the filters shown as boxes in Fig. 10.1(*e*).

It is of interest to note that the final design contains a filter whose amplitude response is

$$\left\{ \frac{\hat{\mathcal{S}}(f)}{\hat{\mathcal{N}}^2(f)} \right\}^{1/2} , \qquad (12.47)$$

where $\hat{\mathcal{S}}(f)$ and $\hat{\mathcal{N}}(f)$ are the power spectra of the signal and the noise, respectively. This formula is of interest since it has a close resemblance to Eq. (7.4) which was derived for the case of a signal of known shape. The important difference is that in Eq. (7.4) the phase structure of the known signal is utilized in the detection process whereas in the present case the signal is noise and no phase structure is available.

Bryn carries through the calculation of array gain for a linear array of five hydrophones and a three-dimensional array of eight hydrophones. It turns out that the detection process shows significant improvement over the standard detector, Fig. 10.1(*a*), only when "$\lambda >$ linear dimensions of the array." The reason offered for this improvement is that "at low frequencies the directivity pattern is superdirective." It will be argued below in Sec. 14.2 that the gain of a superdirective array is achieved only for distant noise sources and that the gain may not be achieved when the noise source is only a few wavelengths from the array.

In conclusion one can say that the results of Bryn's analysis suggest that the performance of the likelihood-ratio receiver does not justify the complexity of its design and construction.

12.8 Suggestions for Further Reading

Although the paper by Mermoz (1964) has been summarized in some detail, there remains much more material in his paper that is well worth reading. The papers by Rudnick (1960) and Bryn (1962) are highly condensed but they will repay the reader the large amount of work necessary to read them carefully. Shor (1966) has analyzed a variation of Mermoz's method that requires the computation of a smaller number of correlation coefficients. The paper contains an example of the design of an array of 23 hydrophones. The problem of the optimum receiver structure for an acoustic array has been considered from a viewpoint more fundamental than that of the present discussion by Middleton and Groginsky (1965).

In the analyses presented in Chapters X and XII it is assumed in every case that the noise is gaussian. Middleton (1962, 1964) has extended the analysis of a few detectors to include a mixture of gaussian noise and non-gaussian noise due to impulses. He develops formulas to show the degradation of performance resulting from the non-gaussian noise.

The reader should not neglect the papers that describe experimental embodiments of the theories such as Anderson (1960) and Allen and Westerfield (1964). Anderson (1958) has discussed the response of three-dimensional arrays similar to those considered by Rudnick and Bryn.

CHAPTER XIII

The Likelihood Ratio and the Likelihood Function

13.1 The Comparison of Different Detection Systems

Analyses of several detection systems have been presented in Chapters VII, X, and XII. The reader probably has experienced a sense of dissatisfaction since a uniform set of hypotheses regarding the nature of the signal and noise and a uniform criterion of performance were not maintained throughout the analyses. Part of this difficulty is real, since the analyses become more complicated as the statistical assumptions become more realistic. On the other hand, the underlying hypotheses regarding the statistics of the noise and signal were sometimes changed so that each of the analyses would be relatively simple. This variability of hypotheses is desirable from a pedagogic point of view since it puts the physical concepts into better view by minimizing the analytic complications.

If one seeks to reorganize the analyses of the different systems into a common framework, the generalized likelihood ratio[1] defined in Eqs. (7.47) or (8.28) furnishes the best standpoint from which to compare the different systems. The advantages of this point of view have already been illustrated. It was shown in Sec. 7.11 that under specialized assumptions regarding the statistics of signal and noise the system which maximizes the signal-to-noise ratio also maximizes the likelihood ratio. Similarly, in Sec. 8.4 it was shown that under certain assumptions the standard detector of Fig. 10.1(*a*) (for the case of one channel) maximizes the likelihood ratio.

These comments suggest the following generalizations for receivers designed to make a decision between the two hypotheses H_0 and H_1. For each set of assumptions regarding the nature of the signal and noise there is a receiver which is optimum. Conversely, for each receiver there is a set of assumptions regarding the signal and noise for which this receiver is optimum. These statements are not precise enough as they stand to admit of proof and so they are offered as guides to one's thinking rather than as mathematical theorems. However, if one follows the spirit of the Bayes system and establishes an average risk as in Eq. (8.8), it should be possible to establish the truth or falseness of these proposed theorems.

---

[1] It is assumed that when there is no *a priori* information regarding the presence of a signal, one sets $p = q = \frac{1}{2}$. In this case the generalized likelihood ratio reduces to the more specialized definition of Eq. (7.46).

As an example of one aspect of these rules, consider the case of a signal obscured with additive gaussian noise. If one knows the shape and the phase of the signal, then the optimum receiver will be the matched filter of Fig. 10.1(*d*). On the other hand, if the signal is a gaussian noise, one will use the standard detector of Fig. 10.1(*a*).

The concept of generalized likelihood ratio does not provide a complete theory of signal detection since it does not provide a value of the threshold, ℓ_0, to be used in the decision process. The receiver operating curves described in Sec. 7.10 provide a graphic way of visualizing the performance of the receiver and they enable one to understand better the effect of the choice of a threshold value, ℓ_0, on the performance of the receiver. The value of the Bayes systems described in Sec. 8.2 is that they show how one can evaluate objectively the problem of selecting the threshold value. Unfortunately, the cost function $C(\vec{S} \mid \vec{\gamma})$ that was introduced in the development of the Bayes system cannot be determined objectively.

It seems likely that the Bayes system provides the complete solution to the problem of signal detection, and that the difficulty of determining the cost function reflects the difficulty of assessing the best military tactics in a given situation. This means that the concept of cost functions must be supplemented by a consideration of the military situation. In other words, the tactical, military situation in which the equipment will be operated must be simulated in order to assess objectively the usefulness of a cost function. It is a common procedure to determine ROC curves experimentally by introducing known noise and signals into the receiver. Consequently, the inclusion of the tactical situation and the cost function is a natural extension of the empirical tests of performance now used. Until experimental data of this type are available it will be necessary to use one's judgement in selecting the cost functions. Of all the statistical quantities discussed so far the probability of false alarm is related most closely to a military requirement that can be assessed objectively. For example, if a ship has a patrol assignment that lasts, say, five weeks, there is a limit to the number of target indications that can be investigated without exhausting the ships' supplies and thereby aborting the mission. This in turn places a limit on the number of false alarms investigated and, hence, on the lower value of the threshold that can be used.

13.2 The Extraction of Signal Parameters in a Noise Background

The theory developed so far has been concerned primarily with signal detection. As soon as the energy in the signal is large enough so that the probability of successful detection is large, the operator will want to measure some of the characteristics of the signal such as bearing and, in the case of active sonar, range and doppler. In more sophisticated systems the designer will try to provide some form of classification. In the case of passive listening it is sometimes possible to make some classification of the source on the basis of spectral properties of the received noise. In the case of active systems one may be able to infer properties of the target from the shape of the returned echo. For example, as mentioned earlier, the finite length of the target will elongate the echo and distributed points of strong reflection may produce a characteristic modulation of the envelope of the echo. The present discussion will be restricted to a brief indication of the theory on which the extraction of signal parameters is based.

Let us follow the notation of Eq. (8.1) and write

$$\vec{V} = \vec{N} + \vec{S}(\vec{\theta}) \tag{13.1}$$

where the functional dependence of $\vec{S}$ on a set of parameters $\vec{\theta}$ $(= \theta_1, \theta_2, \ldots, \theta_K)$ is made explicit. In order to simplify the discussion suppose that $\vec{\theta}$ has only one component θ and that an estimate of the "best" value of θ is sought. The English mathematician, R. A. Fisher, introduced the *method of maximum likelihood* (see Cramér, 1946, Chap. 33) as a general approach to this problem. In brief, for each possible value of the parameter θ the probability of obtaining the observed value $\vec{V}$ $(= V_1, V_2, \ldots, V_M)$ is calculated. This probability density is called the *likelihood function* of the sample and will be denoted $L(\vec{V} \mid \theta)$. For a given sample $\vec{V}$ of the message $L(\cdot)$ is defined as a function of the parameter θ. The method of maximum likelihood asserts that the "best" value of θ is that value which maximizes $L(\vec{V} \mid \theta)$ or, equivalently, $\ln L(\vec{V} \mid \theta)$. Thus one uses the equation

$$\frac{\partial}{\partial \theta} \ln L(\vec{V} \mid \theta) = 0 \tag{13.2}$$

to define θ as an implicit function of $\vec{V}$. If this equation has a solution $\theta =$ constant, this solution will be ignored and only the solution

$$\theta = \theta_e(\vec{V}) \tag{13.3}$$

which depends on the message $\vec{V}$ will be accepted. This value is called the *maximum likelihood estimate,* θ_e, of θ.

If prior knowledge of the probability density of θ is available, the function $L(\vec{V} \mid \theta)$ should be multiplied by this probability density before the maximization is carried out. More commonly it is assumed that the random parameter, say range, bearing, or doppler shift, is restricted to a range of values and that the probability density of the parameter is constant in this range.

The estimate, $\theta_e(\vec{V})$, of θ defined in Eq. (13.3) is a random variable since it is defined as a function of the random variable $\vec{V}$. Therefore it has an expected value and a standard deviation defined by

$$\langle \theta_e \rangle = E\{\theta_e(\vec{V})\} \tag{13.4}$$

and

$$\sigma^2(\theta_e) = E\{[\theta_e - \langle \theta_e \rangle]^2\} . \tag{13.5}$$

Theorems regarding the existence of a solution $\theta_e(\vec{V})$ of Eq. (13.2), and the properties of θ_e and $\sigma^2(\theta_e)$ are given by Cramér (1946, Chapters 32 and 33) to whom the reader is referred. The present discussion is based on the assumption that Eqs. (13.2) and (13.3) provide a practical solution to the problem of parameter estimation.

As an example of this method suppose that the distance to a fixed target is obtained by measuring the two-way travel time θ of an acoustic pulse, and the distance d will be calculated from the formula $d = \theta/2c$. A set of M values $\theta_1, \theta_2, \ldots, \theta_M$ are observed but they are not necessarily the same because of small random variations in the medium and the equipment. If the causes of these variations are small but numerous, one may assume with some justification that each observation θ_i is governed by a gaussian probability density; i.e.,

$$p(\theta_i) = \frac{1}{\sqrt{2\pi}\sigma} \exp[-\frac{1}{2\sigma^2} (\theta_i - \theta)^2] , \tag{13.6}$$

where θ is the "true" value of the travel time. If, further, the M observations are spaced in time so that they are all independent variables, the probability density for the set of values $(\theta_1, \theta_2, \ldots, \theta_M)$ is the product of the M probability densities like Eq. (13.6). In this case the likelihood function becomes

$$L(\theta_1, \theta_2, \ldots, \theta_M \mid \theta) = \frac{1}{(2\pi)^{M/2}\, \sigma^M} \exp\left[-\frac{1}{2\sigma^2} \sum_{i=1}^{M} (\theta_i - \theta)^2\right] . \tag{13.7}$$

A brief calculation shows that Eq. (13.2) becomes

$$\sum_{i=1}^{M} (\theta_i - \theta) = 0 , \tag{13.8}$$

and the maximum likelihood estimates, Eq. (13.3) is

$$\theta = \theta_e(\theta_i) = \frac{1}{M} \sum_{i=1}^{M} \theta_i . \tag{13.9}$$

In this simple case the best estimate is the arithmetic mean as one would expect.

13.3 The Determination of the Amplitude of a Coherent Signal Obscured by Noise

Let us return to the example discussed in Sec. 7.11 and assume that the signal vector $\vec{S}$ is known except for a common factor. Thus it is assumed that

$$S_n = a_o s_n \ , \quad n = 1, 2, \ldots, M \ , \tag{13.10}$$

where the s_n are known but a_o is a random variable whose probability is unknown. When this signal is obscured by the gaussian noise described in Eq. (7.62), the conditional probability of obtaining the message $\vec{V}$ is

$$L(\vec{V} \mid a_o) = \frac{|a_{mn}|^{1/2}}{(2\pi)^{M/2}} \exp\left[-\frac{1}{2} \sum_{m,n=1}^{M} a_{mn} (V_m - a_o s_m)(V_n - a_o s_n) \right] \quad \ldots . \tag{13.11}$$

This is the likelihood function introduced by Fisher, and the optimum choice of a_o is that value which maximizes $L(\vec{V} \mid a_o)$ for the given message $\vec{V}$. The maximization can be obtained more easily by the equivalent process of maximizing $ln\ L(\vec{V} \mid a_o)$. A brief calculation shows that the equation

$$\partial \{ln\ L(\vec{V} \mid a_o)\} / \partial a_o = 0 \tag{13.12}$$

yields

$$a_o{}^* = \frac{\Sigma a_{mn} V_m s_n}{\Sigma a_{mn} s_m s_n} \tag{13.13}$$

where the summations extend from 1 to M on both indices. The asterisk is added to show that this is the estimated value and not necessarily the correct value, a_o.

The estimated value, $a_o{}^*$, of a_o provided by Eq. (13.13) is a function $a_o{}^*(\vec{V})$ of the message $\vec{V}$, and, consequently, $a_o{}^*$ is a random variable. An estimate of this kind is said to be *unbiased* when the expected value $E_{\vec{V} \mid a_o} \{a_o{}^*\}$ averaged over all possible messages $\vec{V}$ is equal to a_o. In terms of a formula, the estimate $a_o{}^*$ is said to be unbiased if

$$E_{\vec{V} \mid a_o} \left\{a_o{}^*\right\} = \int_\Gamma a_o{}^* (\vec{V}) f(\vec{V} \mid a_o)\, d\vec{V} = a_o \tag{13.14}$$

where $f(\vec{V} \mid a_o)$ is the probability density of the message $\vec{V}$ given the true value a_o and Γ is the message space. A brief calculation will show that the value of $a_o{}^*$ defined by Eq. (13.13) satisfies Eq. (13.14) when the probability density $f(\vec{V} \mid a_o)$ is given by Eq. (7.62) with N_m replaced by $V_m - a_o s_m$, $m = 1, 2, \ldots, M$.

PROBLEMS

13.1 Suppose that a random variable x is governed by a gaussian distribution whose mean is zero and whose standard deviation is σ. A set of M independent observations of the variable x yield the values $x_1, x_2, \ldots, x_M$. Use the method of maximum likelihood to show that the best value of the standard deviation is given by $\sigma^2 =$

$$(1/M) \sum_{i=1}^{M} x_i{}^2 .$$

13.2 Show that the estimate of σ^2 obtained in problem 13.1 is unbiased. *Hint:* It is assumed as prior knowledge in problems 1 and 2 that the mean is zero.

13.3 Prove that the value of $a_o{}^*$ defined in Eq. (13.13) satisfies Eq. (13.14) when the noise samples have a gaussian distribution.

13.4 Read Chapter 34 of the book by Cramér (1946) and write an expository essay on the bias and the efficiency of the estimate of a parameter.

CHAPTER XIV

Planar Acoustic Arrays

14.1 Introduction

The acoustic arrays analyzed in Chapters IX, X, XII were composed of omnidirectional point sources. In a sense these are the most general configurations possible, and any configuration of sources may be considered as a specific arrangement of these general point sources. Actually, the transition from a finite number of discrete sources to a continuum of sources is difficult to carry out mathematically, so it is easier to develop from first principles the equations governing the radiation patterns of continuous radiators of finite size. The present chapter has two limited goals. In the first place the relation between Fourier integrals and radiation patterns will be developed. This result will be of interest in view of the dominant role that the Fourier integral has played in this book. In addition, many authors start with Eqs. (14.11) and (14.12) so that the present account will serve as a preparation for the reading of many papers in the scientific literature.

The second goal of the present chapter is the presentation of a brief introduction to the techniques of using multiplication as a method of increasing angular resolution. Significant improvement in this respect has been achieved for isolated, monochromatic signals.

14.2 Radiation Patterns as Fourier Transforms

Suppose that one has a series of transducer elements located in the x',y'-plane and that any area element $dx'dy'$ located at Q contributes to the field pressure at a point $P(x,y,z)$ an amount

$$dp = \frac{p_o(x',y')}{R} e^{-ikR+i\omega t} dx'dy' , \tag{14.1}$$

where $p_o(x',y')$ is a complex function which depends on the amplitude and phase of the transducer motion at the point (x',y'). $R = R(P,Q)$ is the distance from the source point Q to the field point P, and $k = 2\pi/\lambda$. As usual ω is the angular frequency of the source.

The next step in the conventional argument is to integrate Eq. (14.1) over all values of x', y' to get the total pressure at the field point. This gives

$$p(P) = \iint_{-\infty}^{+\infty} \frac{p_0(x',y')}{R(P,Q)} e^{-ikR(P,Q) + i\omega t}\, dx'dy' \qquad \ldots \qquad (14.2)$$

One notices in Eq. (14.1) that it has been tacitly assumed that the source element is omnidirectional and undisturbed by the presence of the other radiators. Alternately, one can justify Eq. (14.1) by restricting the field point P to points $z \geqslant 0$ and say that Eq. (14.1) is the pressure field due to a source located on an infinite, rigid baffle. In addition to the assumption about baffles, it is generally assumed in radiation theory that the motion of each element of the transducer is not influenced by the other elements. This last assumption is not always realistic for experimental transducers. Since a consideration of this feature of real transducers will lead the discussion away from the present goal, it is noted for completeness only.

Assume that there is a finite number E such that $p_0(x',y')$ vanishes identically for all points Q such that $x'^2 + y'^2 > E^2$. If one then restricts the discussion to field points P for which $R \gg E$, one can apply the customary Fraunhofer far-field approximation,

$$R \cong r - \ell x' - my' \ , \qquad (14.3)$$

where

r = distance $\overline{OP}$
ℓ = cosine of the angle between $\overline{OP}$ and the x'-axis
m = cosine of the angle between $\vec{OP}$ and the y'-axis.

It is also assumed in the Fraunhofer theory that the R in the denominator of the integrand in Eq. (14.2) may be treated as a constant equal to r. Hence, one has for the far-field,

$$p(x,y,z) = \frac{e^{-ikr+i\omega t}}{r} \iint_{-\infty}^{+\infty} p_0(x',y')\, e^{+ik(\ell x'+my')}\, dx'dy' \qquad \ldots \qquad (14.4)$$

which may be interpreted as a spherical wave front radiating from the origin which is modified by a directional pattern given by the integral on the right.

The integral depends on the coordinate (x,y,z) of the field point P through the direction cosines ℓ, m.

Define a function

$$F_0(k\ell, km) = \iint_{-\infty}^{+\infty} p_0(x',y')\, e^{+ik(\ell x'+my')}\, dx'dy' \ , \tag{14.5}$$

and introduce the assumption that

$$p_0(x', y') = \bar{p}_1(x')\, \bar{p}_2(y') \ . \tag{14.6}$$

This restriction is not as serious as it might appear at first. When Eq. (14.6) is introduced into Eq. (14.5), one obtains

$$F_0(k\ell, km) = F_1(k\ell)\, F_2(km) \tag{14.7}$$

with

$$F_1(k\ell) = \int_{-\infty}^{+\infty} \bar{p}_1(x')\, e^{+ik\ell x'}\, dx' \tag{14.8}$$

and similarly for $F_2(km)$.

There is no need to make any further simplifying assumptions but it should be noted that the full nature of the function $F_1(k\ell)$ can be understood by restricting the field point P to the x,z-plane. In this case

$$k\ell = \frac{2\pi}{\lambda} \sin\theta \tag{14.9}$$

where θ is the angle between the z-axis, i.e., the normal to the x', y'-plane, and the line $\vec{OP}$. One recognizes Eq. (14.8) as one member of a Fourier transform pair. In order to enhance the similarity with the previous notation, set

$$\left.\begin{aligned} s &= \sin\theta \\ u &= x'/\lambda \\ F_1(k\ell) &= p_1(s) \\ \lambda\bar{p}_1(x') &= \hat{p}_1(u) \end{aligned}\right\} \tag{14.10}$$

so that Eq. (14.8) may be written as

$$p_1(s) = \int_{-\infty}^{+\infty} \hat{p}_1(u)\, e^{+i2\pi su}\, du \tag{14.11}$$

with the inverse transforms

$$\hat{p}_1(u) = \int_{-\infty}^{+\infty} p_1(s)\, e^{-i2\pi su}\, ds \ . \tag{14.12}$$

When one compares Eq. (14.11) with Eq. (14.4), one sees that the function $p_1(s)$ has a simple physical interpretation. For the range of values $-1 \leqslant s \leqslant +1$, $p_1(s)$ is the radiation pattern in the x,y-plane for source distributions that can be factored as in Eq. (14.6). The ambiguity in the inverse equation $\theta = \sin^{-1} s$ can be eliminated if one assumes that the source is located on an infinite, rigid baffle.

This elementary analysis has been given in some detail for several reasons. First, and foremost, the Fourier transforms provide a valuable tool for analyzing pattern formation (Spencer, 1946), and they show clearly the relation between source size and pattern beam width. Further, many authors have stated Eq. (14.11) and (14.12) without showing clearly the circumstances under which they are valid.

The discussion in Sec. 2.3 has shown that if the source is of finite size so that

$$\hat{p}_1(u) \equiv 0, \; |u| > E/\lambda \ , \tag{14.13}$$

the function $p_1(s)$ must be nonvanishing for large real values of s, in particular for $|s| > 1$. This can be explained mathematically by saying that the wave radiates at a complex angle $\pm(\pi/2) + i\,\Sigma$ since

$$\sin(\pm\pi/2 + i\,\Sigma) = \pm \cosh \Sigma \ . \tag{14.14}$$

The physical meaning of these complex angles can be understood when one remembers that the three direction cosines ℓ, m, n of the field point P must satisfy

$$\ell^2 + m^2 + n^2 = 1.$$

Hence, if ℓ^2 is greater than one, that is if $s^2 > 1$, one or both of the values m or n must be imaginary. This leads to waves which are attenuated in the y- and/or z-direction. These waves, which do not contribute to the far-field, are sometimes called evanescent waves.

The preceding discussion has been phrased entirely for radiation, but by appealing to the principle of reciprocity, one can interpret the directivity patterns as receiving patterns. However, one normally measures patterns for plane waves which have real values for the direction cosines (ℓ,m,n). Thus, in the previous example, one would measure $p_1(s)$ only for the range $-1 \leqslant s \leqslant +1$, yet this is considered a complete measurement of the radiation pattern. Similarly, the directivity indices for transducers are defined in terms of integrals over real angles of propagation only. One is now in a position to understand the performance and the limitations of the superdirective array.

If the array has finite size so that Eq. (14.13) is satisfied, Eq. (14.11) becomes

$$p_1(s) = \int_{-E/\lambda}^{+E/\lambda} \hat{p}_1(u)\, e^{+i2\pi su}\, du \,. \qquad (14.15)$$

It is possible to choose $p_1(u)$, $|u| \leqslant E/\lambda$, so that $p_1(s)$ approximates a prescribed radiation pattern for $|s| \leqslant 1$. Thus one can determine a source distribution for a transducer of finite size, i.e., not larger than $2E$, such that the radiation pattern will have a major lobe width as small as desired and such that the heights of the minor lobes are below some arbitrarily chosen level. A source designed to fit these characteristics is often referred to as a *superdirective array*. Unfortunately, this approach to the design of a transducer places no bound on the response $p_1(s)$ for $|s| > 1$.

The possibility that $p_1(s)$ may have large values for $s > 1$ is not serious as long as the discussion is restricted to plane waves from distant sources. Frequently, however, the signals that one wishes to detect are masked by local sources, such as the ship's self-noise, which may produce evanescent waves of significant amplitude. For these reasons it is recommended that the directivity index of a transducer should be redefined to include the response to evanesant waves.

As long as the design is restricted to modest, "well behaved" source distributions, the pair of Eqs. (14.11) and (14.12) offer a lucid explanation of the well-known "trade off" between transducer length and major lobe width.

14.3 Achievement of Increased Directionality by Multiplication

There are two methods by means of which one can obtain major lobe sharpening. It will be shown that if the signals are pure tones one can obtain a sharpening of the major lobe by multiplication. This sharpening of the major lobe does not require any processing in time such as averaging, and therefore, it is not the same process of multiplication discussed in Sec. 9.2 where it was shown that directivity could be bought at the expense of processing time when the signal was a broad-band noise.

As a simple example of a multiplicative array consider a rectangle of length L in the x' direction which is cut in two equal parts, $-L/2 \leqslant x' \leqslant 0$ and $0 \leqslant x' \leqslant +L/2$. Suppose further that there is no shading. One can utilize the principle of reciprocity and utilize Eq. (14.8) to write down an expression for the responses of the right and left halves to waves arriving in the plane $y = 0$. One has

$$F_R(k\ell) = \int_0^{L/2} e^{+ik\ell x'} dx' = e^{+ikL/4} \int_{-L/4}^{+L/4} e^{+ik\ell u}\, du$$

$$F_L(k\ell) = \int_{-L/2}^{0} e^{+ik\ell x'} dx' = e^{-ikL/4} \int_{-L/4}^{+L/4} e^{+ik\ell u}\, du \ ,$$

where the subscripts R and L mean right and left halves, respectively.

These integrals can be evaluated readily to give

$$F_R(k\ell) = 2\left[\frac{\sin(k\ell L/4)}{k\ell}\right] e^{+ik\ell L/4 + i\omega t}$$

$$F_L(k\ell) = 2\left[\frac{\sin(k\ell L/4)}{k\ell}\right] e^{-ik\ell L/4 + i\omega t} \ .$$

After taking the real part of each expression one may multiply these together to obtain the output of the product array. When one uses the trigonometric identity $2\cos(A + B) = \cos(A + B) + \cos(A - B)$, one finds

$$\Re F_R(k\ell)\Re F_L(k\ell) = 2\left[\frac{\sin(k\ell L/4)}{k\ell}\right]^2 \{\cos(k\ell L/2) + \cos 2\omega t\} .$$

The second term in the braces can be removed with a low-pass filter.

On the other hand, if one had utilized the entire array as a detector and formed the square of the real part of the output, one would have obtained

$$[\Re F_{R+L}(k\ell)]^2 = 2\left[\frac{\sin(k\ell L/2)}{k\ell}\right]^2 (1 + \cos 2\omega t) \ .$$

Again, the component of frequency $2\omega t$ can be removed with a low-pass filter.

Figure 14.1 contains a plot of the normalized responses

$$\overline{\Re F_R(k\ell)\Re F_L(k\ell)}\Big|_{\text{Nor}} = \left[\frac{\sin(k\ell L/4)}{k\ell L/4}\right]^2 \cos(k\ell L/2)$$

and

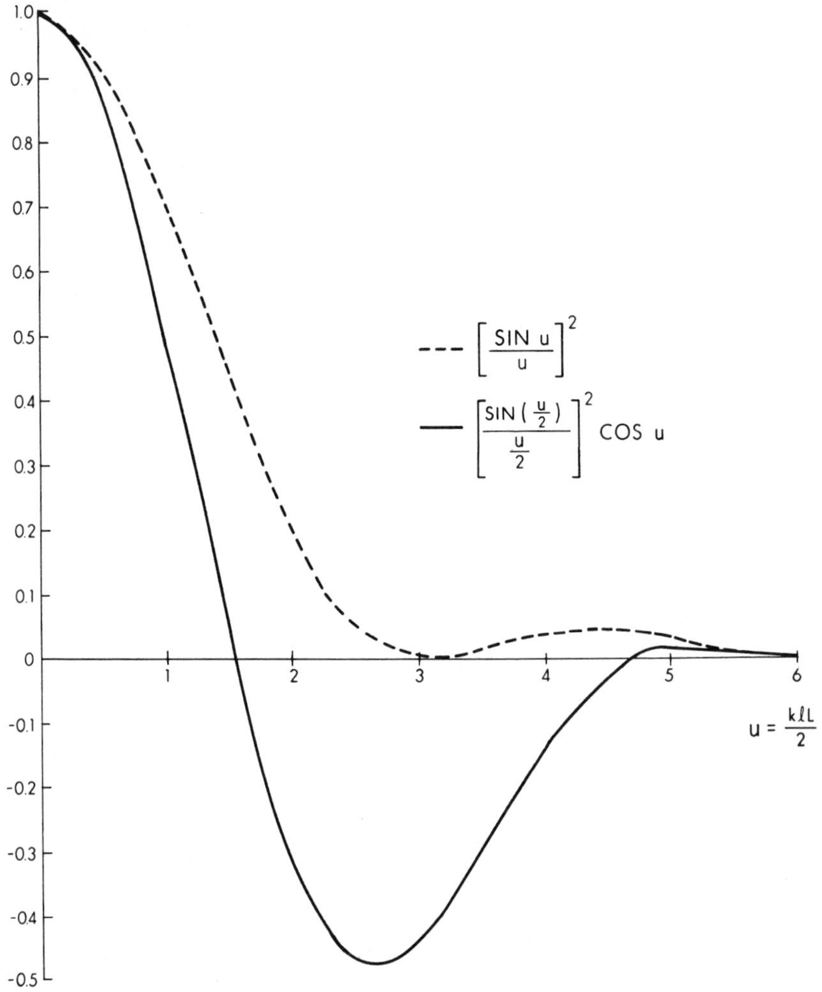

Figure 14.1–The normalized response (- - -) of a standard receiver with hydrophone of length, L, and the normalized response (——) when the halves of this hydrophone are multiplied together.

$$\overline{[\Re F_{R+L}(k\ell)\,]^2}\Big|_{\text{Nor}} = \left[\frac{\sin(k\ell L/2)}{k\ell L/2}\right]^2$$

versus the dimensionless parameter $k\ell L/2$. It should be noted that the normalization hides the fact that the response for the entire line at zero angle, $\ell = 0$, is four times that of the multiplier. One sees from Fig. 14.1 that the response of the multiplier has a sharper major lobe than that of the uniform line. The magnitude of the minor lobe is larger for the multiplier, but the phase of the first minor lobe is negative independently of the phase of the incident signal.

Welsby and Tucker (1959) have pointed out that one might be tempted to infer that if the low-pass filter were followed by a half-wave rectifier, the first minor lobe of the multiplier's pattern would be removed. They also point out that this approach is impractical since the presence of noise will lead to the generation of a dc output. Nonetheless, their experience shows that the response of a cathode ray tube to the acceleration potential leads to the desired reduction of the first minor lobe, but this is an opinion that is not shared by all workers in sonar.

The concept of multiplying the outputs of the two halves of a transducer is not really new. During World War II this effect was achieved under the designation of a "sum and difference sonar." The sum of the outputs of the two halves was squared and from this was subtracted the square of the difference of the two outputs. That this is equivalent to the product can be seen from the identity $(x+y)^2 - (x-y)^2 = 4xy$.

14.4 Multiplicative Arrays with N Similar Hydrophones

It is interesting to extend the discussion of the last section to the case of N identical transducers arranged in a linear array. By virtue of the arguments presented in Sec. 14.2 the discussion will be restricted to the pattern in the x,z-plane. It will be assumed that the n_1 elements on the left are connected together as in Fig. 14.2 and the remaining $n_2(=N-n_1)$ elements on the right are connected together.

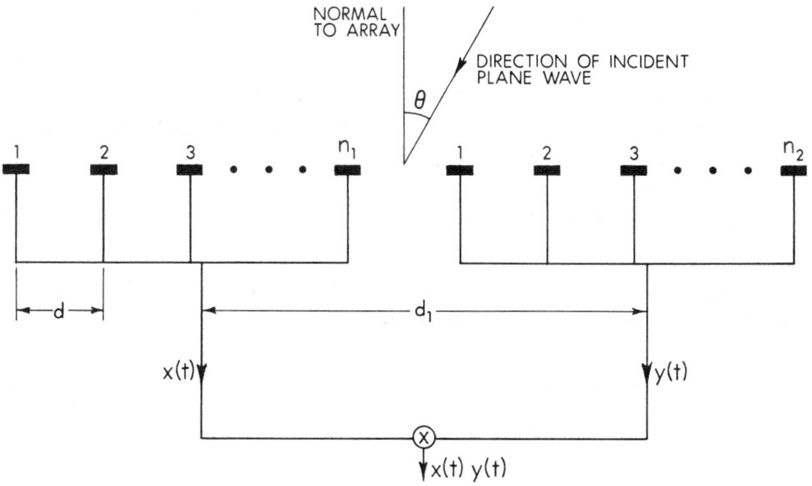

Figure 14.2–The formation of a multiplicative array from $N(=n_1+n_2)$ hydrophones.

It is a well known theorem in radiation patterns (Stratton, 1941, pp. 448-450) that the pattern of an array of identical transducer elements is the product of the pattern of one element and the pattern of an array of omni-directional point elements having the same array geometry. Hence, if one denotes the normalized pattern of one transducer element by $D_o(\theta)$, the normalized pattern associated with the output $x(t)$ of the n_1 elements on the left is

$$D_o(\theta)\, D_1(p) \qquad (14.16)$$

where

$$D_1(p) = \frac{\sin n_1 p}{n_1 \sin p} \qquad (14.17)$$

and

$$p = (kd/2) \sin\theta \;; \qquad (14.18)$$

d is the distance between two adjacent transducer elements. Similarly, for the n_2 elements on the right the normalized pattern associated with the output $y(t)$ is

$$D_o(\theta)\, D_2(p) \qquad (14.19)$$

where

$$D_2(p) = \frac{\sin n_2 p}{n_2 \sin p} \;. \qquad (14.20)$$

Henceforth the common factor $D_o(\theta)$ will be omitted from the formulas.

If the incident wave is a plane wave arriving at an angle θ, the phases of the two outputs $x(t)$ and $x(y)$ will differ by

$$\Psi = kd_1 \sin\theta = (2d_1 p/d) = qp \;, \qquad (14.21)$$

where d_1 is the distance between the acoustic centers of the two groups of transducers. Consequently, one may write

$$x(t) = \sqrt{2}\, \frac{\sin n_1 p}{n_1 \sin p} \cos(\omega t - \Psi + \epsilon) \qquad (14.22)$$

$$y(t) = \sqrt{2}\, \frac{\sin n_2 p}{n_2 \sin p} \cos(\omega t + \epsilon) \;. \qquad (14.23)$$

A common factor that includes $D_O(\theta)$, signal level, hydrophone sensitivity and also two factors n_1 and n_2, the numbers of hydrophones, has been omitted. The phase angle ϵ of the wave is not important when only one wave is present. One may utilize the trigonometric identity $2\cos A\cos B = \cos(A+B) + \cos(A-B)$ to express the product $x(t)y(t)$ as

$$x(t)y(t) = \left(\frac{\sin n_1 p}{n_1 \sin p}\right)\left(\frac{\sin n_2 p}{n_2 \sin p}\right) \times \left\{ \cos \Psi + \cos(2\omega t + 2\epsilon - \Psi) \right\} \cdot \tag{14.24}$$

The second term in the expression in braces may be rejected with a low-pass filter. This gives, using Eq. (14.21),

$$\overline{x(t)y(t)} = \left(\frac{\sin n_1 p}{n_1 \sin p}\right)\left(\frac{\sin n_2 p}{n_2 \sin p}\right) \cos q\,p \ . \tag{14.25}$$

This result should be compared with the output when the system is treated as a standard detector. This is

$$\overline{[x(t)+y(t)]^2} = \left(\frac{\sin N p}{N \sin p}\right)^2 \ . \tag{14.26}$$

When one compares Eqs. (14.25) and (14.26), it becomes obvious that the reduction in the major lobe width results from the factor $\cos q\,p$.

Welsby and Tucker (1959) present an interesting series of graphs of the right member of Eq. (14.25) for $N = 9$ and various combinations of n_1 and n_2. The first minor lobe is smallest for the combination $n_1 = 1$ and $n_2 = 8$, but it can be shown that this is the worst combination when noise is present.

Since the factor $\cos \Psi = \cos p\,q$ is important in the beam formation, it is evident that the beam can be shifted slightly by introducing a time delay in either the output $x(t)$ or $y(t)$ of Fig. 14.2. This is another advantage of the multiplicative array. However, there will be a loss of signal level unless arrangements are made to shift the phases of the outputs of each detector element simultaneously. Hence, if one wishes to obtain optimum beam shifting, one must utilize the arrangement shown in Fig. 14.3

The present discussion is idealized in that only the response to a single, monochromatic plane wave in the absence of noise has been considered. Multiplication is a nonlinear operation so the analysis becomes noticeably more complicated not only when noise is present but even if two or more signals are present. The question of the resolution of two nearby sources with a multiplicative array is a subject of controversy.

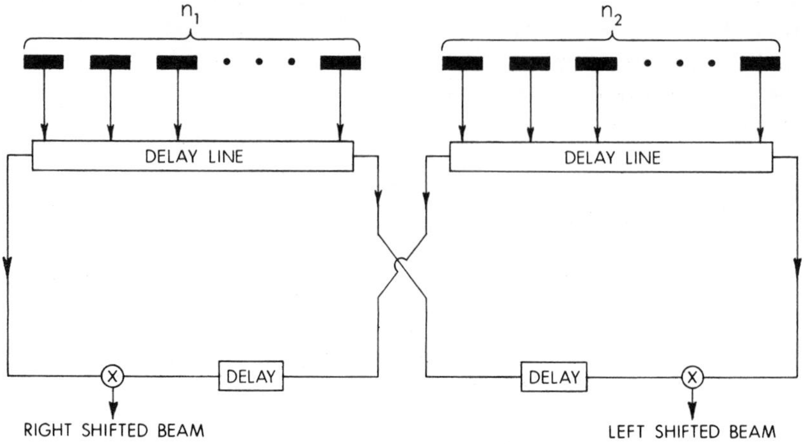

Figure 14.3–The method of using delay lines to shift the major lobe of a multiplicative array.

14.5 Qualifying Comments on Multiplicative Arrays[1]

The subject of multiplicative arrays is relatively new so there does not exist a large body of results upon which there is common agreement. Most workers in the field of sonar technology have been thoroughly conditioned to think in terms of directionality patterns, and it is difficult for them to remember that not all systems can be judged reliably from a consideration of their directivity patterns. This kind of bias is illustrated in the last section. In systems that use simple linear addition a number of important properties are interrelated in such a way that they can all be judged from the directional response pattern, and this makes the response pattern a very simple and powerful criterion for the intercomparison of such systems.

Further, the relation between the power in the main lobe and the side lobes in such systems is relatively insensitive to system changes, and thus the width of the main lobe is a good measure of the processing gain. On the other hand, the multiplicative arrays often have a large negative side lobe like that shown in the solid curve of Fig. 14.1. It was argued in Sec. 14.3 that this lobe could be eliminated in some manner since it was negative. This argument about the response is valid only when the source is a single, plane wave. When there are multiple sources, the large negative lobe adds to the fluctuations of the output and thereby impairs the signal-to-noise level of the output.

In short, one must use great caution in comparing standard, additive systems with multiplicative systems, and especially with systems having

[1]This section is the result of helpful and detailed comments of Dr. P. G. Redgment. He should not be blamed, however, for any errors or lack of appositeness in the discussion.

multiplication at more than one level, until extensive and specific analyses have been made. The gain of the system and the ability to resolve multiple targets in the presence of a noise background must be considered in considerable detail.

14.6 Suggestions for Further Reading

A group at the University of Birmingham, Birmingham, England, working under the leadership of Professor Tucker, has made extensive studies, both theoretical and experimental, of the behavior of multiplicative arrays to noise and multiple targets. Of their many publications one might mention Tucker (1955), Welsby and Tucker (1959), and Shaw and Davies (1964). The paper by Berman and Clay (1957) together with the subsequent paper by Fakley (1959) provide a good discussion of multiplicative arrays.

CHAPTER XV

Future Developments

15.1 Adaptive Systems

At the present time active research is underway on the application of self-adaptive techniques to acoustic signal processing. The phrase "self-adaptive" covers a wide range of sophistication according as "self" refers to the operator or to the equipment. For example, in the most simple form the operator makes repeated measurements of the background noise spectra and changes the threshold and, perhaps, other operating characteristics. At a more sophisticated level the machine is programmed to perform this function automatically and continuously. This is undoubtedly the lowest level of performance to which one can apply the expression self-adaptive.

Another elementary variation in adaptive processes is sequential decision. In this approach, as pointed out before, the length of the sample is variable. This added degree of freedom enables one to set both the false alarm rate and the probability of detection. Thus, instead of one graph like Fig. 7.4 for a single sample length, one has a family of these graphs corresponding to the duration of the sample.

A significant increase in sophistication is provided when the detector has adjustable parameters, such as the coefficients of the correlation function which can be adjusted to give optimum response for known input samples. One realization of this system has been studied at Stanford Electronics Laboratory (Hoff, 1962, Mays, 1963, and Hu, 1963) under the name ADALINE. This word was formed from ADAptive LINEar, which refers to adaptive threshold-logic circuits. Some of the circuits they have studied are similar in form to the quantized version of the standard detector shown in Fig. 10.1(*b*).

A more fundamental approach to adaptive networks has been pursued at Cornell University by Rosenblatt (1962) and his co-workers. They have developed a device, the PERCEPTRON, which simulates the human neural system. A significant feature of the PERCEPTRON is that the circuit utilizes random connections. When a device is able to make internal changes automatically, it is referred to as a self-organizing system. Such a system is more sophisticated than the adaptive systems in which the changes must be made by the human operator.

A system that is intermediate in complexity is under development by Sebestyen (1962) and his associates at Litton Industries. In this approach the detector is able automatically to partition the observation space on the basis of known inputs. This is equivalent to finding empirically the decision function $\delta(\gamma \mid V)$ which maps the message space Γ on to the decision space Δ.

The material presented in this book has dealt solely with hypothesis testing as applied to the question of the presence or absence of a signal. Nevertheless, the important problem of parameter estimation, such as estimates of range and bearing, can be treated, happily, with equal confidence. Less satisfactory is the problem of target classification. A practical and reliable solution to this problem could lead to a substantial reduction in the false alarm rate. It is evident that this classification will require a much greater signal-to-noise ratio since one must extract a much larger amount of information from the signal.

The design of a system for target classification can be approached from two ways. One can design a deterministic system in which the circuits are tailored in accordance with a set of criteria that a target is expected to satisfy. For example, one may decide that a submarine has, say, four or five dominant reflection points or "highlights" so that the output of a crosscorrelation should have not one but four or five peaks in a time interval governed by the length and aspect of the submarine. This criterion is offered not as a solution to the problem of target classification but as an example of the kind of criteria that may be preset into the detector.

Alternately, one can build into the receiver an ability to evaluate a set of criteria but leave the threshold values associated with these criteria to be determined by the receiver. The receiver is trained or taught by presenting to it a series of messages which are known to contain or not to contain signals. For example, in a Bayes detection system the threshold $\mathcal{K}$ of Eq. (8.29) would be determined as follows. A large number of messages would be presented to the receiver and after each message the machine would be told whether or not a signal was present. Thus, in essence, a large number of experimental points would be located in the message space and each point would have a lable "yes" or "no." The receiver then endeavors to construct a surface in this space which provides the best separation of the "yes" points from the "no" points. After this surface has been determined adequately, the receiver is able to judge unknown messages and provide answers to the problem of signal detection. Sebestyen (1962) has described this process in considerable detail.

An interesting application for learning devices can be conceived in connection with bottom bounce sonar. Perhaps a self-adaptive receiver can be trained to utilize the output of the depth sounder to predict the quality of signals reflected from the ocean bottom. This would provide a continuous assessment of the reliability of this mode of sonar operation. This problem is not unlike that of teaching a computer to make weather forecasts (Hu, 1963).

15.2 Developments in Modern Computer Technology

Undoubtedly the most important developments for signal processing are those that have occurred in the area of computer technology. Fundamental in this development are the solid circuit modules which have provided computers which are much smaller and at the same time much faster. This development has made possible the modern technique known as shared time, in which several users can solve their problems *simultaneously* on the same computer. The significance of this for military purposes is immediately obvious. By pooling together the computer requirements for sonar, radar, fire control, and navigation one can install on each ship a large computer that can be shared by all.

The increased computer capacity that is achieved in this manner can be used by the sonar operator to compute correlation matrices such as those of Eq. (12.12), predict quality of bottom reflected echoes, and perform other calculations that are needed to keep his receiver operating in an optimum manner.

Another advantage of this foreseeable increase in computer capability is that one can quantize signal levels in more levels than the two provided by shift registers. There is a large gap between the performance of two-level quantization and the infinite, or continuous, quantization, yet as Professor Bonnet has shown, a modest increase in the number of quantization levels will significantly close this gap.

The use of solid circuit modules in the receiver will lead to significant changes in the approach to circuit designs. One will be more concerned with circuit failures since it will be more difficult, if not impossible, to replace individual elements in the circuits. This will give rise to an increase in the use of redundancy and multiple path logic in the circuits.

15.3 Rearrangement of the Spatial and the Time Processing

It is customary in sonar systems to separate completely those operations which involve the spatial array, i.e., operations of beam formation, from those operations in the time domain, such as filtering and crosscorrelation. It is easy to see why this has been done, but it is not evident that this separation leads to an optimum system. As a matter of fact, this separation will be complete only if the hydrophones are small in size. The output of a finite hydrophone already contains a superposition in time for any signal that arrives from a direction that is not normal to the face of the hydrophone. It is likely that future designers of large sonar arrays will examine more closely the question of the optimum organization of the spatial and temporal processing.

The interplay between the spatial and the temporal processing has been considered by Middleton and Groginsky (1963, 1965) for a passive receiver. They introduce the definition that the receiver will be said to be *factorable* if the processing can be represented as a product of operators depending only on the array and operators depending only on the statistics of the signal and the noise. They proceed to show for some situations whether or not the optimum receiver is factorable. The results of this kind of analysis are clearly important because the conventional method of beam formation will lead to a loss of performance unless the optimum receiver is factorable.

15.4 Oceanographic Surveys

The steady increase in the knowledge of the ocean that results from the many survey programs in progress will contribute significantly to the problem of signal processing. The designer will be required less often in the future to assume the statistics for the noise, and the nature of the degradation of the signal resulting from reflection and propagation will be better understood. Instead, he can determine the receiver characteristics that are optimum for each part of the ocean. For example, in the case of bottom bounce sonar, as the signal characteristics are progressively degraded due to an increase in the roughness of the bottom, one may want to change the receiver from a correlation receiver to a simple energy detector.

15.5 Suggestions for Further Reading

Basic reference for the reader are the books by Rosenblatt (1962) and Sebestyen (1962). A report edited by Wilcox (1964) contains a large number of very brief summaries of the present state of the many fields covered by the term "information sciences." This report is a useful guide to the literature.

The current research in the field of artificial intelligence and automata have not reached the stage of development where they are of immediate applicability to sonar systems. Nonetheless, these fields are of long range interest and the work is of great intrinsic interest independent of its practical potential. The reader is referred to a book *Automata Studies* edited by Shannon and McCarthy (1956) and the *Proceedings of the IFIP Congress 65* edited by Kalenich (1965) for many interesting papers. The latter book contains material on the present and future status of large computers.

BIBLIOGRAPHY

Alexander, M. J., and C. A. Vok: *Tables of the Cumulative Distribution of Sample Multiple Coherence,* Rocketdyne Research Report 63-37, 15 November 1963.

Allen, W. B., and E. C. Westerfield: *Digital Compressed-Time Correlators and Matched Filters of Active Sonar,* J. Acoust. Soc. Am. **36**, pp. 121-139, January 1964. Also reproduced photographically in *Traitement du Signal avec Application Particulière à l'Acoustique Sous-marine,* Centre d'Étude des Phenomènes Aléatoires de Grenoble (CEPHAG), NATO Advanced Study Institute, Grenoble, France, 14-26 September 1964.

Anderson, V. C.: *The Deltic Correlation,* Acoustics Research Laboratory, Harvard University, Tech. Mem. 37, 5 January 1956.

——: *Digital Array Phasing,* J. Acoust. Soc. Am. **32**, pp. 867-870, July 1960.

Arase, E. M., and T. Arase: *Correlation of Ambient Noise in the Ocean,* J. Acoust. Soc. Am. **38**, pp. 146-148, July 1965.

Axelrod, E. H., B. A. Schooner and W. A. Von Winkle: *Vertical Directionality of Ambient Noise in the Deep Ocean at a Site near Bermuda,* J. Acoust. Soc. Am. **37**, pp. 77-83, January 1965.

Bartlett, M. S.: *An Introduction to Stochastic Processes,* Cambridge University Press, Cambridge, 1956.

Beckmann, P., and A. Spizzichino: *The Scattering of Electromagnetic Waves from Rough Surfaces,* Pergamon Press, Oxford, 1963.

Bendat, J. S.: *Principles and Applications of Random Noise Theory,* John Wiley and Sons, New York, 1958.

Beran, M. J., and G. B. Parrent, Jr.: *Theory of Partial Coherence,* Prentice-Hall, Inc., Englewood Cliffs, N. J., 1964.

Berman, A., and C. S. Clay: *Theory of Time-Averaged-Product Arrays,* J. Acoust. Soc. Am. **29**, pp. 805-812, July 1957.

Birdsall, T. G.: *Likelihood Ratio and Optimum Adaptive Detection, Traitement du Signal avec Application Particulière à l'Acoustique Sous-marine,* Centre d'Étude des Phénomènes Aléatoires de Grenoble (CEPHAG), NATO Advanced Study Institute, Grenoble, France, 14-26 September 1964.

Blackman, N. M.: *On Fourier Series for Gaussian Noise,* Information and Control **1**, pp. 56-63, September 1957.

Blackman, R. B., and J. W. Tukey: *The Measurement of Power Spectra,* Dover Publications, Inc., New York, 1958.

Blackwell, D., and M. A. Girshick: *Theory of Games and Statistical Decisions,* John Wiley and Sons, New York, 1954.

Blanc-Lapierre, A.: *Modèles Statistiques pour L'Étude de Phénomènes de Fluctuations,* Masson et Cie, Paris, 1963.

—— et R. Fortet: *Theories des Fonctions Aléatoires,* Masson et Cie, Paris, 1953.

—— et B. Picinbono: *Propriétés Statistiques du Bruit de Fond,* Masson et Cie, Paris, 1961.

Bonnet, G.: *Sur les Correlateurs Utilisant la Quantification des Signaux, Traitement du Signal avec Application Particulière à l'Acoustique Sous-marine,* Centre d'Étude des Phénomènes Aléatoires de Grenoble (CEPHAG), NATO Advanced Study Institute, Grenoble, France, 14-26 September 1964*a*.

——: Editor, *Traitement du Signal avec Application Particulière à l'Acoustique Sous-marine,* Centre d'Étude des Phénomènes Aléatoires de Grenoble (CEPHAG), NATO Advanced Study Institute, Grenoble, France, 14-26 September 1964*b*. Part II. Translations of the Proceedings.

——: *Sur l'Interpolation Optimale d'une Fonction Aléatoire Echantillonnee,* C. R. Acad. Sc. Paris, 260, pp. 780-787, January 18, 1965*a*.

——: *Phénomènes Aléatoires et Traitement du Signal,* Bull. Inf. Scien. Tech. du Commissariat a l'Energie Atomique No. 96, pp. 1-12, September 1965*b*.

Born, M., and E. Wolf: *Principles of Optics,* Pergamon Press, Ltd., London, 1959.

Brekhovskikh, L. M.: *Waves in Layered Media,* Academic Press, New York, 1960.

Bryn, F.: *Optimal Signal Processing of Three Dimensional Arrays Operating on Gaussian Signals and Noise,* J. Acoust. Soc. Am. **34**, pp. 289-297, March 1962.

Campbell, G. A., and R. M. Foster: *Fourier Integrals for Practical Applications,* Bell Telephone System Technical Publications, New York, 1931. Republished by D. Van Nostrand Co., New York, 1951.

Capon, J., R. J. Greenfield, and R. J. Kolker: *Multidimensional Maximum-Likelihood Processing of a Large Aperture Seismic Array,* Proc. IEEE **55**, pp. 192-211, February 1967.

Chandrasekhar, S.: *Stochastic Problems in Physics and Astronomy,* Rev. Mod. Phys. **15**, pp. 1-89, January 1943.

Chernov, L. A.: *Wave Propagation in a Random Medium,* McGraw-Hill Book Co., Inc., New York 1960.

Clay, C. S.: *Use of Arrays for Acoustic Transmission in a Noisy Ocean,* Reviews of Geophysics **4**, pp. 475-507, November 1966.

Cooley, J. W., and J. W. Tukey: *An Algorithm for the Machine Calculations of Complex Fourier Series,* Math. of Computation **19**, pp. 297-301, April 1965.

Cramér, H.: *On the Theory of Stationary Random Process,* Ann. Math, **41**, pp. 215-230, 1940.

——: *Mathematical Methods of Statistics,* Princeton University Press, Princeton, N. J., 1946.

Cron, B. F., and A. H. Nuttall: *Phase Distortion of a Pulse Caused by Bottom Reflection,* J. Acoust. Soc. Am. **36**, pp. 486-492, March 1965.

Davenport, W. B., Jr., R. A. Johnson and D. Middleton: *Statistical Errors in Measurements on Random Time Functions,* J. Appl. Phys. **23**, pp. 377-388, 1952.

—— and W. L. Root: *An Introduction to the Theory of Random Signals and Noise,* McGraw-Hill Book Co., Inc., New York, 1958.

Dirac, P. A. M.: *The Principles of Quantum Mechanics,* Oxford University Press, 1930.

Doob, J. L.: *Stochastic Processes,* John Wiley and Sons, Inc., New York, 1953.

Duflos, J.: *Étude des Effects de l'Echantillonnage en Detection des Signaux Foibles,* l'Onde Electrique, Paris, No. 443, February 1964.

Dunham Laboratory. R. A. McDonald, P. M. Schultheiss, F. B. Tuteur, and T. Usher, Jr.: *Processing of Data from Sonar,* Yale University, September 1963.

Dwork, B. M.: *Detection of a Pulse Superimposed on Fluctuation Noise,* Proc. IRE, pp. 771-774, July 1950.

Eckart, C., Editor: *Principles of Underwater Sound,* Vol. 7, NDRC Summary Technical Reports, Distributed by Research Analysis Group, Committee on Undersea Warfare, National Research Council, undated.

——: *Optimal Rectifier Systems for the Detection of Steady Signals,* University of California, Marine Physical Laboratory of the Scripps Institution of Oceanography, La Jolla, California, Sponsored by Bureau of Ships, Reference 52-11, 4 March 1952.

Erdelyi, A., W. Magnus, F. Oberhettinger and F. G. Tricomi: *Tables of Integral Transforms,* Vols. I and II, McGraw-Hill Book Co., Inc., New York, 1954.

Fakley, D. C.: *Comparison between the Performance of a Time-Averaged Product Array and an Intraclass Correlator,* J. Acoust. Soc. Am. **31**, pp. 1307-1314, October 1959.

Faran, J. J., and R. Hills: *Correlators for Signal Reception*, Tech. Mem. 27, Acoustics Research Laboratory, Harvard University, September 15, 1952*a*.

—— and ——: *The Application of Correlation Techniques to Acoustic Receiving Systems,* Tech. Mem. 28, Acoustics Research Laboratory, Harvard University, November 1, 1952*b*.

Faure, P.: *Theoretical Model of Reverberation Noise,* J. Acoust. Soc. Am. **36**, pp. 259-266, February 1964.

Fisher, R. A.: *Statistical Methods and Scientific Inference,* Oliver and Boyd, Edinburgh, 1956.

Flinn, E. A.: *Editor of Special Issue on The MIT Geophysical Analysis Group Reports,* Geophysics **32**, pp. 411-525, June 1967.

Fox, G. R.: *Ambient-Noise Directivity Measurements,* J. Acoust. Soc. Am. **36**, pp. 1537-1540, August 1964.

Freeman, J. J.: *Principles of Noise,* John Wiley and Sons, New York, 1958.

Gabor, D.: *Theory of Communication,* J. Inst. Elec. Engrs. Part III, **93**, pp. 429-457, 1946.

Goodman, N. R.: *On the Joint Estimation of the Spectra, Cospectrum and Quadrature Spectrum of a Two-Dimensional Stationary Gaussian Process,* Dissertation, Princeton University, March 1957.

Green, M., and A. Swets: *Signal Detection Theory and Psychophysics,* John Wiley and Sons, Inc., New York, 1966.

Green, P. E., Jr.: *Radar Astronomy Measurement Techniques,* Tech. Report No. 282, M.I.T. Lincoln Lab., Lexington, Mass., December 1963.

Guillemin, E. A.: *The Mathematics of Circuit Analysis,* The Technology Press, M.I.T., John Wiley and Sons, Inc., New York, 1956.

Hannan, E. J.: *Time Series Analysis,* Methuen and Co., Ltd., London, 1960.

Helstrom, C. W.: *Statistical Theory of Signal Detection,* Pergamon Press, Ltd., London, 1960.

Hoff, M. E.: *Learning Phenomena in Networks of Adaptive Switching Circuits,* Tech. Report No. 1554-1, Electronic Technology Laboratory, Aeronautical Systems Division, Air Force Systems Command, U. S. Air Force, Wright-Patterson Air Force Base, Ohio, July 1962.

Honnest-Redlich, G.: *Radio Control for Models,* A Harborough Publication, Leighton Buzzard, 1950.

Hu, M. J.: *A Trainable Weather-Forecasting System,* Tech. Report No. 6759-1, Electronic Technology Laboratory, Air Force Avionics Laboratory, Air Force Systems Command, U. S. Air Force, Wright-Patterson Air Force Base, Ohio, June 1963.

Hunt, F. V.: *Perturbation and Correlation Methods for Enhancing the Space Resolution of Directional Receivers,* Proc. IRE **39**, p. 840, July 1951.

Jeffreys, H.: *Theory of Probability,* third edition, Oxford University Press, Oxford, 1961.

Kalenich, W. A.: Editor *Proceedings of IFIP Congress 65,* Spartan Books, Inc., Washington, D. C., May 1965.

Kendall, M. G.: *The Advanced Theory of Statistics,* Vol. 1, fourth edition, Charles Griffin and Co., Ltd., London, 1948.

Khinchin, A. I.: *Mathematical Foundations of Statistical Mechanics,* Dover Publications, Inc., New York, 1949.

Khintchine, A.: *Korrelationstheorie der stationaren stochastischen Prozesses,* Math. Ann. **109**, pp. 604-615, 1934.

Kohlenberg, A.: *Exact Interpolation of Band-limited Functions,* J. Appl. Phys. **24**, pp. 1432-1436, December 1953.

Kolmogorov, A. N.: *Foundations of the Theory of Probability,* Chelsea Publishing Company, New York, 1950.

Lerner, R. A.: *Signals with Uniform Ambiguity Functions,* IRE Nat'l. Conv. Rec., Part 4, pp. 27-36, 1958.

Levy, P.: *Processus Stochastiques et Mouvement Brownien,* Gauthier-Villars, Paris, 1948.

Linnette, H. M., and R. J. Thompson: *Directivity Study of the Noise Field in the Ocean, Employing a Correlative Dipole,* J. Acoust. Soc. Am. **36**, pp. 1788-1794, October 1964.

Loève, M.: *Fonctions Aléatoires du Second Ordre,* note in *Processus Stochastiques et Mouvement Brownien,* Gauthier-Villars, Paris, 1948.

Mays, C. H.: *Adaptive Threshold Logic,* Tech. Report No. 1557-1, Electronic Technology Division, Air Force Avionics Laboratory, Air Force Systems Command, Wright-Patterson Air Force Base, Ohio, April 1963.

Mermoz, H.: *Filtrage Adapté et Utilisation Optimale d'une Antenne, Traitement du Signal avec Application Particulière à l'Acoustique Sout-marine,* Centre d'Étude des Phénomènes Aléatoires de Grenoble (CEPHAG), NATO Advanced Study Institute, Grenoble, France, 14-26 September, 1964.

Middleton, D.: *An Introduction to Statistical Communication Theory,* McGraw-Hill Book Co., Ind., New York, 1960.

——: *Topics in Communication Theory,* McGraw-Hill Book Co., Inc., New York, 1965.

——: *A Statistical Theory of Reverberation and Similar First-order Scattered Fields,* IEEE Trans. on Inform. Th. **IT-13**, Part I, pp. 372-392; Part II, pp. 393-414, July 1967.

——: and H. L. Groginsky: *Detection of Random Acoustic Signals by Receivers with Distributed Elements, Optimum Receiver Structures for Normal Signal and Noise Fields,* Tech. Report, Raytheon Company, Submarine Signal Division, Portsmouth, Rhode Island, August 1963.

—— and D. van Meter: *Detection and Extraction of Signals in Noise from the Point of View of Statistical Decision Theory,* J. Soc. Indust. Appl. Math., Part I, **3**, pp. 192-253, December 1955; Part II, **4**, pp. 86-119, June 1956.

Milne, A. R., and J. H. Ganton: *Ambient Noise under Arctic-Sea Ice,* J. Acoust. Soc. Am. **36**, pp. 855-869, May 1964.

Officer, C. B.: *Introduction to the Theory of Sound Transmission,* McGraw-Hill Book Co., Inc., New York, 1958.

Ol'shevskii, V. V.: *Characteristics of Sea Reverberation,* Consultants Bureau, New York, 1967.

Peirce, B. O.: *A Short Table of Integrals,* Ginn and Company, Boston, 1929.

Pekeris, C. L.: *Propagation of Sound in the Ocean,* Geol. Soc. of Amer. Mem. No. 27, October 15, 1948.

Peterson, W. W., T. G. Birdsall and W. C. Fox: *The Theory of Signal Detectability,* Trans. IRE **PGIT-4**, pp. 171-211, September 1954.

Price, R., and P. E. Green, Jr.: *Signal Processing in Radar Astronomy–Communication via Fluctuating Multipath Media,* Tech. Report No. 234, M.I.T. Lincoln Lab., Lexington, Mass., October 1960.

Rayleigh, Baron: *Theory of Sound,* Vol. I, p. 41, Macmillan Co., London, 1937.

Rice, S. O.: *Mathematical Analysis of a Random Noise,* Bell System Tech. J. **23**, pp. 184-294, 1944, and **24**, pp. 133-183, 1945. Reprinted in Selected Papers on Noise and Stochastic Processes (N. Wax, Editor), Dover Publications, Inc., New York, 1954.

Rosenblatt, F.: *Principles of Neurodynamics,* Spartan Books, Inc., Washington, D. C., 1962.

Rosenblatt, M., Editor: *Time Series Analysis,* from Proceedings of the Symposium in Time Series Analysis held at Brown University, 11-14 June 1962, John Wiley and Sons, Inc., New York, 1963.

Rudnick, P.: *Small Signal Detection in the DIMUS Array,* J. Acoust. Soc. Am. **32**, pp. 871-877, July 1960.

——: *Likelihood Detection of Small Signals in Stationary Noise,* J. Appl. Phys., pp. 140-143, February 1961.

Saks, S.: *Theory of the Integral, Monografje Matematyczne,* Vol. II, Wurszawa, 1937.

Schiff, L. I.: *Quantum Mechanics,* McGraw-Hill Book Co., Inc., New York, 1949.

Screaton, G. R., Editor: *Dispersion Relations,* Oliver and Boyd, Ltd., Edinburgh, 1961.

Sebestyen, G. S.: *Decision-Making Processes in Pattern Recognition,* The MacMillan Company, New York, 1962.

Shannon, C. E.: *Communication in the Presence of Noise,* Proc. IRE **37**, pp. 10-21, 1949.

—— and J. McCarthy, Editors: *Automata Studies,* Princeton University Press, Princeton, New Jersey, 1956.

Shaw, E., and D. E. N. Davies: *Theoretical and Experimental Studies of the Resolution Performance of Multiplicative and Additive Aerial Arrays,* Symposium on Signal Processing in Radar and Sonar Systems: Paper No. 7, Reprinted from The Radio and Electronic Engineer **28**, No. 4, October 1964.

Siebert, W. M.: *A Radar Detection Philosophy,* Trans. IRE **PGIT-2**, pp. 204-221, September 1956.

Spencer, R. C.: *Fourier Integral Methods of Pattern Analysis,* Radiation Laboratory, Massachusetts Institute of Technology, Cambridge, Massachusetts, Report 762-1, 21 January 1946.

Stewart, J. L., and E. C. Westerfield: *A Theory of Active Sonar Detection,* Proc. IRE **47**, pp. 872-881, May 1959.

Stocklin, P. L.: *Signal Processing of Underwater Acoustic Fields,* Underwater Acoustics, (V. M. Albers, Editor), pp. 339-349, Plenum Press, New York, 1963*a*.

——: *Space-Time Sampling and likelihood Ratio Processing in Acoustic Presssure Fields,* J. Brit. I.R.E., **26**, pp. 1-12, July 1963*b*.

Stone, J.: *Problems Associated with the Measurements of Ambient-Noise Directivity by Means of Linear Additive Arrays,* J. Acoust. Soc. Am. **34**, pp. 328-333, March 1962.

Stratton, J. A.: *Electromagnetic Theory*, McGraw-Hill Book Co., Inc., New York, 1941.

Talham, R. J.: *Ambient-Sea-Noise Model,* J. Acoust. Soc. Am. **36**, pp. 1541-1544, August 1964.

Thomas, J. B., and T. R. Williams: *On the Detection of Signals in Nonstationary Noise by Product Arrays,* J. Acoust. Soc. Am. **31**, pp. 453-462, April 1959.

Titchmarsh, E. C.: *The Theory of Functions,* second edition, Oxford University Press, Oxford, 1939.

——: *Introduction to the Theory of Fourier Integrals,* Oxford University Press, Oxford, 1959.

Tolstoy, I., and C. S. Clay: *Ocean Acoustics,* McGraw-Hill Book Co., Inc., New York, 1966.

Tucker, D. G.: *Signal/Noise Performance of Multiplier and Addition (or Integrating) Types of Detection,* J. Inst. Elec. Engrs. **102C**, pp. 181-190, February 1955.

——, Chairman: *Signal Processing in Radar and Sonar Directional Systems,* Symposium held at the University of Birmingham, England, 6-9 July 1964.

Turin, G. L.: *An Introduction to Matched Filters,* Trans. IRE **PGIT-6**, pp. 311-329, 1960.

Usher, T., Jr.: *Signal Detection by Arrays in Noise Fields with Local Variations,* J. Acoust. Soc. Am. **36**, pp. 1444-1449, August 1964.

van der Pol, B., and H. Bremmer: *Operational Calculus Based on the Two-Sided Laplace Integral,* Cambridge University Press, Cambridge, 1950.

Van Melle, F. A.: Editor of *Vela Uniform, Special Issue I,* Geophysics **29**, pp. 151-300, April 1964a.

——, Editor of *Vela Uniform, Special Issue II,* Geophysics **29**, pp. 663-771, October 1964*b*.

Van Meter, D.: *Optimum Decision Systems for the Reception of Signals in Noise,* Thesis, Harvard University, Cambridge, Mass., January 1955.

van Schooneveld, C.: *Analytischen Signalen,* Rappart No. Ph. L. 1963-49, Rydsverdediglings-Organisatie TNO, November 1963.

———: *Some Remarks on Sampling Methods for a Bandpass Signal, Traitement du Signal avec Application Particulière à l'Acoustique Sous-marine,* Centre d'Étude des Phénomènes Aléatoires de Grenoble (CEPHAG), NATO Advanced Study Institute, Grenoble, France, 14-26 September 1964.

Van Vleck, J. H., and D. Middleton: *A Theoretical Comparison of the Visual, Aural, and Meter Reception of Pulsed Signals in Presence of Noise,* J. Appl. Phys. **17**, pp. 940-971, 1946.

—— and ——: *The Spectrum of Clipped Noise,* Proc. IEEE **54**, pp. 2-19, January 1966.

Wald, A.: *Statistical Decision Functions,* John Wiley and Sons, Inc., New York, 1950.

Webb, E. L. R.: *On the Distribution of the Product of Diode Detector Waveforms,* Can J. Phys. **34**, pp. 679-691, July 1956.

———: *Note on the Product of Random Variables,* Can. J. Phys. **40**, pp. 1394-1396, October 1962.

Webster, F.: *Some Perils of Measurements from Moored Buoys,* Trans. of the 1964 Buoy Technology Symposium, pp. 33-48, March 24, 25 1964.

Welsby, V. G., and D. G. Tucker: *Multiplicative Receiving Arrays,* J. Brit. I.R.E. **19**, pp. 369-382, June 1959.

Whittaker, E. T., and G. N. Watson: *A Course of Modern Analysis,* fourth edition, Cambridge University Press, Cambridge, 1927.

Widder, D. V.: *The Laplace Transform,* Princeton University Press, Princeton, N. J., 1946.

Wiener, N.: *Generalized Harmonic Analysis,* Acta Math. **55**, pp. 117-258, 1930. Reprinted in Selected Papers of Norbert Wiener, M.I.T. Press, 1964.

———: *The Fourier Integral and Certain of its Applications,* Cambridge University Press, Cambridge, 1933. Reprinted by Dover Publications, Inc., New York, 1951.

———: *Cybernetics,* The Technology Press, M.I.T., John Wiley and Sons, Inc., New York, 1948.

Wilcox, R. H., Editor: *Information Systems Summaries,* ONR Report ACR-97, Office of Naval Research, Department of the Navy, Washington, D. C., July 1964.

Woodward, P. M.: *Probability and Information Theory with Applications to Radar,* Pergamon Press Ltd., London, 1953.

ANSWERS TO SOME OF THE PROBLEMS

2.1 (a) $\hat{Y}(f) = (1+i2\pi fT)^{-1}$

$h(t) = 0, t<0$

$= (1/T)\exp(-t/T), t>0.$

(b) $\hat{Y}(f) = i2\pi fT(1+i2\pi fT)^{-1}$

$h(t) = \delta(t), t<0$

$= \delta(t) - (1/T)\exp(-t/T), t>0.$

(c) $\hat{Y}(f) = \left\{1+iQ\left(\frac{f}{f_o} - \frac{f_o}{f}\right)\right\}^{-1}$

$h(t) = 0, t<0$

$= 4\pi f_o \tan\phi \cos(2\pi f_o \cos\phi t - \phi)\exp(-2\pi f_o \sin\phi t)$

where

$\cot\phi = (4Q^2-1)^{1/2}$

2.2 (a) $E_{out}(t) = 0, t<0$

$= E_o\{1-\exp(-t/T)\}, 0 \leqslant t \leqslant T_1$

$= E_o\{\exp(T_1/T)-1\}\exp(-t/T), T_1 \leqslant t.$

(b) 0.214

2.3 (a) The output may be imaginary. There may be an output before there is an input.

(b) Restrict the given definition of $\hat{Y}(f)$ to positive frequencies and define $\hat{Y}(-f) = \hat{Y}^*(+f)$.

2.5 $\hat{H}(f) = 1/i2\pi f$

2.6 No. The Fourier integral will give the correct answer if it is deformed below the origin $f = 0$.

2.7 4

2.10 $\Psi^2(\tau_d, f_d) = \exp\{-(\pi f_d/a)^2 - (a\tau_d)^2\}.$

3.3 Clipping decreases the normalized autocorrelation function.

3.6

$$f(x_1, x_2) = \frac{1}{2\pi\sigma\sqrt{1-\rho^2}}\, e^{-\frac{1}{2\sigma^2(1-\rho^2)}[x_1^2 - 2\rho x_1 x_2 + x_2^2]}$$

4.4 (a) $E(T)/W_O{}^{1/2} = (2T)^{-1/2}$
(b) $E(T)/E_O = \pi^{1/4} \sqrt{\nu}\, e^{\nu} \{1-\Phi(\nu)\}^{1/2}$
where
$\nu = \sigma/\sqrt{2}\,T$ and $\Phi(\cdot)$ is the error integral.

4.6 (a) $E\{x\} = 1/12$
(b) $E\{x^2\} = 15/32.$
(c) $f(x) = 0 \quad x < -1$
$f(x) = 2(1+x) \quad -1 < x < -1/2$
$f(x) = (1/4)\,\delta(x + 1/2), \quad -1/2\text{-}\epsilon < x < -1/2+\epsilon$
$f(x) = 0 \quad -1/2 < x < +1/2$
$f(x) = 1 \quad 1/2 < x < 1$
$f(x) = 0 \quad 1 < x$

4.7 (c) The difference is that in the present case the phases are correlated so that amplitudes must be summed.

5.1 The mode is $R = \sigma$. $E\{R\} = a\sqrt{\pi/2}$

$E\{R^2\} = 2\sigma^2$.

5.2 (a) The prior probability, $P(w)$

w	0	1	2	3	4
$P(w)$	3/40	10/40	14/40	10/40	3/40

(b) The posterior probability, $P(z = 0 \mid w)$, that $z = 0$ given w.

w	0	1	2	3	4
$P(z=0 \mid w)$	1.0	0.7	0.5	0.3	0

5.12 $p(s) = \int f(r, r/s) \mid r/s^2 \mid dr$

5.13 (a) $p(s) = (1/\pi) \mid a_{ij} \mid^{1/2} \{a_{11}s^2 + 2a_{12}s + a_{22}\}^{-1}$
(b) $E\{s\} = -a_{12}/a_{11}$.

5.17 $\mu_{12}(t) = \sigma^2 \rho \sqrt{s(t_1)s(t_2)}$

7.1

(a) $G(t) = \int_{-\infty}^{+\infty} E_i(-\tau)\Omega(t-T-\tau)\, d\tau$

where $\Omega(t)$ is the Fourier transform of $[W(f)]^{-1}$

7.8 **No.** These two errors do not exhaust the possible combinations of likelihood ratios and hypotheses.

8.3

$$\ell n\, \Lambda = \ell n(p/q) + \frac{1}{2p^2}\left\{\sum_{m,n=1}^{M} a_{mn} V_m V_{n-M}\right\}$$

9.5 (b) 8.6 deg

NAME INDEX

SUBJECT INDEX

☆ U. S. GOVERNMENT PRINTING OFFICE : 1969 O - 365-775